BIOSOCIAL
CRIMINOLOGY

Introduction and Integration

Anthony Walsh
Boise State University

anderson publishing co.
2035 Reading Road
Cincinnati, OH 45202
800-582-7295

Biosocial Criminology: Introduction and Integration

Copyright © 2002
Anderson Publishing Co.
2035 Reading Rd.
Cincinnati, OH 45202

Phone   800.582.7295 or 513.421.4142
Web Site www.andersonpublishing.com

Library of Congress Cataloging-in-Publication Data

Walsh, Anthony, 1941-
    Biosocial criminology : introduction and integration / Anthony Walsh.
        p. cm.
    Includes bibliographical references and index.
    ISBN 1-58360-532-0
    1. Criminology. 2. Criminal behavior--Physiological aspects. 3. Criminal behavior--Genetic aspects.
4. Human beings--Effect of environment on. 5. Sociobiology. 6. Environmental psychology. I. Title.

HV6025 .W365 2001
364.2--dc21

                                                2001037311

Cover design by Tin Box Studio, Inc.

EDITOR Ellen S. Boyne
ACQUISITIONS EDITOR Michael C. Braswell

Foreword

It is an honor for me to introduce Anthony Walsh's *Biosocial Criminology: Introduction and Integration*, which I do with great enthusiasm. This book not only provides an excellent and comprehensive explanation of biosocial perspectives regarding criminality, but it also takes this approach further by incorporating the various biosocial concepts and propositions with dominant sociological theories of crime. Such integration of these traditionally distinct genres has long been advised but never undertaken. *Biosocial Criminology* represents the first significant attempt to show the similarities and dissimilarities of the biosocial and sociological theoretical frameworks, and it is clearly successful in accomplishing this objective. A variety of readers, from undergraduate students to well-established criminologists, will gain much insight from this book, and I expect that it will come to be known as the authoritative work in this area of theoretical development.

The author makes it known from the very first page of the Preface, as well as throughout the book, the need for the field to become interdisciplinary. This transition has not occurred despite many calls by leaders in the field to do so, which are evident in several recent addresses by presidents of the American Society of Criminology (ASC) and the Academy of Criminal Justice Sciences (ACJS). It should be noted that the title of the journal produced by the former society is called *Criminology: An Interdisciplinary Journal*. Walsh's emphasis on the biological-environment relationship (i.e., nature via nurture) at the outset sets a great tone, and one that is so important for such a book. Furthermore, this book takes the biosocial approach to a place that has been advised by the most recognized leaders of the field, and fills a theoretical void that has not yet been addressed.

A lot of the biosocial issues and propositions that are discussed in this book are considered controversial by many, if not most, criminologists and criminal justice practitioners. However, consideration of these issues is necessary because such knowledge is vital in developing a better understanding of human behavior, both by individuals and in groups. Only by improving such understanding can we develop more effective methods to reduce and prevent crime in our society. Furthermore, the author has gone to great lengths to present findings from

iii

empirical studies that are relevant to the theoretical propositions presented throughout the text. In light of such evidence, it will be hard for even the most ardent critic to dismiss the value of biosocial theory as a vital element in the etiology of offending behavior.

As discussed in the Preface and Chapter 1, the author's organization of the material is logical and beneficial in that it presents most of the substantive information regarding biosocial perspectives in the first several chapters of the book. In the first four chapters, the author explains the three major biosocial perspectives of human behavior. These general categories include behavioral genetics, evolutionary theory, and neurological factors. I think readers will find that the clarity and specificity of the explanation of each biosocial framework is outstanding, particularly regarding the way in which the author relates the principles to modern human behavior. By the end of the Chapter 4, it is very apparent that the author has accomplished the task of applying the core propositions of each biosocial perspective to deviant tendencies.

In subsequent chapters, he evaluates the propositions of the traditionally dominant sociological theories of crime while incorporating the concepts and principles of biosocial theory. More specifically, the author reviews the basic assumptions and propositions of most traditional theories of crime, including strain, social learning, social control, ecological, and conflict theories. This book succeeds in comprehensively reviewing these theories in the light of the biosocial perspectives, while giving due attention to the empirical support that has been accumulated regarding the validity of these theories without the biosocial factors being included. Additionally, Chapter 9 includes a discussion of feminist theories of crime, which I think is a significant advantage over other texts (particularly most biosocial reviews) that do not address the issue of gender differences. The examination of differences between males and females is especially important in criminology because of the drastic discrepancies across gender regarding propensities to commit crime. The ability of the biosocial perspectives to help us understand such discrepancies is reason enough to include them in our theoretical models of criminality.

One of the most advantageous aspects of the book is that the author is quite skilled in his use of analogies and examples, which makes the sometimes complex material much more understandable to readers who do not have a strong background in physiological processes of the human body and their role in how people behave. Without such illustrative examples, the material would be incomprehensible, as it is in many recent biosocial reviews. Fortunately, Walsh has a talent for applying these analogies, such as presenting the functioning of a thermostat to convey the importance of environment in determining the expression of genes (see Chapter 2), which is a rather effective demonstration of the importance of the environment in triggering biological dispositions. Another effective analogy (see Chapter 3) is the author's use of a heat-producing automobile engine to demonstrate the difference between adaptions and exaptations. Similar types of ingenious analogies and examples are included throughout the book, and they will help readers not only understand and retain the information but provide clear ways of explaining the material to others (e.g., students, colleagues).

One of the author's primary goals in this book is to encourage vertical integration of the existing criminological theories, which tend to be sociologically based, with more well-developed disciplines, such as behavioral genetics and neurosciences. Instead of simply recommending this type of theoretical integration, Walsh backs this up by providing an impressive and elaborate example of how such integration can be done successfully. Ultimately, *Biosocial Criminology* provides the most persuasive arguments to date for incorporating biologically influenced factors into contemporary explanations of criminality. All who are interested in the origins of human behavior will find this book to be insightful and captivating.

Stephen G. Tibbetts, Ph.D.
California State University–San Bernardino

Preface

Former President-elect of the American Society of Criminology (ASC) C. Ray Jeffery once opined that criminology should have dropped "anomie, opportunity theory, differential association, social learning theory, conflict theory, and labeling theory," 20 (now more than 40) years ago (1977:284). For a president-elect of the ASC to argue that his discipline should drop its major theories is rather peculiar, but Jefferey has long campaigned for a more biologically informed criminology, arguing that criminology must meet the biological challenge "or sink into the mire" (1977:285). Although Jeffery's point that criminology needs biology is correct, I believe that he was too radical in his blanket condemnation of existing criminological theories. The longevity enjoyed by these theories suggests that there are conceptual cores to each of them with sufficient logical appeal and empirical support to have captured the attention of generations of criminologists. These theories are not wrong; they are merely incomplete, encompassing the first one or two stages (demographics and correlates) in the search for causes. Criminology is an inherently interdisciplinary science, and the causes of criminal behavior can be sought at many levels as long as each level is part of a coherent and mutually reinforcing whole.

Most criminologists would probably agree in the abstract that criminology is inherently interdisciplinary, but in practice they tend to ignore any perspective other than the one they were trained in and with which they have become comfortable. Criminologists with different disciplinary orientations conduct their research and formulate their theories apparently oblivious to what is going on in other camps. Biological factors do not operate in an environmental vacuum, nor do environmental factors operate in a biological vacuum, and we must cease formulating our theories as if they do. I argue that scientific progress is only possible when young sciences are vertically integrated with the more mature and fundamental sciences. Vertical integration has been observed across many scientific disciplines, although many practitioners in the early history of those disciplines stoutly resisted it.

Although this book argues for applying insights from evolutionary psychology, behavior genetics, and the neurosciences to criminological theorizing, it is not a call for a "biological" criminology, for such a criminology is not possible. Nor is it a book introducing a new criminological theory, for we already suffer an embarrassment of riches in this area. It is a call for more biologically informed criminological theories. More precisely, it is a work that examines how *existing* criminology theories can be better understood, expanded, and revised by incorporating relevant methodological, conceptual, and theoretical insights from the biological sciences. This should be welcomed by criminologists who favor environmental explanations because, as many biosocial scientists have pointed out, insights from the biological sciences provide us with a deeper understanding and appreciation of the vital role of the *environment* than strictly environmentalist theories ever could (Crawford & Anderson, 1989; McGue et al., 1993; Plomin, 1995; Reiss, 1997).

I make the argument for a *biosocial* criminology in the context of traditional criminological concepts that have served as explanations of criminal behavior such as socioeconomic status, age, race, gender, conflict, the family, and child abuse and neglect.

Chapter 1 makes the argument for vertical integration with biology. It briefly explores the history of the animus between sociology and biology and why this animus has retarded the progress of sociology (and by extension, criminology) as a science. It does this primarily by examining how other sciences in their youth resolved the same kinds of tensions between them and the more mature science adjacent to them. Chapter 1 also explores the deep ideological barriers that separate criminologists, the resistance to biological explanations among them, the reasons for the resistance, and rebuttals to arguments frequently used to reject biological thinking in the human sciences.

Chapter 2 introduces the theories, concepts, and methods of behavior genetics and contrasts them with what has been called the *standard social science model* (SSSM). The issue today is not whether genes affect behavior, but rather *how* they do. We explore twin and adoption study designs that allow behavior geneticists to separate genetic from environmental effects and to calculate heritability coefficients. The genetic influences on criminal behavior are explored via the concepts of gene x environment interaction and gene/environment correlation. The changing effects of genes on personality and behavior over the lifespan, and how genes are differentially expressed in different environments are also explored. This kind of behavior genetic research offers an unprecedented opportunity for criminologists to assess the shifting balance of genetic and environmental factors over time and place. Challenges to the assumptions and methods of behavior genetics are examined in the final section.

Chapter 3 examines the evolutionary origins of behaviors that modern societies have come to define as criminal. The basic concepts and logic of evolutionary psychology are examined by discussing some of the many misunderstandings of evolutionary logic, such as "organisms are designed to be directly concerned with maximizing their fitness," or "what is natural is good." I then discuss altruism and cooperation, how these behaviors create a niche for "cheats" (criminals), the mechanisms that have evolved for detecting cheats, and discuss whether the coevolutionary "arms race" between cooperators and cheats may have resulted in a psychopathic genotype that makes cheating an obligatory strategy. The relationship between violence, status, and reproductive success is also discussed in this chapter. The chapter concludes with brief introductions to four specific evolutionary theories of criminal behavior.

Chapter 4 looks at the contributions to criminological theory from the neurosciences. Genes have surrendered much of their control of human behavior to a much more plastic organ we call the brain. The brain physically "captures" the environment as it wires itself in response to environmental experience. However, the brain has many assumptions built into it over eons of evolutionary time; it is no *tabula rasa*. The evolutionary importance of attachment is explored in terms of the neurological consequences of nonattachment. The effects of child abuse and neglect on various neurological structures that are important to prosocial and antisocial behavior are also discussed. The chapter concludes with a brief introduction to neurologically specific criminological theories and how they help to illuminate the consequences of abuse and neglect.

The remaining five chapters attempt to show the relevance of the preceding material to traditional criminological theories in the context of major theoretical concepts contained in those theories. Chapter 5 examines the anomie/strain tradition and status. After briefly exploring the evolution of this tradition from Emile Durkheim to Robert Agnew, the book examines what the biosocial sciences have to tell us about the central concepts of this tradition; for example, determinants of occupational success, coping with strain, and status striving.

Chapter 6 explores the differential association/social learning tradition, with emphasis on the childhood precursors of antisocial behavior. It then examines the differences between persistent offenders and those who limit their offending to adolescence. The peculiarities of the endocrinology and neurology of adolescence are explored in an attempt to understand the age effect, which some criminologists (e.g., Gottfredson and Hirschi, 1990) have asserted is essentially impervious to explanation.

Chapter 7 examines the social control/self-control tradition with emphasis on the evolutionary importance of human attachment and the family. The biology of low self-control is also examined.

Chapter 8 examines the human ecology tradition and race. It examines the "people versus places" debate, the sex ratio and illegitimacy, the ecology of the inner city, and testosterone and dominance in so-called *honor subcultures*.

Chapter 9 examines critical and feminist theories, with the emphasis on conflict. Marxism is discussed first in terms of its compatibility with evolutionary psychology. Feminist theory is explored in the context of the neurohormonal and evolutionary origins of the gender gap in crime. Feminist concerns about rape and domestic violence are examined in an evolutionary context.

Chapter 10 provides a summary and conclusion, followed by a discussion of further ethical concerns.

Acknowledgments

I would like to gratefully acknowledge the contributions of Drs. John Crank, Lee Ellis, and Craig Hemmens for reading and critiquing certain chapters, and to Dr. Stephen G. Tibbetts for his review and foreword. I would also like to thank Michael Braswell, Acquisition Editor, and Susan Braswell, Acquisitions Coordinator, for their advice and encouragement during the early stages of this project. Grateful thanks also go to my editor, Ellen Boyne, whose careful eye spotted many an error. Without her, this book would have been less readable.

My most special thanks are reserved, as ever, for my wife, Grace (aka "the face") for her patience, love, wit, devotion, and support over this and many other projects. She is truly a treasure, and I am a truly lucky man. Thanks for everything, Facie. Love ya.

Contents

Chapter 1

Why Criminology Needs Biology

This book is an attempt to convince fellow criminologists that the biological sciences have a bounty of treasures to offer our discipline, and that we should seek theoretical integration with them. There is no single biological approach to the study of criminal behavior any more than there is a single environmental approach. David Buss (1990) identifies three broad biological approaches to the study of human behavior: *evolutionary*, *behavior genetic*, and *[neuro]physiological*. Although they employ different theories and methods and work with different levels of analysis, their principles are conceptually consistent across all three levels. Furthermore, all three approaches are so "environment-friendly" that I am tempted to call them "biologically informed environmental approaches," although *biosocial approaches* is a more succinct way of describing them. This book explores these biosocial approaches in the context of traditional criminological theories that have their home in sociology.

Why should criminologists, most of who are ideologically left-leaning (Walsh & Ellis, 1999), concern themselves with incorporating the biological sciences into their discipline? Biology as applied to human behavior is still, after all, associated with illiberal politics by many social scientists. The short answer is that a review of the behavior genetic literature led the reviewer to remark that behavior genetics studies often reach the *same conclusions about environmental solutions to social problems* that "left-leaning sociologists" do (Herbert, 1997:80, emphasis added). If this is so, why should we burden ourselves by becoming familiar with another body of literature telling us the same thing? The short answer is again supplied by Herbert in pointing out that the conclusions arrived at by behavior geneticists were arrived at using "infinitely more sophisticated tools." The basic premise of this book is that these "infinitely more sophisticated tools" (theories, models, concepts, instruments, methodologies) developed by behavior geneticists (as well as evolutionary psychologists and neuroscientists) can be

brought to bear on the concepts and assumptions of traditional criminological theories as quality control devices functioning to separate
the wheat from the chaff.

There is a lot of chaff in traditional criminological theories, but
there is also a lot of wheat. Criminology's problem is that it is largely blind to the difference. Much of the discipline's inability to focus its
vision and move forward by allying itself with more robust sciences lies
in the ideological barriers it has constructed for itself. Ideological
barriers are the mental processes at work that prevent those behind
them from acknowledging that "alien" ideas have any possibility of
helping to illuminate the phenomenon they study. Moir and Jessel
(1995:10) put it well when they asserted that "the evidence that biology is a central factor in crime, interacting with cultural, social, and
economic factors, is so strong . . . that to ignore it is perverse." Yet it
is largely ignored, and few criminologists consider themselves "perverse" for doing so.

SOCIOLOGY CONTRA BIOLOGY

We cannot discuss the state of criminology without first discussing
the state of sociology, its parent discipline. The decade of the 1990s saw
an increasing number of social scientists voicing their displeasure
about the sad state of sociology and its refusal to even consider the possibility that the biological sciences can tell us anything of value about
human social behavior (e.g., Crippen, 1994; Ellis, 1996a; Lopreato &
Crippen, 1999; Neilsen, 1994; Udry, 1995; Walsh, 1995a). Having
observed the natural sciences develop coherent, logical, and florescent
theories from which have flowed a cascade of testable propositions and
hypotheses resulting in robust explanations of biological phenomena,
these critics see no reason why the social sciences cannot follow suit.
Tooby and Cosmides (1992:23) offer one of the most stinging of these
criticisms:

> After more than a century, the social sciences are still adrift,
> with an enormous mass of half-digested observations, a not
> inconsiderable body of empirical generalizations, and a con-
> tradictory stew of ungrounded, middle-level theories expressed
> in a babble of incommensurate technical lexicons. This is
> accompanied by a growing malaise, so that the single largest
> trend is toward rejecting the scientific enterprise as it applies
> to humans.

These and many other critics urge the social sciences to integrate
themselves vertically with biology. That is, the social sciences must make

themselves consistent with what is known in the natural sciences so that there is a harmonious interlocking of causal explanations running from biology to psychology to sociology. There is no defensible *scientific* reason why sociology should not be continuous with biology in the same way that biology is continuous with chemistry, and chemistry with physics.

Ward, Durkheim, and the Demon Biology

The schism between biology and sociology can be traced to the work of Lester Ward, the first president of the American Sociological Society (later to become the American Sociological Association after acronyms became trendy) in 1906 (Ritzer, 1988). Ward, a biologist turned sociologist, saw sociology as a potential guide to creating a better society. He was vehemently opposed to the misuse of Darwinist principles by the social Darwinists and eugenicists who were quite active in his time. Ward's reformist campaigns against these doctrines set the stage for sociology to become the self-appointed conscience of science, ever on the lookout to expose and oppose any proposition or hypothesis that threatened to promote insidious social policies.

This is a noble and valuable mission, and sociology is to be applauded for staking out science's moral high ground. However, advocacy must not be confused with science. Sociology's agenda has led to it becoming "so enmeshed in the politics of advocacy and the ideology of self-righteousness that it is simply unaware of, much less able to respond to, new conditions in the scientific as well as social environments in which it finds itself" (Horowitz, 1993:5). The scientific ignorance and ideological blinders Horowitz refers to often lead to misidentifying the causes of the problems sociologists seek to ameliorate. This misidentification leads to interventions that do not work, which eventually leads policymakers and scientists in other disciplines to mistrust and discount anything further these well-meaning reformers may have to say. Ward himself persisted in his belief in Lamarckism (the inheritance of acquired characteristics) because he felt it was more optimistic and progressive than Darwinian natural selection (Degler, 1991:22).

If Ward and his colleagues fought the battles, the rallying cry was provided by Emile Durkheim. In what is probably the most cited passage in all of sociology, Durkheim proclaimed that: "The determining cause of a social fact should be sought among antecedent social facts and not among the states of the individual consciousness" (Durkheim, 1982:134). This dictum has become a sociological mantra used to assert and defend the ontological autonomy of the discipline. What it has actually done, according to Lopreato and Crippen (1999:52), is to isolate sociology "from the rest of the scientific community and to seek fundamental causes [in class, race, gender, etc.] where only intervening variables could be found." According to Richard Udry (1995:1267), however, while Durkheim meant his social factist statement to be a boundary axiom defining sociology's purview, sociologists came to think of it as "a true statement about the nature of the world instead of a set of deliberate blinders to help them focus their attention."

Thus, Ward provided the moral model for sociology's role as advocate for the oppressed and deprived, and Durkheim provided the intellectual foundation justifying its existence as an independent science. Both men fought their battles against biology, so it is not all that surprising that any sort of biological explanation of human social behavior is not politely received by contemporary sociologists. Largely due to the twin legacies of Ward and Durkheim, generations of sociologists have been professionally nurtured to view nonsocial causes of human behavior as inconsequential and probably malignant. Because of the perception that such explanations threaten both the autonomy of the discipline and the well-being of society's less fortunate members, sociologists have not been content simply to ignore biological explanations, they have gone out of their way to attack and discredit them (Degler, 1991; Wright & Miller, 1998). Unfortunately, the content of much of this criticism makes it plain that they are not being informed by any semblance of biological insight, for most sociologists are not simply oblivious to biology; "they are militantly and proudly ignorant" (van den Berghe, 1990:177).

For much of the twentieth century, sociology seemed to have achieved its goal of becoming a respected and autonomous science. Although there were always sociologists who yearned to link their discipline with biology, sociology's view of human nature as socially constructed and largely biology-free had more or less become the view accepted by the liberal democracies of the western world following their clash with the racist dogmas of Nazism. A major challenge to sociology's autonomy emerged with the publication of Edward O. Wilson's *Sociobiology* (1975), a 697-page book that, with the exception of the "infamous" Chapter 27, dealt with the social behavior of nonhuman animals. The opening paragraph of Chapter 27, titled "Man: From Sociobiology to Sociology," seemed to relegate sociology to a minor branch of biology:

> Let us now consider man in the free spirit of natural history, as though we were zoologists from another planet completing a catalog of social species on earth. In this macroscopic view the humanities and social sciences shrink to specialized branches of biology; history, biography, and fiction are the

research protocols of human ethology; and anthropology and sociology together constitute the sociobiology of a single species (1975:547).

Such a bold statement was guaranteed to raise the hackles of sociologists already hostile to "biologizing." There followed numerous attacks on sociobiology and on Wilson by such groups as Science for the People (1978), who saw sociobiology as "biological determinism" and as a legitimizer of all the alleged evils of the status quo. Yet Stephen Jay Gould, one of the contributors of the Science for the People article, later argued that it is wrong to view sociobiology as motivated by a political agenda, stating that if social scientists find the theory wanting, "They must find and use a more adequate evolutionary biology, not reject proffered aid and genuine partnership" (1991:51).

A fair number of esteemed social/behavioral scientists have taken Gould's advice. They have sought more adequate explanations of their research findings and have adopted biosocial approaches. Among the most famous of these "apostates" are:

- Alice Rossi, past president of the ASA, a liberal, and a feminist, began her professional career as an ardently traditional sociologist. In an article in *Daedalus* (1964), she defended the thesis of the interchangeability of the sexes. In the same forum 13 years later, she found her previous biology-free position "wanting" and corrected it (1977:2). Her 1983 ASA presidential address focused strongly on the biological underpinning of sex roles (Rossi, 1984), and she continues to this day to try to convince her colleagues that any biology-free position related to human behavior is "wanting."

- Jerome Kagan, one of the most eminent developmental psychologists in the world today, reports often "wincing at my early [antibiological] credulity." Kagan was the classical liberal environmentalist who did not give biology the time of day. "For the first twenty years of my career, I wrote essays critical of the role of biology and celebrating the role of the environment. I am now working in the opposite camp because I was dragged there by my data." (quoted in Wright, 1999:93).

- Cultural anthropologist Medford Spiro, a self-confessed "cultural determinist," was also dragged from his biophobia by his data. Expecting to find "natural androgyny" in Israeli kibbutzim (which was one of the major aims of the movement) after three generations of indoctrination toward that end, what he actually found forced him into "a kind of Copernican revolution in my own thinking" (1980:106). He had expected to find "how a new culture produces a new human nature [but] I found (against my own intentions), that I was observing the influence of human nature on culture" (1980:106).

- Anthropologist Donald Brown used to be a cultural relativist in the Boas-Benedict-Mead tradition until he wagered fellow anthropologist Donald Symons that he could find exceptions to the sex differences claimed by Symons to be universal. Brown lost the bet and "began to think more carefully about the role that human biology plays in human affairs" (Brown, 1991:vii).

Many other former strict environmentalists could be added to this list, but even more exciting are the calls for more biologically informed theories made in the context of social science presidential addresses. These include Alice Rossi's (1984) address to the American Sociological Association, Sandra Scarr's (1992) address to The Society for Research in Child Development, and Richard Udry's (1994) address to the Population Association of America. More pertinent for criminologists are two presidential addresses to the American Society of Criminology by Charles Wellford (1997) and Margaret Zahn (1999), both of which called for a more biologically informed criminology. These addresses inform us that some influential social scientists have accepted the reality of the continuity that exists between biology and the social sciences.

Reductionism

There is a great deal of resistance to the idea of a seamless continuity with biology among many sociologists, who view their subject matter as radically different from the subject matter of biology and thus requiring an ontologically different set of principles to understand. "Biologizing," or even "psychologizing," what is claimed to be a social phenomenon is almost sure to be met with one of sociology's favorite "boo words"—*reductionism*. However, reductionism is nothing more sinister than the process of examining a complex phenomenon at a more fundamental level. Edward O. Wilson (1998:187) cites sociologist James Coleman as an example of this aversion to reductionism. Coleman asserts that whenever two or more individuals interact, "the *essential requirement* is that the explanatory focus be on the system as a unit, not on the individuals or other components which make it up" (emphasis added). While it is true that the interaction of elements (whether they are chemicals, people, or what have you) often produce effects not predictable a priori from their respective constituent parts, the claim that it is *essential* to focus explanatory efforts only on the whole unit to the exclusion of the parts is unnecessarily constraining. In response to Coleman, Wilson points out that biology "would have remained stuck around 1850 with such a flat perspective" if biologists took seriously any claims that "the essential requirement is that the explanatory focus be on the organism as a unit, not on the cell or molecules which make it up" (1998:187). Holistic explanations may sometimes be more coherent and useful than reductionist explanations, but reductionism has been the "royal road," though not the only road, to progress in science.

Thomas Nagel, the doyen of the philosophy of science, claims that nonreductionist accounts simply *describe* a phenomenon, while reductionist accounts *explain* it (in Rose, 1999:915). Let us examine this claim in the context of the search for the cause of AIDS.

Lubinski and Humphreys (1997) note that sociology and medical epidemiology both deal with broad categories of people (races, genders, ethnic groups, and other subpopulations), and both seek to determine the location, spread, and prevalence of the phenomenon of interest. Having identified an at-risk category for AIDS (gay men), the next step epidemiologists took was to identify what behaviors and practices (exchange of bodily fluids, anal sex, intravenous drug use) that separate those with the disease from those in the same at-risk category who did not have it. Epidemiologists continued to narrow their focus in this way until a particular pathogen (the HIV) believed to cause the disease was identified. Notice that the term *cause* is not invoked until the lowest relevant level of analysis is reached. The at-risk population identified is certainly not considered a cause of the disease, and the behaviors and practices discovered are not causes either, but rather descriptions of events and situations that separate those with the disease from others in the same at-risk population who do not have it.

Social scientists who study broad categories of people do not typically turn their attention toward lower levels of analysis when they have identified categories associated with the problem with which they are concerned. How often have we seen demographic variables such as race, gender, and age, invoked as causes in phrases such as "Gender explains X%, age Y%, and race Z% of the variance in delinquency"? These variables are predictors, not explanations, and they "necessarily beg the question" (Lopreato & Crippen, 1999:52). If any attempt at explanation is ventured beyond identifying the associated demographics, it commonly involves invoking higher-level constructs assumed to be operating, such as racism, discrimination, and classism. Dennett (1995:82) likens this kind of science to a "yearning for skyhooks," by which he means yearning for a sort of *deus ex machina* that will lift us miraculously out of scientific difficulty. Invoking higher-level variables such as these that are more often assumed than measured is reminiscent of the nineteenth-century physicist's use of ether for the same purpose. I am not saying that racism, discrimination, and so forth do not exist. I am only saying that they are too readily invoked as blanket explanations that relieve researchers of their obligation to explore further.

Dennett contrasts skyhooks with cranes. Unlike skyhooks suspended on nothing, cranes are solidly grounded devices that also serve to lift us out of difficulty but do so with solid, non-question-begging science (1995:80). There is no excuse for yearning for skyhooks when we have perfectly good cranes available. Invoking higher-level categories (or at least not invoking lower-level ones) may be true to Durkheim's dictum that only social facts should be used to explain other social facts, but it is poor science. As Lubinski and Humphreys (1997:177) suggest: "Whatever the causes of group differences in social phenomena are, measures of individual differences typically reflect those causes more effectively than does membership in demographic groups." Lubinski and Humphreys (1997) and Walsh (1997) provide several examples of the superiority of lower-level measures with reference to major demographic variables such as gender, race, age, and socioeconomic status (SES).

This is not to say that identifying the causes of a phenomenon such as criminal behavior found to be more prevalent in one group than in another is as simple as identifying a pathogen more prevalent in one group than in another. Few would dispute that the former is immensely more complicated than the latter. Nor am I saying that reductionism is the only legitimate way to explain phenomena. Even if the practices identified as responsible for passing on the HIV virus do not cause AIDS in the strict sense, refraining from engagement in these practices prevents one from acquiring it, so the practices constitute causes in a practical sense. There are certainly times when nonreductionist explanations are more coherent, satisfying, and useful than reductionist ones, but these must be decided on a case-by-case basis, not by disciplinary fiat. For instance, propositions about biological entities such as genes, hormones, and neurons do not contain terms that define the human condition at its most meaningful level. How do we reduce the likes of love, justice, morality, and honor to such terms? We do not, but they can *assist* us in our attempts to understand them. I would condemn Dennett's (1995:82) "greedy reductionist" (a greedy reductionist is a person who skips over several layers of higher complexity in a rush to fasten everything securely to a supposedly solid foundation) just as surely as I would a naive antireductionist. The trick is to determine when it is useful to engage in reductionist analysis and when it is not.

The history of science shows consistently that higher-level (emergent) theories and explanations of many phenomena existed long before their underlying mechanisms were discovered and elucidated. Higher-level theories are not necessarily abandoned when lower-level theories come along; physicists and engineers still find classical physics quite useful despite relativity theory and quantum mechanics. Unlike social scientists, natural scientists have long recognized the complementarity of reductionist and holistic explanations. Useful observations and hypotheses now go in both reductionist and emergent directions in those sciences. Cell biologists know that at bottom they are dealing with subatomic particles and seek to understand their properties. They also know, however, that there are properties of the cell that cannot be deduced from those particles *a priori* and that functional explanations of the whole cell are required, as well as information on how that cell fits into a network of other cells to form a larger whole (the organism). This is why we will always need social science regardless of how sophisticated we become about the genetic and neurohormonal bases of human behavior. Science is eclectic by nature and can pose questions and offer explanation at several levels of understanding.

Part of the fear of reductionism has always been the intellectual threat the more fundamental sciences are perceived as posing to the autonomy of the more immature sciences. Edward Wilson (1990) coined the term *antidiscipline* to describe the relationship between a young science and an adjacent older science. Initially, there is tension between the two disciplines, although it is felt most acutely by the younger one because the "upstart" science poses little threat to the autonomy or the reputation of the established science. As the younger science gains confidence, it is less threatened and it begins to experiment with how the ideas and theories of the mature science can be of use to it. After a period of creative interplay, the younger science becomes fully complementary with its erstwhile antidiscipline. With complementarity accomplished, the younger science begins to realize great gains in theoretical and methodological sophistication. The younger discipline prospers from the thrust provided by the more mature science in ways it could never have done had it not shaken itself free of those more interested in autonomy than in progress. Let me briefly illustrate from the history of chemistry, biology, and psychology.

In the late 1860s, a series of sometimes rancorous debates took place at the Chemical Society of London over the intrusion of physics and its atomic theory into chemistry. Oxford chemistry professor Benjamin Brodie argued for an "ideal [pure] chemistry" based on explanations involving qualitative (the transformation of substances such as a solid to a gas) and quantitative (weight changes due to transformation) changes. Brodie's argument was that any reference to these newfangled things called atoms (if indeed they existed) was reductionist and unnecessary because chemical compounds possessed emergent properties not predictable *a priori* from their constituent parts. He claimed that chemical compounds are *sui generis* entities that transcend their constituent parts. This position was supported by the majority of chemists of the London Chemical Society at the time. However, many changed their minds shortly thereafter when "the deductive power of the atomic theory [became] evident. . . . the atomic theory now enabled definite predictions and detailed explanations to be made. The experimental and deductive aspects of chemistry were cohering at last" (Knight, 1992:124).

Chemistry soon became fully integrated with physics, and the pair of them turned their curious eyes on biology. In the first half of the twentieth century, chemists and physicists were bringing a molecular (and thus, a reductionist) approach into biology, much to the chagrin of University of London biologist and philosopher Joseph H. Woodger. Woodger (1948) argued that biology has a characteristically biological way of thinking that is not reducible to the thinking of chemistry or physics. He went on to claim in a very Durheimian way that biological facts should be explained only by other biological facts. Woodger may have felt that he stood on firmer ground than Brodie in claiming autonomy for his discipline, for surely the step from the inorganic to the organic is the most momentous discontinuity in all nature. Yet it was only five years after the publication of Woodger's *Biological Principles* that James Watson and Francis Crick decoded the "language of life" by an examination of the chemistry, and hence the atomic structure, of the DNA molecule.

Watson and Crick won the Nobel Prize by ignoring the constraints of discipline orthodoxy, as did the Swedish chemist Svante Arrehenius for his elucidation of ionic bonding in the nineteenth century. It is instructive that central concepts of modern chemistry and biology (ions and genes, respectively) were once considered to be reductionist and therefore outside the domains of those disciplines. Today, chemists learn physics and biologists learn chemistry; any suggestion that this should not be so would be met by puzzled stares by chemical and biological scientists. These three disciplines now form a seamless web of connected explanations of phenomena ranging from subatomic particles in physics to ecosystems in biology. Biologists today would no more dream of advancing a hypothesis that contradicts principles of chemistry than a chemist would dream of formulating a proposition at odds with the elegant laws of physics.

Psychology, with its specialties such as physiological psychology, has never been as antibiology as sociology. Nevertheless, there have been many instances in its history when psychologists have made efforts to distance their discipline from biology. John Watson's extreme statement that he could take any healthy infant at random and make him into any type of specialist regardless of "his talents, penchants, tendencies, abilities, vocations, and race of his ancestors," and Zing Yang Kuo's assertion that psychology "needs the concept of heredity as much or as little as the concept of god," are prime examples of noted psychologists discounting biology (cited in Degler, 1991:155-159).

Modern psychology has not embraced biology as intimately as biology has embraced chemistry, or chemistry physics, but it is at least on much friendlier terms than it was in Watson and Kuo's time. Even archenvironmentalist B.F. Skinner (1966) readily acknowledged that to understand why a reinforcer reinforces, we must understand the evolutionary history of the species as well as the history of the organism being reinforced. It is interesting that many leading behavior geneticists are psychologists, and as behavior genetics flows naturally into molecular genetics, they will surely go along for the ride. While there is no psychological analogy to the ion or the gene that has forced psychologists to surrender their antireductionism, many of them appear to agree that to fail to consider genetic, evolutionary, or neurohormonal evidence is to neglect the guidance of compasses that have demonstrated their predictive power time and again.

Sitting on the top rung of Comte's ladder are acrophobic sociologists stubbornly refusing to look downward for guidance from the sciences below, many convinced that monsters are at rest on the lower rungs awaiting those who would dare carry *social* facts down there for analysis. Any approach smelling of biology is open to accusations of genetic determinism, of being in league with Hitler, being anti-immigrant (especially of brown- or black-skinned immigrants), being reactionary and/or racist, or simply being insensitive. Sociologist Garland Allen (1999) manages to touch on all these alleged crimes in his comments about the so-called *Violence Initiative* funded by the Department of Health and Human Services. This initiative was the brainchild of Louis Sullivan, an African-American physician who was then the secretary of health and human services, and was designed to apply biological insights (a public health or medical approach) to the problem of inner-city violence. Rather than applaud efforts that would bring new insights to a problem that has defied traditional sociological efforts to understand and control, social scientists saw a political conspiracy and staged a successful campaign to halt the conference (although it was subsequently reborn with a more politically correct title).

CRIMINOLOGY AND BIOLOGY

Having examined the attitude toward biology in criminology's parent discipline, let us now examine the attitude specifically in criminology. Although criminology is inherently interdisciplinary, it has perhaps been the subfield of sociology that has been most resistant to biology. According to Gottfredson and Hirschi (1990:70), sociology possesses "a conceptual scheme that explicitly den[ies] the claims of other disciplines potentially interested in crime." Our discipline deals with behavior that is so negatively valued that many of us are reluctant to allow persons who engage in it to be tarred with the same negative brush that taints their behavior. To explore the characteristics of individuals engaged in crime would do just that, and thus place the blame for their actions on them. Now that is a really radical idea! Traditional criminologists often seem to claim that everything and everybody is responsible for crime—except the criminal. As Hirschi and Hindelang (1977:571) put it: "Few groups in American society have been defended more diligently by sociologists against allegations of difference than ordinary delinquents. From the beginning the thrust of sociology has been to deny the relevance of individual differences as an explanation of delinquency, and the thrust of sociological criticism has been to discount research findings apparently to the contrary." It is a strange discipline that seeks to "protect" individuals by denying them the dignity of responsibility for their own actions and by implicitly denying human diversity.

For many criminologists over the past few decades, even the thought of embracing biology bordered on the perverse and the unthinkable. A content analysis of criminological textbooks published between 1961 and 1970 showed that coverage of biological topics (at least any sort of positive coverage) was virtually taboo (Wright & Miller, 1998). For instance, Wright and Miller (1998:9) quote Don Gibbons's 1968 edition of *Society, Crime, and Criminal Behavior*, in which he characterized biological research on crime as "unfruitful" and noted that "whatever the explanation of lawbreaking, it is not to be found in defective heredity, biological taint, or in . . . other formulations." The treatment of biocriminology in textbooks softened from 1987 through 1997 as knowledge in the natural sciences increased by leaps and bounds—and as criminologists became more sophisticated in their thinking about it. In the 1992 edition of Gibbons's text, he changed his assessment of the place of biology in criminology to: "There is empirical evidence that lawbreaking is often the product of biological, psychological, and sociological factors operating [together] in complex ways" (cited in Wright & Miller, 1998:9).

Wright and Miller report significantly greater proportions of textbooks in this latter period relative to the earlier period being devoted to biological topics, except for books written by radical/Marxist authors. Wright and Miller (1998:14) conclude their study stating: "Sadly, twenty recent books link biological explanations of crime to sexism, racism, and fascism, a common tactic used by some criminologists (especially those embracing critical perspectives) to discredit these arguments." It is indeed sad that criminologists feel that they have to resort to name-calling to refute research they do not like (and likely do not understand). Resorting to branding work one finds personally distasteful with labels such as racism or sexism serves only to foreclose on further discourse, which disadvantages labeler and labelee alike.

It is probably fair to say that even given the somewhat positive trend toward accepting biological arguments, we are still a long way from embracing them as willingly as we embrace sociological arguments. Perhaps they will never gain such acceptance in our time because of the "evil" taint applied to them when the current crop of criminologists was in graduate school. Academics appear to have a significant psychological investment in ideas that were painfully assimilated in graduate school, as a survey of British criminologists indicates. This survey found British criminologists to be a homogeneous group who entered the discipline en masse during the liberal/radical period of the late 1960s to early 1970s (Rock & Holdaway, 1998). Consequently, they have become very familiar with each other, adopted more or less the same theoretical orientation (various mixtures of liberal, Marxist, and feminist approaches), and have settled into a kind of "internalized coziness" that is not conducive to adopting insights from other disciplines (Rock & Holdaway, 1998:6).

There are reasons to believe that American criminologists are likewise fairly cozy with the concepts, theories, and ideologies they assimilated when they entered the field (many in the same period as their British colleagues). Lawrence Cohen (1987:204) points out that sociology is "the only branch of social science that has . . . failed to recognize openly the possible influence of nature on human behavior, and nowhere is it more evident than in our studies of crime." Ellis and Hoffman (1990:57) contend that the reason "that most criminologists continue to resist the incorporation of biological factors into their understanding of criminal behavior is ideological. As part of their liberal academic tradition, criminologists tend not to blame individuals for their ill behavior, preferring to blame society and its institutions." This assertion was based on a survey of the opinions of American criminologists conducted in 1986.

A similar survey of American criminologists by Walsh and Ellis (1999), which was conducted a decade later, found that little had changed. American criminologists did not appear to be quite as ideologically homogeneous as their British counterparts, but the strict environmental flavor or American criminology was strongly in evidence. Even within this predominantly environmentalist paradigm, American criminology appears to be fragmented by ideology. No fewer than 23 different theories were listed by participating criminologists when asked which theory they believed had the most empirical support in terms of explaining variance in persistent and serious criminality. Each of these theories doubtless contributes something to our understanding of criminality, for there is no more a single cause of it than there is for illness. One can become a criminal by almost as many pathways as one can become ill, and criminality, like illness, varies tremendously in its frequency, intensity, and duration. However, they obviously cannot *all* enjoy "the most empirical support."

Table 1.1 lists the theories in order of popularity. Social control theory was listed by more criminologists than any other theory, which mirrors the similar survey conducted by Ellis and Hoffman (1990). The only theory to garner support from each ideological category was Terrie Moffitt's (1993) taxonomical developmental theory. As the statistics indicate, favored theories were strongly associated with self-reported sociopolitical ideology. Gender ideology was also important. All seven respondents who listed feminist theory as enjoying the most empirical support were female and liberal, although most women (86%) listed theories other than feminism.

To no one's surprise, ideology also intrudes into opinions regarding the causes of crime. (I prefer to view criminal behavior as the result of an accumulation of risk factors rather than something that is "caused.") Respondents were asked to assign a number ranging from 0.0 (not important at all) to 9.0 (extremely important) indicating their assessment of the causal importance of 24 alleged causes of crime. The overall pattern was that conservatives and moderates favored individual-level explanations, and liberals and radicals favored structural explanations. The top three causal factors for conservatives were *lack of empathy, impulsiveness*, and *lack of supervision*. Moderates favored *poor discipline practices, lack of supervision*, and *lack of empathy*. Liberals favored two structural variables (*unfair economic system* and *lack of educational opportunities*) and one individual-level variable (*lack of empathy*) most strongly. Radicals favored macrosocial factors exclusively—*unfair economic system, lack of educational opportunities*, and *bias in law enforcement*.

The study also found that, taken as a whole, criminologists of all ideological persuasions view alleged biological causes of crime (*hormonal factors, genetic factors, evolutionary factors,* and *low intelligence*) as relatively unimportant. This does not mean that they reject the role of biology in criminal behavior entirely, only that they consider biological factors to be less important than environmental factors. For instance, only 25.2 percent of the respondents indicated (by assigning a score of zero) that genetic factors are of no importance at all, which means that almost 75 percent did feel that genetic factors are of *some* importance. The percentages of respondents assigning a score of zero for hormonal, evolutionary, low intelligence, and neurological factors were 17.0, 48.3, 15.5, and 11.6, respectively. The percentage of respondents who considered biological variables to be of great importance (a score of five or more) were: evolutionary factors (9.1), genetic factors (13.1), hormonal factors (17.0), neurological factors (29.9), and low intelligence (34.3). It can be concluded that the majority of criminologists are open to the possibility that biosocial factors play at least some part in the etiology of criminal behavior, and a small minority considers them to be very important. On the whole, however, these findings support Voigt and his colleagues (1994:188) in their contention that "most criminologists continue to be reluctant to accept any biological theories of criminal behavior, and they generally do not support genetically based arguments."

Table 1.1
Theories Favored by American Criminologists, Broken Down by Political Ideology

Theory	Political Persuasion				
	Conservative	Moderate	Liberal	Radical	Total
social control	3	10	10		23
self-control	4	8	2		14
differential association	2		10		12
conflict			7	3	10
Moffitt's developmental theory	2	5	1	1	9
traditional anomie			8	1	9
social learning	2		7		9
strain		2	5		7
routine activities	4		3		7
feminist			7		7
developmental	2	4			6
biosocial	1	4			5
Marxist				4	4
social disorganization			4		4
differential opportunity	1		2		3
radical			2		2
labeling			1		1
critical				1	1
integrated		1			1
classical	1				1
criminal personality		1			1
neo-Darwinian			1		1
ecological	1				1
Total	23	35	70	10	138

$X^2 = 177.23$, df = 66, p < .0001; Cramer's V = .65

The lack of interest in biology's role in criminology among criminologists is at least partially attributable to their lack of exposure to it. Respondents were overwhelmingly trained in the social sciences (sociology, criminal justice, and political science). The mean numbers of undergraduate and graduate sociology classes taken were 6.23 and 9.10, respectively. The mean number of undergraduate and graduate classes in psychology was 3.71 and .94; and in biology, it was 1.69 and .028.

Two major conclusions about the current state of criminology can be offered based on this survey: (1) there is a great deal of theoretical excess, and (2) allegiance to a theory appears to be rather strongly related to ideology. Any field generating this much theoretical excess (and there are other theories not represented in the sample) to explain the same phenomenon can reasonably be accused of lacking in scientific rigor. However, it is highly unlikely that any one theory or perspective will ever be able to provide a full explanation of such complex and heterogeneous phenomena as crime and criminality. Perhaps all of these theories have something to offer. Likewise, any field in which a practitioner's sociopolitical ideology predicts his or her favored theory with a fair degree of accuracy can reasonably be accused of lacking in objectivity. Ideology implies a selective interpretation and understanding of the data in terms of "how things should be" rather than an objective and rational evaluation of the evidence.

Bernard (1998) makes a similar point about theoretical excess when he observes that every new edition of a criminology textbook grows fatter as new theories are added, with few being dropped because they have been falsified. He goes on to state: "This suggests an astounding lack of scientific progress over a forty-year period of increasingly vigorous and sophisticated empirical research" (1998:x). We may still be chasing our tails in another 40 years unless we drop our unreasonable fear of biology and accept its nourishment. It is fair to say that criminology (or sociology in general, for that matter) has failed to discover even a single central principle enabling it to systematically organize the empirical facts obtained from its "increasingly vigorous and sophisticated" research. The switch from simple hand-calculated chi-squares and gammas of 40 years ago to today's computerized LISREL modeling is an example of technology outpacing theory. No matter how sophisticated the methods we use, if we do not look in the right places, we are bound to find the same things over and over.

Typical Objections to Biological Thinking in Criminology

I have thus far tried to outline some general reasons why criminology should incorporate biological theories, concepts, and methods into its theories—and why criminologists in general have been resistant to doing so. I will now outline some of the specific objections criminologists raise to the idea of incorporating biological ideas into their theories. Many of these objections have been around since the birth of criminology and have been answered many times. The same objections continue to be voiced, however, and thus require further responses. These objections include the following.

Biosocial theories are deterministic and socially dangerous.

When scientists speak of determinism, they simply mean that every event stands in some causal relationship to other events. Surely we are all determinists in this sense. When social scientists use the term *determinism* in the context of criticizing biosocial theorizing, however, they have something different in mind, such as the accusation that it implies that social behavior is a *direct* outcome of genetic programming absent any influence from the environment (Woodward, 1992). Colin Trudge (1999:96) asserts that such accusations represent either mere rhetoric or simple ignorance. "For a start, no evolutionary psychologist [or behavior geneticist or neuroscientist] doubts that a gene is in constant dialogue with its surroundings, which include the other genes in the genome, the rest of the organism, and the world at large." If only those who made accusations of biological determinism would take the time to learn something about human biology, they would not embarrass themselves with such pronouncements.

As for being socially dangerous, I suggest that far more damage to humanity has been done by those holding "blank slate" views of human nature than has ever been done by those holding nativist views. The environmental determinism implied by an "empty organism" view of human nature is a more sinister form of determinism because the forces supposedly determining behavior are external to the actor. The idea that humans are empty organisms is a totalitarian's dream, for if humans are *tabula rasa* at birth, they can be knocked into any shape dictated by state ideology (Daly & Wilson, 1988a:296; Fox, 1991:17-18). Stalin, Mao, Pol Pot, and their like, murdered in excess of 100 million people in their belief that they could take empty organisms and turn them into the "new Soviet, Chinese, or Cambodian man" (van den Berghe, 1990:179). A view of human nature that sees each person as a unique individual born with a suite of biological traits with which to interact with the world is more scientifically defensible—and more respectful of human dignity—than blank-slate views that delight the political megalomaniacs of the world who would like to see everyone made to their specifications.

Many criminologists may fear that biocriminology is social Darwinism in new clothes and can likewise be used for antiprogressive purposes, such as offering support for the status quo as it relates to racial, class, and gender inequalities. Human nature will be what it is regardless of whether we acknowledge it. Politicians, racists, and bigots of all stripes will use any theory—biological, political, religious, or economic—that will give their hatreds and goals whatever support they think they find in them. Nazi beliefs in the biological inferiority of Jews (more a philosophy than a theory underpinned by any semblance of science) were soundly trounced when exposed to science's self-correcting discourse, but ideologies such as those advocated by Stalin, Mao, and Pol Pot are, almost by definition, impervious to reasoned discourse. Science, which in the context of human behavior means everything subsumed by biology and the social/behavioral sciences, must be our unfettered guide. We cannot let censors or bigots (from the left or from the right) define scientific agendas, for as Bryan Vila points out, "biological findings can be used for racist or eugenic ends only if we allow perpetuation of the ignorance that underpins these arguments" (1994:329). Social justice is a moral imperative regardless of what science does or does not have to say about any observed inequalities in society.

Because crime is socially constructed, there cannot be any genes for crime.

This criticism most clearly illustrates the biological ignorance of those who make it. The argument is captured by Senger (1993:6), who argues: "Those who claim to have found a gene for criminality must explain how any gene knows what is a crime, why, when, and where. They will also have to abolish the concept of guilt, for the born criminal can hardly be more responsible for his supposed criminality than for the color of his eyes." In other words, if crime is a social invention, how can a person inherit a disposition for it? Senger is, of course, correct. There are no genes "for" crime, but there are genes that lead to particular traits (e.g., low levels of empathy, IQ, self-control, fear, conscientiousness, and high levels of sensation-seeking, egoism, negative emotionality, and aggression) that increase the probability of criminal behavior, more so in some environments than in others.

It is de rigueur these days to think of almost everything as "socially constructed," that is, having little or no objective reality. It is true that crime is socially constructed in the sense that certain acts are given names and criminalized, but these acts most certainly have a reality beyond being named and punished. Those who make the "socially constructed" argument conflate the distinction between *mala in se* and *mala prohibita* crimes. *Mala in se* crimes are universally condemned, and the litmus test for determining what constitutes such a crime is that no one (except in the most bizarre of circumstances) wants to be the victim of one. *Mala in se* crimes violate the core of human nature because they most threatened the survival and reproductive success of our ancestors in evolutionary environments, and thus fit firmly into a materialist reality (Krebs, 1998; Walsh, 2000b). *Mala prohibita* crimes are not universally condemned, and the act of criminalizing them is often arbitrary. However, the legal status of the act is less important than the willingness of some individuals to violate any standard of fairness or decency to satisfy their urges and to acquire resources, and to largely discount the negative consequences to self and others of doing so.

If a problem is considered biological, therapeutic nihilism will ensue.

This argument carries with it the assumption that any behavior said to have a biological basis is impervious to treatment, and if accepted as such, will lead to the cessation of treatment efforts via environmental improvement. For instance, in her argument against genetic explanations of problem behaviors, Diana Baumrind (1993:1313, emphasis added) states that "the purpose of identifying undesirable predispositions of individuals should be to devise more health-promoting interventions, not to discourage such attempts on the supposition that these predispositions are genetically based *and therefore intractable.*" Sandra Scarr (1993:1351) replies that only ignorance of genetics could motivate such a statement and that the fear of genetics among many social scientists would be allayed if only they would learn something about it.

The assumption that is it is easier to treat the kind of problems that are correlated with criminal behavior in environmental ways rather than biological ways is wrong in certain instances. A number of problems of concern to criminologists have shown significant improvement after their biological correlates had been identified and pharmacological treatments were developed for them. With the advent of antipsychotic medications, many people who would have been incarcerated in mental institutions in previous years now lead reasonably normal lives (Buckley et al., 1996); the treatment of sex offenders with antiandrogen medication such as Depo-Provera and Andocur dramatically reduces recidivism (Marsh & Walsh, 1995); alcohol and drug antagonists such as Antabuse, Naloxone, and Disipramine have proven to be of great help in the treatment of alcoholics and drug abusers (Ling, Wesson, Charuvastra & Klett, 1996); and extreme symptoms of PMS and depression have been greatly alleviated by administering progesterone (Trunnell, Turner & Kaye, 1988) and Prozac (Kramer, 1993), respectively. None of these pharmacological interventions are panaceas. They all must be supplemented by psychosocial treatment, but they represent a dramatic improvement over the days when treatment modalities for these problems were exclusively of a psychosocial nature (or simply imprisonment, which is hardly the most liberal of solutions to the crime problem). These psychosocial treatments, however, are treatments for various syndromes, some of which are associated with *criminality*, not treatments for *crime*. Problems associated with crime (i.e., the incidence and prevalence of criminal acts) can only be addressed socially, economically, and politically. *The most beneficial anticrime strategies are environmental because they seek to reduce the proportion of a population that becomes criminal.*

Conservatives as well as liberals are sometimes upset about alleged biological causes of criminal behavior, feeling that to accept such allegations removes moral responsibility. It does no such thing. Explanations can never become excuses for criminality. As we shall see time and again, certain biosocial variables constitute risk factors for criminal behavior. Whatever those factors are, they are not deterministic causes, and they never relieve the individual possessing them of the obligation to behave decently and obey the law.

Crime cannot have a biological basis because crime rates change rapidly and changes in genes require many generations.

This argument conflates the distinction between *crime* and *criminality*, between the prevalence of criminal behavior in a population and the differential propensity of individuals to engage in it. Beirne and Messerschmidt (2000:221) do this in their criticism of self-control theory when they inform us that the United States has seven to 10 times the homicide rate of most European countries and ask: "Is it because the U.S. population somehow has less self-control, or is it something to do with the nature of social organization in the United States?" Such a criticism is a red herring. As has already been acknowledged, crime rates have relatively little to do with individual differences, but criminality has a lot to do with them. It is indisputable that crime rates reflect fluctuating social, economic, and political phenomena operating on relatively constant genotypes. Because causal status can only be conferred on factors that vary, fluctuating environments have to be the only causes of fluctuating crime rates. However, environmental (macro-level) factors lower or raise individual thresholds for engaging in crime, and this is where individual (micro-level) factors come into play. Some individuals would engage in criminal behavior in the most noncriminogenic of environments, while others would remain noncriminal in the most criminogenic of environments. In between these two extremes are individuals with traits conducive to criminal behavior that lie dormant until triggered by appropriate environmental events. It is in attempting to explain why individuals differ in their propensity to commit criminal acts in similar environments, and in attempting to explain person-by-environment interactions, that biosocial criminology makes its contribution. In any science, micro and macro levels of analysis (once the difference is appreciated) should take place side by side without recriminations.

Biological theories tend to be insensitive to people's feelings.

Even if critics do not go so far as to accuse biosocial theorists of having a racist, classist, or sexist agenda, they may feel that the cold stare of science can be discomforting for some and thus perhaps should not be brought to bear on certain "sensitive" topics. For example, psychologist J. Philippe Rushton's evolutionary r/K theory rank-orders "Negroids," "Caucasoids," and "Mongoloids" along a number of biological and social dimensions such as maturation rates, gamete production, twinning rates, stability of bonded relationships, rates of child abuse and neglect, and early onset of sexual activity. Because these rankings are almost invariably found to be unfavorable (at least from a white, middle-class, European-American point of view) to people of African origin and favorable to Asians, with people of European origin fitting between, many social scientists view Rushton's work to be at least insensitive or, at worst, racist. For example, after admitting that the assemblage of data on race collected by Rushton is "not readily dismissible, although many have tried," Daniel Freedman states that his major problem with Rushton's work is not with his data "but with the emotionally distant nature of [Rushton's] scientific presentations." He goes on to opine that in the realm of human studies, "cold science will not do, *for only with love and warmth will the proper things be looked at, the proper things said, and a sympathetic picture of the study participants emerge*" (1997:61, emphasis in original).

This statement from a respected empirical psychologist seems to be saying that ignorance is sometimes bliss. What are the "proper things" to be looked at? What are the "proper things" to be said? Do we lie, cheat, and fudge the data so that we do not offend anyone's sensibilities? Should we always seek a "sympathetic image" of human subjects, even if they happen to be serial killers, Nazis, terrorists, torturers, muggers of old ladies, career criminals? Isn't science supposed to be "emotionally distant," that is, detached? There is no doubt that many would like to see the likes of Rushton silenced, and some have tried to do so by threats, intimidation, and even legal action (Rushton, 1994). Such a response to unpopular research is an unconscionable affront to the spirit of science. In his defense of science against ignorance, Carl Sagan (1995:430) quoted English philosopher John Stuart Mill's declaration that silencing an unpopular opinion is "a peculiar evil." Mill stated:

If the opinion is right, we are robbed of the "opportunity of exchanging error for truth"; and if it is wrong, we are deprived of a deeper understanding of the truth in its "collision with error." If we know only our own side of the argument, we hardly know even that; it becomes stale, soon learned only by rote, untested, a pallid and lifeless truth.

We may conclude that sociology, and by extension, criminology, is the soft underbelly of science. The subject matter of our discipline assures us that we can never achieve the "washboard abs" of the natural sciences, but we can at least embark on a regimen of theoretical exercises to at least firm them up. If we do not, we will forfeit the study of criminal behavior to disciplines with sturdier midsections. We cannot, and must not, bend to the whims of those who dismiss the guidance of theories that have proven their worth time after time on purely ideological grounds. Ignorance is not bliss; it is simply ignorance. "Paradigm shifts" are always a little frightening for those who find comfort in the familiar, but they are also extremely invigorating. As Thomas Kuhn so well put it:

Led by a new paradigm, scientists adopt new instruments and look in new places. Even more important, during revolutions scientists see new and different things when looking with familiar instruments in places they have looked before. It is rather as if the professional community has been suddenly transported to another planet where familiar objects are seen in a different light and are joined by unfamiliar ones as well (1970:111).

Chapter 2

Behavior Genetics and Criminality

Behavior (or behavioral) genetics is the application of quantitative genetics to the study of human personality, characteristics, and behavior. It seeks to estimate the relative contributions of heredity and environment to variance in quantitative measures of phenotypical traits and behaviors such as IQ, extroversion, and delinquency. Behavior geneticists are interested in much the same sort of issues as other behavioral scientists, but they employ different research designs and operate with different assumptions.

The seeds of behavior genetics were sown in the nineteenth century by Charles Darwin's theory of evolution, Gregor Mendel's experiments with garden peas, and Francis Galton's statistical work on hereditary genius. Darwin's theory required that there be variation among organisms for a variety of traits (for anatomical structures and for physiological and "mental" processes) and a selection process by which the most useful variants were retained and harmful ones eliminated. The theory also required a hereditary mechanism by which these advantageous traits were passed down from generation to generation. Darwin was unaware of the nature of the mechanism that allowed for the transmission of traits across the generations, but he knew that there had to be one.

Gregor Mendel's meticulous experiments provided preliminary details about this mechanism of selective retention and elimination. Mendel noticed that although the traits of his peas (size, color, shape) remained fairly constant over the generations, a trait occasionally disappeared and reemerged several generations later. He also noted that certain trait attributes were dominant over others, such as tallness over shortness, because the offspring of crossbred tall and short plants were always tall. When his tall-short hybrids were interbred, however, he found that about one-fourth of the offspring were short. Mendel deduced from this that traits such as shortness are not lost when combined with tallness, but are "hidden" and can only be expressed in the absence of the dominant trait. He also concluded that there are two

23

"factors" for every trait, one of which is dominant and the other recessive. We now call Mendel's "factors" *genes* and their alternate forms (one each from maternal and paternal sources) *alleles*.

Like his cousin Charles Darwin, Francis Galton was ignorant of Mendel's work. Galton's interests lay in the area of hereditary individual differences in human traits, particularly in cognitive and temperamental traits. Galton's contributions to behavior genetics were theoretical, methodological, and statistical. His *Hereditary Genius*, published in 1869, provided early evidence of the intergenerational transmission of cognitive and personality traits. As far as is known, Galton was the first to stress the importance of using twins to study human traits in order to disentangle the effects of heredity and environment. Galton and his students/followers (Karl Pearson, Ronald Fisher, Sewall Wright) invented a variety of statistical methods (correlation, regression, chi-square, analysis of variance, path analysis) for the express purpose of estimating the transmission of genetic variance (Rushton, 1990:119).

WHAT ARE GENES?

According to evolutionary biologist Richard Dawkins (1982:13), genes have a "sinister, juggernaut-like reputation" among social scientists. A juggernaut is an inexorable force that crushes everything in its path. If social scientists really do tend to think of genes in this way, then it is reasonable for them to believe that if the source of any social problem has been declared "genetic," it is beyond the influence of anything in the environment to prevent, ameliorate, or change. This kind of thinking may go back to Biology 101, in which we learned that genes had alternate forms called alleles that occupy the same locus on a chromosome. We placed these alleles in Punnett squares (big T for tall, little t for short, big S for smooth, little s for wrinkled, and so forth), and learned that if a plant had "TtSs" alleles, its immutable destiny was to be tall and wrinkled, no matter what. If we think that genes work on human personality and behavior in the same way, then it is understandable that we should fear the "sinister" notion that genes have anything to do with those things.

On the other hand, rather than viewing genes as juggernauts, we might go to the opposite extreme and dismiss them as irrelevant to understanding human personality and behavior, reasoning that "genetic" means "inevitable," and because we know that nothing about human social behavior is inevitable, genes cannot be involved in it. Both of these positions arise from dichotomous nature-versus-nurture thinking ("if genetic, then not environmental; if environmental, then not genetic"), and both are absolutely wrong.

To begin with, the genetics underlying human traits and behavior do not typically follow the deterministic Mendelian dominant/recessive rules that pea plants do (eye color is an example of one trait that generally does). For instance, the offspring of tall and short human human parents are usually of intermediate height, and the offspring of dark- and light-skinned parents typically have skin color of intermediate hue. Human height and skin color are examples of *incomplete dominance*, which means that dominant and recessive traits blend their traits in the phenotype. The traits of interest to criminologists (aggression, impulsiveness, intelligence, empathy, etc.) are not underlain by discrete single-gene distributions governed by the rules of dominance and recession. Rather, they are polygenetic traits (produced by complexes of coordinated genes each having minor additive effects) governed by incomplete dominance.

A gene is simply a strand of DNA that codes for the amino acid sequence of a protein or the base sequence of an RNA molecule. Genes do not code for any kind of behavior, feeling, or emotion. There is no neat cryptography by which certain kinds of genes build certain kinds of brains, which in turn produce certain kinds of behavior. These protein products of gene activity are enzymes, hormones, or cell-structure proteins. Hormones (including neurotransmitters) obviously have a lot to do with how we behave or feel, but they do not *cause* us to behave or feel one way or another, they *facilitate* our behavior and our feelings. These substances produce tendencies or dispositions to respond to the environment in one way rather than in another. Even this might be too deterministic a slant to put on the role of genes. It might be better yet to think of genes as modulators of how we respond to the environment, because the gene products that facilitate behavior and emotions are produced in response to environmental stimuli.

One can use a thermostatic image to convey the importance of the environment to the expression of genes. A thermostat sitting on the wall senses when the temperature surrounding it is above or below its setting. When this information arrives at its sensory mechanism, it activates the furnace or air conditioner to restore the house temperature to the comfort level desired by its inhabitants. Thus, the operation of the heating/cooling system depends on environmental information (the temperature of the room and the perceptions of the person who sets the thermostat regarding what is a comfortable temperature) to restore the equilibrium between being too cold or too warm. Far from people being slaves to their genes, genes are usually at the beck and call of people.

Think of the nucleus of a cell, which is sitting and waiting to instruct its DNA to unwind and transcribe itself into a slice of *messenger RNA* (mRNA), as the furnace. The afferent, or sensory, nerves (eyes, ears, skin, etc.) that transmit information about the state of the environment to the spinal cord (if a required response is reflexive) or to the brain (if the information needs to be processed before responding) may be thought of as a set of physiological thermostats. Upon receiving information from the environment that requires attention, the "furnace" in the nucleus of the cell kicks on and sends instructions via its mRNA into the protein-building factory in the cellular cytoplasm outside the nucleus. These instructions are in the form of triplets of bases called *codons*. *Transfer RNA* (tRNA) "reads" the coded message and picks up and transports the appropriate *anticodons* (sets of bases that complement the codons on the mRNA) to the mRNA strand where they are slotted into place by molecules of *ribosomal RNA*. When this is complete, we have a protein that will help the organism respond effectively to the environmental challenge by activating our efferent, or motor, nerves.

The protein manufactured depends on the nature of the challenge facing the organism. If the challenge is a cut finger, genes will automatically manufacture fibrin, which criss-crosses the cut to entangle blood cells, thus preventing excess bleeding. If it is something requiring conscious decisions, such as whether to fight or to flee, or whether to give in to a prurient sexual urge, several different proteins may be manufactured to facilitate the person's response regardless of the decision made. Note that just as information from the environment activates the furnace, so information from the environment activates the genetic machinery. Genes are not little automatons pulling strings in our heads and determining the directions in which our lives will go; rather, they help us to get there once the direction has been decided. This is not to say, however, that variability in genes and gene products does not bias us in certain directions, doing so weakly or strongly at different stages of development and within different environmental contexts. Differential responses to environmental challenges may be most proximally determined by the person's phenomenology, but phenomenology itself depends on a causal chain involving prior learning, enduring personal traits, developmental history, genetic inheritance, and the evolutionary history of the species.

BEHAVIOR-GENETIC RESEARCH DESIGNS VERSUS SSSM DESIGNS

The standard social science model (SSSM) of socialization and development explores how parents, through parenting style, modeling, and explicit instructions, influence and mold the personality, attitudes, and behavior of their offspring. The research design usually includes sampling a single child from a number of families and correlating a number of predictor variables (e.g., parenting style) with outcome variables (e.g., antisocial attitudes and behavior). These studies tend to find such things as (1) children who are treated affectionately are less antisocial than those who are treated abusively, and (2) parents who manage their lives well and get along with others have children who manage their lives well and get along with others. As many self-confessed former SSSM researchers (J. Harris, 1998:30; Maccoby, 1992) have pointed out, such studies are essentially useless because they ignore (1) the role of genes and (2) the role of children's effects on parents. They are uninterpretable unless we are willing to defend the positions that genes have zero effect on human traits and that children's personality and behavior have zero effect on parental behavior.

David Rowe (1994:2) provides an example that highlights the difference between SSSM and behavior genetic socialization research. Suppose medical researchers want to determine the effects of psychotherapy and a new drug on depression. A well-designed study to assess this question would require four comparison groups: (1) drug plus therapy, (2) drug alone, (3) therapy alone, and (4) a control group receiving no treatment. Suppose, however, that researchers use only Groups 1 and 4, find that members of Group 1 have fewer and shorter depressive episodes than Group 4, and then announce that the drug works. The medical community would soundly reject such a study because the findings could be the result of the therapy rather than the drug, or vice-versa. The only way we can possibly tell which of the methods accounted for what percentage of the variance in treatment effects is to disentangle their combined effects, which would be accomplished by examining the results from Groups 2 and 3 as well as from Groups 1 and 4.

Let us recast this hypothetical study in the form of socialization research on the effect of parenting style on children's antisocial behavior. Let Group 1 stand for the joint effects of genes (shared by parents and offspring) and parenting style, Group 2 for parent/offspring genetic similarity only, and Group 3 for parenting style only (a control group is not required). SSSM socialization researchers typically look only at parenting style (Group 3) and announce that parenting style affects children's antisocial behavior, which ignores genes and the effects of children's behavior on parenting style.

An announcement such as this generally does not generate skepticism among sociologically oriented socialization researchers, who would rather continue to operate as though genes really do not matter. Psychologically oriented socialization researchers, however, have responded to behavior-genetic criticisms and findings. Many of these researchers have responded with extremely sophisticated designs that in some ways augment classic behavior-genetic designs using direct and specific environmental measures (which are not typically a part of behavior genetic studies) in addition to genetic measures (Collins et al., 2000).

In order to disentangle genetic from environmental effects, behavior-genetic models randomize genes to determine the effects of environments and randomize environments to determine the effects of genes. My discussion of these methods will center on intelligence (as measured by IQ scores) because this is the human trait that has been studied more than any other by behavior geneticists and psychologists. Literally thousands of behavior genetic studies of IQ have been conducted around the world with remarkably consistent results. I make no attempt here to defend against accusations that IQ tests are biased or that genes are not substantially involved in intelligence. These allegations have been examined and rejected by the National Academy of Sciences (Seligman, 1992), the overwhelming majority of 1,020 Ph.D.-level experts surveyed by Snyderman and Rothman (1988), and the American Psychological Association's Task Force on Intelligence (Neisser et al., 1995). Recent studies involving neuroimaging techniques and molecular genetics have increased confidence in the genetic basis of intelligence (reviewed by Plomin & Petrill, 1997; see also the special edition of the journal *Intelligence*, guest edited by Linda Gottfredson, 1997a).

THE CONCEPT OF HERITABILITY

A concept of central importance to behavior genetics is that of *heritability* (h^2). Heritability is the ratio of genetic variance to total phenotypical variance of a particular trait or characteristic. It is a quantification (ranging between 0 and 1) indicating the extent to which variance in a trait or characteristic is due to genetic influences. Much of behavior genetics involves partitioning phenotypical variance (the observed, measured variance in a trait) into genetic and environmental components, and is thus important for evaluating environmental as well as genetic effects on the trait in question. All cognitive, behavioral, and personality traits have been shown to be heritable (Buss, 1995; McGue, 1994).

There is a lot of confusion among nonbiologists about the terms *inherited* and *heritability*, a confusion that is itself related to the failure to understand polymorphism. Polymorphism refers to the differences in allelic combinations at chromosomal loci that make us different from one another within the species. All humans have all the genes it takes to make us human, that is, all the genes for species-defining physical and mental structures. Thus, all human structures and traits are *inherited* because they are coded for in the DNA bequeathed to us by our ancestors, but they are not *heritable*. There are no "heritability estimates" for the presence or absence of human intelligence, aggression, altruism, noses, sex organs, bipedalism, and so on. Barring environmental insults, we all have these things, and they function the same way for each of us. Variance in the presence or absence of a nose, for instance, would reflect environmental factors, such as an accident, not genetic factors. It is the *variance* in their quantitative properties governed by the effects of polymorphism on such characteristics as strength, range, threshold, size, color, and so forth, not the properties per se, that is the basis for calculating heritability.

A heritability coefficient is a statistic estimating genetic and environmental variance components in a trait within a *population*. It varies among populations as well as within the same population as it experiences different environments. It is important for social scientists to realize that heritability does not place constraints on environmental effects; that is, knowing what percentage of the variance in a trait in a population is attributable to genes does not set limits on creating new environments that could influence the trait (Bronfenbrenner & Ceci, 1994). Nor does the decomposition of variance into genetic and environmental effects tell us how much of the trait itself is due to these factors. It only tells us how much of the *variance* in the trait is accounted for by those effects (Plomin, 1994). Heritability estimates the proportion of variance in a trait attributable to *actualized* genetic potential, and whatever the unactualized potential may be, it cannot be inferred from h^2 (Bronfenbrenner & Ceci, 1994:315). Seeds from a prize-winning rose are very likely to realize their maximum genetic potential in a Virginia garden but are unlikely to thrive at all if planted in the Nevada desert.

Because heritability estimates fluctuate among different populations and in different environments, behavior-genetic studies allow us to assess the relative importance of the mix of genetic and environmental factors over time and place (Plomin, 1995). This fact should excite social scientists, but because many of still think in "nature versus nurture" terms, it probably doesn't. As useful as heritability estimates are, they unfortunately help to perpetuate this false nature/nurture dichotomy because these estimates divide trait variance into "genetic" and "environmental" components (Freedman, 1997:59). Unlike those who speak in terms of nature versus nurture, behavior geneticists are aware that genes and their environment are not separable ingredients in the real world and that heritability is simply a formula that *statistically* transforms them into such. Genes and environments have the same relationship to *phenotype* as hydrogen and oxygen have to water, and length and width have to area—each meaningless without their complement in terms of the wholes they describe. If behavior geneticists say that genes are more important in accounting for variation in X in a given population than the environment (or vice versa), they are using shorthand for what they and their colleagues know is the result of a complex interaction of both.

The determination of heritability in any trait of interest requires that every genotype be exposed to identical environments because variance can only be attributed to factors that vary. A random sample of genetically heterogeneous corn seeds planted in identically nourishing environments would yield phenotypical trait variance (sweetness, color, size, etc.) that is *entirely* attributable to genes (i.e., h^2 would be 1.0). Because the environment was held constant across variable genotypes, it cannot be considered a source of phenotypical variance. Likewise, a random sample of genetically homogeneous corn seeds planted in diverse environments would yield trait variance that is 100 percent attributable to the environment (h^2 would be zero) because genetic material was held constant across variable environments.

Because many social scientists exhibit a tendency to believe that anything "genetic" implies immutability, it is necessary once again to point out that even if h^2 is 1.0 for a trait, it does *not* mean that it is beyond the power of the environment to change. It would be absurd to read "$h^2 = 1.0$" as meaning that the environment has no effect. After all, genes cannot be expressed in any way without an environment. As Lykken (1995:85) reminds us, without the environment, one's genome would create "nothing more than a damp spot on the carpet." High heritability tells us that the *present environment at the present time* accounts for very little variance in the trait; it does not tell what other environments *may* affect variance in the trait.

Let us perform another "corn seed thought experiment." This time, we will select two random samples of heterogeneous seeds and plant them in environments that are each homogeneous within themselves but heterogeneous with respect to each other. That is, we make Environment A more conducive to the realization of the potential inherent in each genotype than Environment B. Because the environments are constant and the genetic material is variable in each sample, phenotypical variance in the corn cobs from each sample will be entirely attributable to genetics ($h^2 = 1.0$). However, although the *within-sample* variance for both samples is entirely a function of the genetic differences among the seeds, the *between-sample* variance is entirely a function of the different environments in which the two samples were grown (example adapted from Lewontin [1982:132]). Bringing Environment B up to the standards of Environment A will improve phenotype quality commensurately, despite h^2 being 1.0 for Environment B's phenotype.

Human beings, of course, are genetically heterogeneous and live in diverse environments, making it much more difficult to decompose phenotypic variance in human traits neatly into genetic and environmental effects. We cannot control environmental effects very well, but we can control genetic variability by the twin-study and adoption methods, as will be demonstrated below.

Shared and Nonshared Environments

In addition to sorting genetic from environmental effects, heritability studies also enable us to further decompose variance into shared and nonshared environmental effects. Just as shared genes serve to make those who share them more alike and nonshared genes serve to make them different, shared environments serve to make people similar and nonshared environments serve to make them different. In behavior genetics, shared (or common) environment refers to the environment experienced by children reared in the same family. Shared environmental variables include parental SES, religion, values and attitudes, parenting style, family size, intactness of home, and neighborhood. Nonshared (or unique) environment can be familial or extrafamilial. Familial nonshared variables include gender, birth order, perinatal trauma, illness, and parental favoritism. Extrafamilial nonshared factors include having different peer groups and teachers; experiencing a different, time-dependent culture (e.g., the "placid" 1950s versus the "far out" 1960s); and any other idiosyncratic experiences. Behavior-genetic studies report the percentage of variance in traits that is attributable to environmental factors, but as previously stated, they do not typically endeavor to determine what those factors are; they leave that to the social scientists.

Various environmental features may sometimes be considered either shared or nonshared. For instance, parenting style may not be uniform for all siblings and may be more a function of the evocative style of each child than anything else. This is supported by studies showing that monozygotic twins *reared apart* assess their affectual experiences with their different adoptive parents significantly more similarly than do dizygotic twins *reared together* (Baker & Daniels, 1990; Plomin & Bergeman, 1991). These findings indicate that just as there is environmental mediation of genetic effects, there is genetic mediation of environmental effects. These effects will be explored in the context of a later discussion of the concept of gene/environment correlation.

One of the most interesting findings of behavior genetics is that shared environmental effects on cognitive and personality traits, although moderate during childhood, disappear almost completely in adulthood. This is *not* to say parents have no effect on children apart from the genes they provide. The expression of many heritable traits often depends to various degrees on parental factors (Collins et al., 2000). Parental effects on their adult children's attitudes, values, behavior, and choice of leisure activities and professions do not necessarily disappear, although such effects are surely confounded with genetic effects. It is only averred that parental effects on personality and cognitive traits that made siblings somewhat similar while they shared a home fail to survive after the period of common rearing. The nonshared features of the "common" environment appear to be much more salient with respect to the formation of an individual's personality and cognitive traits. Genetic effects on personality and cognitive traits, however, continue to increase throughout the lifespan (McGue, Bouchard et al., 1993). I am reminded here of the old saying: "The older I get, the more I become myself."

The Twin Method

Behavior geneticists are able to determine the genetic and environmental sources of variance by comparing interclass correlations for a trait between monozygotic (MZ) twin pairs and same-sex dizygotic (DZ) twin pairs. The twin-study method takes advantage of the fact that MZ twins are genetically identical; that is, the coefficient of their genetic relationship is 1.0. DZ twins, on average, share one-half of their genes, so their coefficient of genetic relationship is 0.5. If genes are an important source of variation for a trait, individuals who are more genetically similar should be more alike on that trait than individuals who are less genetically similar. If this were not so, it would be empirically and logically impossible to calculate heritability coefficients significantly greater than zero. Under the assumption of a purely polygenetic model (no environmental effects), the theoretical correlation between a trait and genes between MZ twins should be 1.0, it should be 0.5 between DZ twins and full siblings, 0.25 for half siblings, and zero for unrelated individuals. Departures from these theoretically expected correlations reflect environmental (everything not transmitted by DNA is considered environmental) effects plus measurement error.

Differences in the correlations between different kinship pairs on measured traits are used to determine the heritability of those traits. Table 2.1 shows the average weighted correlations between IQ scores of pairs of individuals with various degrees of genetic relatedness obtained from 111 different studies (Bouchard & McGue, 1981). The predicted correlations are those we would expect (ignoring measurement error) if: (1) IQ depended entirely on genes and the environment was irrelevant, and (2) if IQ depended entirely on the environment and genes were irrelevant.

The fact that both genes and the environment are important to IQ is demonstrated by the correlations actually observed. We see that the greater the degree of genetic relatedness between pairs, the higher the correlation between paired IQs. MZ twins reared together have the highest average correlation (.86), followed by MZ twins reared apart (.72). A strict genetic theory would predict a correlation of 1.00 in both cases, because MZ twins are genetically identical. The difference between the two correlations provides a rough estimate of shared environmental effects. The pattern and magnitude of the correlations by degree of genetic relationships across 111 studies involving thousands of kinship pairs provides impressive support for the claim that genes are substantially involved in cognitive functioning as it is measured by IQ tests. Although we expect minor variation in the magnitude of the correlations from study to study, the same robust pattern is invariably found (Loehlin & DeFries, 1987; Plomin & DeFries, 1980; Rowe, 1997; Seligman, 1992; Snyderman & Rothman, 1988).

Table 2.1
Average Weighted Correlations for Various Kinship Pairings on IQ and Predicted Correlations Based on Degree of Genetic and Environmental Relatedness*

Relatedness	Actual	Genetically Predicted	Environmentally Predicted
Monozygotic twins reared together	.86	1.00	1.00
Monozygotic twins reared apart	.72	1.00	.00
Dizygotic twins reared together	.60	.50	1.00
Biological siblings reared together	.47	.50	1.00
Half siblings reared together	.36	.25	1.00
Adoptive siblings reared together	.34	.00	1.00
Siblings reared apart	.24	.50	.00

*Actual *r*s from Bouchard & McGue, *Science*, 1981, p. 1057.

Computing Heritability

In order to compute h^2, we take the correlation for a given trait between pairs of subjects with one degree of genetic relatedness and compare it to the correlation obtained from pairs of subjects with a different degree of genetic relatedness. MZ and DZ twins reared together constitute the two most common genetic relationship pairs used to calculate h^2.

Let CG stand for "common genes," CE for "common environment," and r for the correlation coefficient relating how closely, averaged over all twin pairs, one twin's score matches the other's. CG = 1.0 for MZ twins and 0.5 for DZ twins. Because all MZ and DZ twin pairs were reared together, in both cases, CE = 1.0. The correlations are taken from Table 2.1. The formula for calculating heritability from correlations obtained from MZ and DZ twins reared together is:

$$h^2 = 2(rMZ - rDZ) \text{ substituting } h^2 = 2(.86 - .60) = 2(.26) = .52$$

The logic behind the formula may be grasped as follows:

Kinship Pairs	CG		CE		r
MZ twins reared together	1.0	+	1.0	yields a correlation of	.86
DZ twins reared together	0.5	+	1.0	yields a correlation of	.60
Difference	0.5	−	0.0	=	.26
Difference x 2 =	1.0			=	.52

more formally

$$h^2 = 2 \left[(v_{CG} + v_{CE}) - (1/2\ v_{CG} + v_{CE}) \right] = 2\ (1/2\ v_{CG}) = v_{CG}$$
where v_{CG} = variance attributable to common genes
  v_{CE} = variance attributable to common environment

Thus, the heritability coefficient is equal to twice the difference between the MZ and DZ correlations. We double the difference because the reported correlations are due to common genes and common environments for both sets of twin pairs. If we subtract rDZ from rMZ, we have taken away all IQ variance due to common environment and one-half of the variance due to common genes $[(v_{CG} + v_{CE}) - (1/2\ v_{CG} + v_{CE})]$. Thus, rMZ − rDZ (.86 − .60 = .26) equals one-half of the difference (or variance) in IQ due to genes. Because it is equal to only one-half, it must be doubled to arrive at an estimate of the total variance in IQ attributable to genes.

We may compute h^2 from the MZ and AS (adopted siblings) correlations as follows:

$$h^2 = rMZ - rAS \qquad \text{substituting} \qquad h^2 = .86 - .34 = .52$$

The coefficient of genetic relationship for adopted siblings is zero; they share no common genes. Thus, the correlation of .34 between their IQ scores is entirely the result of their common environment, and the .52 difference between the MZ and AS correlations is therefore entirely the result of the genetic relatedness of MZ twins.

Kinship Pairs	CG		CE		r
MZ twins reared together	1.0	+	1.0	yields a correlation of	.86
Adopted sibs reared together	0.0	+	1.0	yields a correlation of	.34
Difference	1.0	−	0.0	=	.52

Because some kinship relationships tend to overestimate h^2 and others tend to underestimate it, all kinship relationships should be computed and the average h^2 taken as the estimate. We have presented the most basic method of computing h^2, but the logic is the same for all

methods and the results do not vary significantly from more sophisticated methods. Some theorists (Lykken, 1995; Rowe, 1994) argue that
the best estimate of h^2 is simply the correlation between MZ twins
reared apart. Note that r is not squared to express the percentage of
total variance shared by pairs, the correlation itself does that. We are
not predicting one twin's score from the other's; we are determining the
extent to which the observed variance is due to shared variance
(covariance) among the pairs (Plomin & Daniels, 1987:16).

The proportion of variance in IQ accounted for by the environment
can be further broken down into common environmental (c^2) and
specific environmental (e^2) sources. Recall that common environmental influences are those shared environmental experiences that
make people similar to one another, and specific environmental influences are those nonshared experiences that make them different from
one another. We may estimate CE from the correlations in Table 2.1
by the following formula:

$$c^2 = 2rDZ - rMZ = 1.20 - .86 = .34.$$

To illustrate the logic:

Kinship Pairs	CG		CE		r
MZ twins reared together × 2	1.0	+	2.0	yields a "correlation" of	1.20
MZ twins reared together	1.0	+	1.0	yields a correlation of	.86
Difference	0.0	−	0.1	=	.34

More formally,

$$c^2 = [2(1/2 \, v_{CG} + v_{CE})] - (v_{CG} + v_{CE}) = (v_{CG} + 2v_{CE}) - (v_{CG} + v_{CE})$$
$$= v_{CE}$$

The DZ correlation is doubled to equalize the proportion of variance accounted for by shared genes with the proportion accounted for
by shared genes among MZ twins. Once genetic variance is eliminated by subtraction, we have only that portion of the variance accounted for by common environment.

Thus, genetics and common environmental experiences together
account for 86 percent of the variance in IQ (which is equal to the correlation for MZ twins reared together). The variance accounted for by
specific environment is simply $1 - (h^2 + c^2)$, which is the same as $1 -$
rMZ. In the present case, $e^2 = 1 - (.52 + .34) = .14$.

The great majority of the 111 studies on which these calculations
are based were studies of children and adolescents. As indicated earlier, shared environmental effects (which appear substantial from our
calculations) essentially fall to zero in adulthood. Nonshared envi-

ronmental effects remain stable, albeit modest, into adulthood, and genetic effects increase, with estimates of adult h^2 for IQ as high as .80 (see McGue et al., 1993; Plomin & Petrill, 1997; and Rowe, 1997, for reviews).

Broad and Narrow Heritability

There are two types of assessed heritability: broad and narrow. Broad heritability refers to trait variance accounted for by all sources of genetic variance, that is, *additive*, *dominance*, and *epistasis*; narrow heritability includes additive variance only. Additive genetic variance is the sum of the mean effects of a number of genes at different chromosomal loci across the genotype. The process is analogous to summing r-squared values in multiple correlation when there is no shared variance among the predictor variables. Additive effects are the effects that are transmitted to the offspring, and as such, they are relevant to predicting average offspring phenotypes from "gene dosage" and are thus the "expected value" of a trait.

Dominance and epistasis effects are nonadditive interaction effects that are not transmitted to offspring and are thus not relevant to the prediction of average offspring phenotypes. Dominance effects represent the interaction of alleles at a single homologous locus, with only the dominant allele of a dominant/recessive pair being expressed in the offspring phenotype. The alleles themselves, of course, are transmitted to offspring; it is the allelic interactions per se that are not transmitted. In contrast to dominance effects, which represent interaction at one chromosomal locus, epistasis effects result from the interaction of alleles at a number of chromosomal loci. Dominance and epistasis effects are deviations from the expected value of a phenotype predicted by gene dosage that decrease similarity between parental and offspring phenotypes.

Because dominance and epistasis usually have quite small effects on most human characteristics, behavioral geneticists often ignore them. However, to the extent that nonadditive variance influences a trait, twin-study methods tend to inflate heritability estimates (Plomin, Chipuer & Loehlin, 1990:229). This may be important because while MZ twins share all sources of genetic variability, DZ twins share only about one-quarter of the variance due to dominance and very little due to epistasis. The importance of nonadditive affects thus depends on the trait in question. If a computed value of h^2 is greater than the correlation between MZ pairs reared together (the upper limit of h^2), we know that trait variance is significantly affected by nonadditive genetic variance (Plomin, Chipuer & Loehlin, 1990:227).

Heritability in Different Environments

As previously noted, heritability is not a constant. Like other population parameters, it changes with the composition of the population and with changes in the environment. Numerous studies have shown that heritability of human traits is different in different environments and that genetic effects are expressed or repressed to varying degrees in different environments (Goldsmith, 1994). Because variation can be attributed only to sources that vary, it follows that the more environments are equalized (the less variability there is within them), the greater will be the genetic effects—and thus the larger h^2 will be. Conversely, the more variable the environment, the lower the heritability of any such traits. A high heritability coefficient for a given trait indicates that a society is doing a good job with respect to equalizing the relevant environment for that trait.

In addition to the homogeneity/heterogeneity of environments, heritability varies with environmental quality. More advantageous environments allow for greater genetic expression, more disadvantaged environments depress full expression (Bradley & Caldwell, 1991; Walsh, 1992). For instance, Scarr-Salapatek (1971) computed the heritability of IQ to be .34 and .72 for African-American twins reared in disadvantaged and advantaged environments, respectively, and Fischbein (1980) computed heritability coefficients of .30 and .78 for IQ among white twins reared in low and high SES environments, respectively.

The Adoption Method

The second method used in behavior genetics to disentangle genetic and environmental effects is the adoption method. The adoption method allows us to randomize genes in order to investigate the effect of common environments and to randomize environments to investigate the effect of common genes. In the first instance, phenotypical trait similarities between genetically unrelated individuals reared in the same home must be entirely a function of their common environment. In the second instance, any similarities between genetically related individuals reared in different homes must be a function of their shared genes. This method also allows us to compare trait similarities between adoptees and both their biological and adoptive parents.

Adoption studies do tend to show that being raised in an environment more advantageous than that which could be provided by biological parents of adoptees can have beneficial effects on personality and cognitive traits. This is to be expected because most adoptions involve higher-than-average SES couples adopting children from lower-than-average SES backgrounds. However, adoptees tend to more close-ly resemble their biological parents than their adoptive parents on most measures of personality and cognitive functioning. For instance, the Bouchard and McGue (1981) data cited earlier show that the averaged weighted correlation between adopted mothers' and adopted chil-dren's IQs is .19, while the correlation between adopted children and their biological mothers is .22. While these correlations are not sig-nificantly different from one another, both are significantly different from the .42 between biological mothers and their children reared by them. This difference underscores the synergistic effect of genes and environment.

GENE/ENVIRONMENT INTERACTION AND CORRELATION

Gene/environment (G/E) interaction and G/E correlation are impor-tant concepts in behavior genetics. The concept of G/E interaction involves the reasonable assumption that different genotypes will inter-act with and respond to their environments in different ways; that is, people are differentially sensitive to identical environmental influ-ences. For instance, a relatively fearless and impulsive child is genet-ically more vulnerable to opportunities for antisocial behavior in its environment than is a more fearful and less impulsive child. Cast in terms of parental effects on children's behavior, we might say that the effect of parental practices on children's behavior varies across different children's genotypes. The robust finding that shared environmental effects are negligible for many personality and cognitive traits may be due to the differing effects of parental practices on their children (i.e., parental practice x child interaction) rather than the lack of parental influence per se (McGue, 1994). That is, nonshared environment can be subjective as well as objective in that the exact same objective event can lead to different consequences for one or the other of a pair of nonmonozygotic siblings.

Consistent with McGue's (1994) point, Turkheimer and Waldron (2000) make the important observation that what we call G/E inter-action gives us the erroneous impression that environmental effects are directly mediated by a person's genotype. The influence of an envi-ronmental event on the person depends on the person's phenotype *at the time*, and the person's current phenotype is the cumulative result of numerous previous interactions of his or her phenotype with the envi-ronment (Turkheimer & Waldron, 2000). Certainly, the genotype underlies and guides phenotypical development, but once the genotype sets the person on a particular developmental trajectory, it is genes and experience (i.e., the phenotype) that interact with the environment.

Plomin, DeFries, and McClearn (1980:360) have pointed out that despite its usefulness, G/E interaction has taken on an "almost mystical aura," and that its most connotative idea, that of the organism's active transactions with its environment, is better conveyed by the concept of G/E correlation. The concept of G/E correlation avers that genotypes and the environments they encounter are not random with respect to one another (Plomin, 1995; Scarr & McCartney, 1983). Included in the concept is the proposition that genetic factors influence complex psychosocial traits by influencing the range of individuals' experiences (McGue, 1994). The concept thus enables us to conceptualize the indirect way that genes help to determine what aspects of the environment will be salient and rewarding to us. We must again keep in mind that G/E correlation is shorthand for what is actually *genes + accumulated experience* (phenotypical) */environment correlation*. There are three types of G/E correlation: passive, reactive, and active.

Passive G/E correlation refers to the association between genotype and environment imposed on individuals in their earliest years. Biological parents provide infants with genes for certain traits and an environment favorable for their expression—genotype and its environment are positively correlated. For instance, a child born to intellectually gifted parents is very likely to receive genes conducive to above average intelligence and an environment in which intellectual behavior is modeled and reinforced. The child is thus set on a trajectory independent (passively) of his or her actions. This does not mean that the child does not actively engage its environment, it only means that he or she has merely been *exposed* to it and has not been instrumental in forming it. The pertinent environment for passive G/E correlation is limited to that shared with parents and siblings during infancy, the earliest years of life. As the scope of environmental interaction widens, the influence of passive G/E correlation wanes rapidly (Scarr, 1992).

Reactive G/E correlation picks up the trajectory from passive G/E correlation as the phenotype develops. Reactive GE correlation refers to the way parents, siblings, teachers, peers, and all others in the social environment react to the individual on the basis of his or her evocative behavior—the typical social science explanation of children's behavior that it is shaped only by the way others treat them. Behavior geneticists, on the other hand, aver that the treatment of children by others is as much a function of children's evocative behavior as it is of the interaction style of those who respond to them. Children bring with them traits that increase or decrease the probability of evoking certain kinds of responses when they interact with others. A well-behaved, pleasant, and compliant child generates different reactions from others than does a bad-tempered, moody, and mischievous child. Socialization is not something parents do to the child, it is a reciprocal process that parents and children do together.

Some children may be so resistant to parental control that parents either resort to extreme forms of punishment or give up on the child altogether. Social science researchers observing such children some time later will probably attribute their behavioral problems to their parents' "harsh" or "permissive" parental style, ignoring completely that "parental styles" evolved in response to the children's behavior. Either the punitive or permissive response will serve to exacerbate the child's already antisocial personality and drive him or her to seek social environments in which such behavior is accepted. Individuals similarly disposed usually populate such environments. Reactive G/E correlation thus serves to magnify differences among phenotypes.

Active G/E correlation refers to what Scarr and McCartney (1983) call "niche picking"; that is, the seeking of environments compatible with our genetic dispositions. Our genes, within the range of cultural possibilities and constraints, help to determine what features of the environment world will be salient and rewarding to us and what features will not. Active G/E correlation gains momentum as individuals mature and acquire the ability to take greater control of their lives. The effects of genes on forming these environments can be gauged by studies showing that the intelligence, personalities, and attitudes of MZ twins are essentially unaffected by whether or not they were reared together. That is, MZ twins reared apart construct their environments about as similarly as they would have had they been reared together, and considerably more similarly than DZ twins reared together (Bouchard et al., 1990).

The concept of G/E correlation is liberating in that it emphasizes that our minds and personalities are not simply the products of external forces, nor are our choices simply passive responses to social situations. G/E correlation is akin to the social psychological concept of *agency,* a concept developed in response to the "oversocialized" vision of human nature held by many social scientists. The agency concept maintains that people are active agents who, in the process of striving for autonomy, create their own environments just as they are created by them (Sztompka, 1994). The difference between the concepts of G/E correlation and agency is that the former provides a mechanism that accounts for environmental "niche picking."

BEHAVIOR GENETICS AND CRIMINAL BEHAVIOR

Adoption studies are useful to help determine if children at genetic risk for a particular disorder or behavior pattern experience more environmental risks (via G/E correlation) for those things than do children who are not at genetic risk (Nigg & Goldsmith, 1998). A study of this type conducted by O'Connor (1998) and his colleagues illustrates the role of G/E correlation mechanisms for antisocial behavior in late childhood/early adolescence. A number of adopted children were classified as either being or not being at genetic risk for antisocial behavior on the basis of their biological mothers' self-reported antisocial behavior collected prior to the birth of their children. It was found that from ages seven to 12, children at genetic risk for antisocial behavior consistently received more negative parenting from their adoptive parents than did children not at genetic risk. This effect was interpreted as reactive G/E correlation in that the poor behavior of the children was seen as evoking negative parenting. Genetic risk thus has an independent effect on environmental risk.

Another adoption study focused on G/E interaction (the differential effects of similar environments on different genotypes). Cadoret and his colleagues (1995) examined the antisocial history of adopted children separated at birth from biological mothers with verified antisocial histories, compared with other adoptees with biological mothers with no known history of antisocial behavior. It was found that adverse adoptive home environments (divorce/separation, substance abuse, neglect/abuse, marital discord) led to significant increases in antisocial behavior for adoptees at genetic risk but not for adoptees without genetic risk. Both genes and environments operating in tandem (interacting) were required to produce significant antisocial behavior, while neither seemed powerful enough in this study to produce such effects independent of the other. That is, genetically at-risk children reared in positive family environments did not display antisocial behavior, and children not at genetic risk did not become antisocial in adverse family environments.

Antisocial behaviors, especially adolescent antisocial behaviors, are an interesting exception to the modest shared environmental influences typically discovered for most human characteristics. Shared group influences reflect the socializing influences of peer groups, although such influences cannot be considered apart from the tendency of similar people to befriend one another (Rowe & Gulley, 1992). The shifting pattern of genetic and environmental effects is readily seen in studies of juvenile and adult offending. DiLalla and Gottesman's (1989) review of behavior-genetic studies of delinquency reported weighted average concordance rates of .87 and .72 for MZ and DZ twins, respectively. While this shows a modest genetic effect, the DZ concordance rate suggests a much higher environmental effect. Further, a large study of 3,226 twin pairs found that genes accounted for only 7 percent of the variance in antisocial behavior among juvenile offenders but 43 percent among adult offenders (Lyons et al., 1995). Shared environment accounted for 31 percent of the variance among the juveniles but only 5 percent among the adults (which supports other work indicating the limited *lasting* effects of shared environment on personality and behavior). On the other hand, nonshared (specific) environment accounted for more variance than genes for both juveniles and adults (62 and 52 percent, respectively).

The fluctuating role of genes in antisocial behavior is nicely illustrated in the well-known Danish adoption study conducted by Mednick, Gabrielli, and Hutchings (1984). They found that 24.5 percent of the males whose biological and adoptive fathers had criminal records had records themselves. Twenty percent of those who had a criminal biological father but a noncriminal adoptive father had a record, and 14.7 percent whose adopted but not biological father had a record had records themselves. Among males with neither a biological or adoptive father with a criminal record, only 13.5 had a record themselves. This pattern of findings reveals a genetic effect, albeit a very weak one. Far more instructive is the 37 male adoptees who had biological fathers with three or more criminal convictions. This mere 1 percent of the cohort accounted for fully 30 percent of all adoptee convictions in the cohort. This suggests that genetic influences on antisocial behavior beneath some unknown threshold may be weak to nonexistent, while above that threshold they may be very strong. It also suggests that pooling subjects possessing minimal genetic risk for antisocial behavior (the majority of delinquents) with the small minority possessing a large genetic vulnerability will elevate the estimate of the effect of genes on antisocial behavior overall, while simultaneously minimizing it for those most seriously involved. Genetic effects on antisocial behavior appear most likely to be found, then, among those who DiLalla and Gottesman (1989) call *continuous antisocials*, or who Moffitt (1993) calls *life-course-persistent* offenders.

Using data from a number of studies, Lykken (1995:97) estimates the heritability of criminality to be in the .30 to .40 range and ponders why h^2 is so small for criminality when it is much larger for the traits associated with criminality (e.g., fearlessness, aggressiveness, sensation-seeking, impulsiveness, and intelligence). He asks us to imagine two hypothetical environments in which: (1) all parents are equally feckless and negligent in their parental duties, and (2) all parents are equally diligent and skilled in their parental duties. To the extent that the only environmental factor that mattered was parenting quality, h^2 would be 1.0 in both instances because parenting under these hypothetical conditions is a constant across all families. However, there would be much more antisocial behavior in the first case, because feckless and negligent parents have created a situation in which only the most fearful, nonaggressive, and conscientious would refrain from antisocial behavior. Conversely, in the second case, only the most fearless, aggressive, and impulsive children would become antisocial. In the real world, there is a wide variation in the quality of parenting, and parents have greater control over their offspring's behavior than they do over their personality traits. That, asserts Lykken (1995:109), is why "the heritability of criminality is less than the more basic psychological traits" [that are its constituent parts].

Another reason that behavior-genetic studies of juvenile delinquency typically find very little genetic influence is the high base rate for delinquency. It is often claimed that the adolescent male who is *not* delinquent in some way is statistically abnormal (Moffitt, 1993). Because the great majority of adolescents engage in behavior that could lead them to become involved with criminal justice authorities, differences in concordance rates between MZ and DZ twins are minimized, thus yielding only small heritability coefficients (DiLalla & Gottesman, 1989).

The differing genetic effects on IQ in different environments also apply to delinquent and criminal behavior. In environments where resistance to crime is low, very little variance in criminal behavior will be attributable to genes; in environments where resistance to crime is high, the genetic contribution will be high. Venables (1987), for example, found that (low) tonic heart rate was a significant predictor of antisocial behavior among children from high SES families but not among children from low SES families. Similarly, Walsh (1992) found that cognitive imbalance (as measured by verbal/performance IQ discrepancy scores) significantly predicted violent delinquency in advantaged environments but not in disadvantaged environments. This does not mean these studies found that low tonic heart rate or cognitive imbalance was more prevalent in advantaged environments; quite the contrary. What it means is that environmental causes tend to overwhelm putative genetic causes in disadvantaged environments (Gottesman & Goldsmith, 1994). Differences in heritability on traits associated with criminality within different environments could provide criminologists with additional indices of relative environmental advantage/disadvantage. Because heritability changes, "[a] relatively unexplored benefit of the concept of heritability is that it can describe changes in the mix of genetics and environmental factors in various populations, times, or developmental stages" (Plomin, DeFries & McClearn, 1980:225). If criminologists become sensitive to genetic data for no reason other than this, the benefits to the field will be great.

TYPICAL OBJECTIONS TO BEHAVIOR GENETICS' ASSUMPTIONS AND RESEARCH DESIGNS

A number of criticisms of behavior-genetic assumptions and research designs have been offered to discount the role of genetics in human behavior ("seriously flawed" seems to be a favorite, if not very specific, one). According to Sandra Scarr (1981: 523-524), "Standards of evidence are elevated when one is defying the zeitgeist . . . our work is subjected to the scrutiny of an electron microscope when the rest of psychology is examined through the wrong end of a telescope." Personally, I am glad that behavior geneticists are held to higher standards than strict environmentalists. Criticism, even virulent criticism, is good, for sentries fall asleep and troops grow fat and complacent when there is no enemy at the gates. Behavior genetics has become very muscular indeed from standing up to this scrutiny. It has become arguably as meticulous in its methods as any branch of science, and certainly more meticulous than any other branch of the social/behavioral sciences.

A number of studies have been conducted specifically to address these alleged assumptive and design problems of behavior genetics empirically. Kenneth Kendler (1983) wrote a review article outlining the findings of these studies. Kendler's article documents the great lengths to which behavior geneticists have gone in order to demonstrate the soundness of both their assumptions and their research designs. The primary criticism is that MZ twins share more of their social environment than do same-sex DZ twins, and it is this similarity of environment and the similarity of the treatment received within them, rather than similarity in genes, that make MZ twins more similar than DZ twins. This criticism has been examined in a number of different ways and found to be groundless.

The "similar environment" criticism assumes that only twins reared together would develop similar behavioral, cognitive, and personality phenotypes. The corollary assumption is that MZ twins reared apart would not develop similar phenotypes. Kendler cites four studies that specifically address this criticism by comparing twin pairs whose zygosity was misidentified. Some DZ twins look so much alike that they are often misidentified as MZ twins, and some MZ twins look so unalike that they are often misidentified as DZ twins. If the "similar environment" argument were correct, MZ twins falsely identified as DZ twins would achieve test results showing a similarity level more like DZ twins than MZ twins, and DZ twins wrongly identified as MZ twins would test more like MZ than DZ twins. This was not the case. Twins behaved consistent with their genetic similarity (their true zygosity) rather than on the basis of social expectations derived from their falsely perceived zygosity. As we have seen, many studies conducted after Kendler's review have confirmed that the phenotypic similarity of MZ twins is largely uneffected by whether or not they grew up together or apart, and that MZ twins reared apart are considerably more alike than same-sex DZ twins reared together (Bouchard et al., 1990). These robust and consistent findings should end the "equal environments" criticism forever but probably won't.

Other studies reviewed by Kendler attempted to determine if twins with a large degree of physical similarity were behaviorally more similar than twins less physically similar, the assumption being that the more physically alike twins were, the more they would be treated alike. Although physical similarity did tend to lead to similarity of treatment, none of the studies reported by Kendler found any relationship between treatment similarity and similarity of scores on the various behavioral, personality, or cognitive measures utilized. It was also found by other studies that MZ twins whose parents made every effort to *emphasize* the twins' sameness did not score any closer to each other on various behavioral, personality, or cognitive measures than twins whose parents made every effort to *minimize* the twins' sameness. Treatment similarity or dissimilarity apparently has no effect on making MZ twins any more or less similar on a variety of measures.

In terms of comparing MZ twins with DZ twins on treatment received by parents, studies do find that MZ twins are treated more alike. However, when parental behavior was divided into parent-initiated and twin-initiated behaviors, it was found that parent-initiated behavior was similar for MZ and DZ twins, but parental behavior was significantly different when responding to actions initiated by MZ and DZ twins. Parental responses to MZ twin-initiated behavior was significantly more similar than parental responses to DZ twin-initiated behavior, leading researchers to conclude that parents *treat* MZ twins more similarly than DZ twins because MZ twins *behave* more similarly than DZ twins. This example of reactive G/E correlation shows that parents respond to differences among their offspring rather than create them.

Another "similar treatment"-type argument is the selective-placement argument for MZ twins reared apart. This argument states that the similarity between MZ twins reared apart is explained environmentally by the tendency of agencies to place MZ twins put up for adoption in similar homes. It is true that there is a small correlation (about .30) on indices such as educational attainment and SES between the adoptive homes of MZ twins adopted out separately. However, as Lykken (1995:76) points out, these same correlations between DZ twins and other siblings reared together is 1.0, and MZ twins reared apart score significantly more similarly than DZ twins reared together on almost every behavioral, personality, cognitive, and attitudinal measure studied. Additionally, almost all adoption studies have found that adoptees tend to resemble their biological parents more than their adoptive parents on these measures (Bouchard et al., 1990).

Kendler also looked at studies assessing the possibility of "reverse bias," that is, factors that may lead to an *underestimation* of genetic effects. There are three such factors, the first being assortative mating. Assortative mating refers to the tendency of individuals with similar phenotypes to mate with each other at a rate significantly greater than would be expected by chance—like seeks like. Such a mating pattern has the effect of producing DZ twins more genetically similar than would be the case with random mating. Assortative mating has no effect on MZ similarity, however, because such twins share 100 percent of their genes regardless of whether they are the products of random or assortative mating. According to Kendler, assortative mating results in an approximate 11 percent underestimation of the importance of genetic factors in intelligence because DZ twin correlations are inflated by assortative mating while MZ correlations are unaffected, thus leading to lower heritability estimates than would be obtained under conditions of random mating.

The second factor that may lead to underestimating genetic effects is the phenomenon of *anastomosis*, or the "twin tranfusion" syndrome. This syndrome exists when one twin transfuses blood from the other in the uterine environment, resulting in the recipient twin being born physically healthier and larger than the donor twin. Anastomosis may also affect cognitive and behavioral outcomes. The syndrome may have the result of underestimating genetic effects because it occurs in two-thirds of MZ twins who shared the same chorionic membrane. All DZ twins are dichorionic and are thus not susceptible to the transfusion syndrome. A significant number of MZ twins are thus exposed to an environmental factor that may make them less similar than their shared genes would have otherwise made them, but DZ twins are not.

The final factor turns the "equal environments" criticism on its head. Kendler cites two studies in which MZ twins reared apart were more similar in personality than MZ twins reared together. The implication is that MZ twins reared together often attempt more assiduously than DZ twins to be different from one another in order to assert their individuality.

Behavior-genetic assumptions and research designs are thus very robust. For environmentalist researchers to achieve the same level of precision, asserts Eric Turkheimer (2000:162), they would have to have "'identical environmental twins' whose experiences were exactly the same, moment by moment, and another variety who shared exactly (but randomly) 50% of their experiences." Of course, there are no mono- or di-"envirogotic" twins, but we don't need them. Behavior genetics informs us of the environmental contribution to any human trait as surely as if there were such twins. This is why criminologists must embrace the powerful methods of behavioral genetics if the discipline is to make the progress it promised but failed to deliver in the twentieth century.

GENES AND HUMAN FREEDOM

It is appropriate to end this chapter by again explaining why accusations of genetic determinists aimed at biosocial scientists are both unfair and uninformed. As we shall see in Chapter 4, there are far too few genes for them to exercise anything like primary control over human behavior. Complex organisms in complex environments are always better off if left to their own devices rather than being hardwired for every possible situation they could encounter. Think of the almost limitless kinds of situations humans could possibly face, and then consider how absurd it is to think that we could possibly be preprogrammed to respond to them in fixed, undeviating ways. To program such an organism would require a gazillion genes carrying a series of "if this/then do that" algorithms rather than the 30 to 40 thousand that we actually have. What genes actually do regarding our behavior is to provide us with some very general rules, such as "avoid snarling creatures," "be kind to close kin," "fear heights," or even more generally, "seek pleasure and avoid pain," and then leave the specifics to the judgment of the organism. Biologists call these general rules that help us to survive and achieve reproductive success *epigenetic rules*.

Badcock (2000) employs the concept of epigenetic rules to assert human freedom, using the analogy of a person wishing to take a trip by air. If you decide to fly somewhere, you do not have to book your own flight, load your own luggage, work the control towers, fly the plane, or build the plane. You temporarily employ others to do these things for you because they can do them better than you can. In order for them to do their jobs properly, you must allow them the freedom and judgment to exercise their individual competencies to do so. Genes are in the same position as airline passengers; they must allow their agents freedom to do what they must do on the genes' behalf. Badcock goes on to state the consequences of the inability of genes to do all the necessary tasks required to run an organism:

> [O]rganisms will have all kinds of independent competencies, expertise and abilities that their genes in themselves lack. They will be expert systems in their own right and will have to have the freedom and discretion to act as such. *Genes don't deny*

human freedom; they positively guarantee it because their agents could not function without it. And without their agents genes would go nowhere save to extinction (2000:71, emphasis added).

We shall meet the primary agent—the brain—in Chapter 4, where we will learn the epigenetic rules by which the brain wires itself in response to environmental input. After completing Chapters 1 through 4, the reader should come to realize that it is the purveyors of blank-slate images of human nature that implicitly deny human freedom, and not biosocial scientists.

Chapter 3

Evolutionary Psychology and the Origins of Criminal Behavior

As shown in the previous chapter, almost all human characteristics associated with criminal behavior are substantially heritable. If we accept these data on face value, we must ask why genes promoting criminal behavior exist. We know enough about evolutionary theory to be aware that genes that currently exist in the gene pool of any species are there because they somehow conferred an advantage on ancestral organisms. Could criminal behavior be something that has survived across the generations because it served a useful evolutionary purpose? This chapter explores that issue.

Evolutionary psychology is a branch of psychology that utilizes a Darwinian theoretical framework to animate its research agenda. Although the vocabulary of evolutionary psychologists is replete with biological terms such as natural selection, Darwinian algorithms, inclusive fitness, and adaptation, in a sense it is even more "environmentally friendly" than behavior genetics. Behavior genetics focuses on differences among people, whereas evolutionary psychology focuses on the exploration of the universal features that all people share. Evolutionary psychology is interested in ultimate-level explanations (the most fundamental explanations in terms of the evolutionary history of the species), but it never fails to emphasize that evolved behavior is always expressed contingently. Evolutionary criminologists explore how behaviors we now define as criminal may have been adaptive in ancestral environments. Because adaptations (somatic or behavioral structures, patterns, or processes that contributed to an organism's reproductive success in the environment in which it evolved) apply to all members of a species, unlike behavior geneticists, evolutionary psychologists look exclusively for *environmental* sources of variation in criminal behavior.

THE RELEVANCE OF EVOLUTIONARY THEORY TO SOCIAL SCIENCE

Evolution may be very simply defined as changes in a population's gene pool over time. No other theory lends itself more to misunderstanding and confusion than evolutionary theory when it is applied to human behavior. There is such abundance and variety of evidence supporting biological evolution theory that no scientist seriously disputes it. They may argue about the precise details of *how* evolution takes place, but not about the fact that it did and does. It is often said that very little in biology makes sense without the theory of evolution, but biologists frequently carry on their research looking for proximate-level explanations without making reference to ultimate-level evolutionary factors. However, the theory is available to them as a theoretical umbrella enabling them to link their work to other subfields of biology, and as a theoretical guide enabling them to understand their own work in ultimate-level terms. Because human beings are as much products of evolution as plants and other animals, a growing number of leading social and behavioral scientists in anthropology (e.g., Barkow, 1992; Brown, 1991), psychology (e.g., Buss, 1999; Tooby & Cosmides, 1990), and sociology (e.g., Ellis, 1998; Lopreato & Crippen, 1999) believe that the theory of evolution can lead to a deeper understanding of the phenomena of their disciplines, although evolutionary social scientists are still distinctly in the minority.

Many social scientists share an aversion to evolutionary thinking as it applies to humans and their behavior, apparently believing that humans are "above all that." Such an attitude is scientifically indefensible. Humans are certainly unique in many ways, but so is every other animal species in one way or another. The attitude that humans are so special that they are set above nature (and thus require a different set of ontological principles to understand them) delays our understanding of human nature. Human nature is the sum of human adaptations, and an understanding of it is fundamental to any branch of the human sciences. Few social scientists balk at the notion that human anatomy and physiology are products of evolution. We observe some aspect of human morphology and correctly infer that it was selected over alternate designs because it best served some particular function that proved useful in assisting the proliferation of its owners' genes. Unless we are believers in divine creation (and even if we are, as the within-species evolution—micro-evolution—with which we are concerned is not disputed by creationists), we have to make that inference because there is no other scientifically viable explanation for morphological design.

While it is true that there is no other scientifically viable explanation for the origin of *basic* behavioral design, most social scientists dismiss the idea that human behavioral patterns are products of the same natural process. Commenting on this, Kenrick and Simpson

(1997:1) state that "to study any animal species while refusing to consider the evolved adaptive significance of their behavior would be considered pure folly . . . unless the species in question is *Homo sapiens*." If pressed, social scientists might take the position that while our species' behavioral repertoire must have been designed by natural selection, evolved behaviors lost their relevance once the species developed culture. In an announcement that would surprise biologists, Jacques Ruffie (1986:297) takes such a position: "The beginning of mankind's psychosocial development represents the end of biological evolution." Ruffie does not specify what environmental pressures resulting from our "psychosocial development" might have led to the elimination of the alleles underlying the evolved traits that were supposedly rendered irrelevant. Unless those evolved traits became detrimental to survival and reproductive success in a cultural setting, the genes underlying them remain in the human gene pool. This does not mean that evolutionary psychologists consider culture unimportant in explaining human behavior. Indeed, they consider it to be of the utmost importance, and they would probably all agree that culture accounts for almost all the variance in behavioral differences *between* cultures. Evolutionary psychologists simply ask us to remember that "psychology underlies culture and society, and biological evolution underlies psychology" (Barkow, 1992:635). It is true that the fine nuances of life as subjectively experienced are lost as we move from proximate-level to ultimate-level explanations, but ultimate-level explanations seek to complement, not supplant, proximate explanations.

NATURAL SELECTION

Although the idea that life evolved naturally had been around since at least the time of Plato, it was the nineteenth-century British botanist Charles Darwin who first organized the evidence into a scientific theory. Darwin's theory (first published in 1859 in *On the Origin of Species by Means of Natural Selection*) has stood the test of time, requiring only a few modifications. Darwin's basic point was that populations of plants and animals grow until they strain the ability of the environment to support all members. The production of excess offspring results in a struggle for existence in which only the "fittest" survive.

Darwin also noted that individuals within populations exhibit a considerable degree of *variation* with respect to observable traits and characteristics (color, size, speed, height, aggressiveness, cunning, etc.). Variants of a trait sometimes gave their possessors an edge in the struggle for survival in prevailing environmental conditions. The edge, whatever it may be, meant that those possessing it would be more likely than those not possessing it to survive and reproduce, thus passing the edge on to future generations. For instance, if slightly more aggressive males in a breeding population were more likely, on average, to produce slightly more offspring than their less aggressive counterparts, then the average level of aggression in that population would increase from generation to generation. On the other hand, if most males of the population became so aggressive that they killed one another fighting over mating opportunities, or attacked and killed females and their offspring, aggression would be selected against. Hyperaggressive males would leave fewer offspring than males who obtained mating opportunities with cunning rather than ferocity. The particular trait variant selected is selected because it best "fit" its possessors into the environmental conditions existing *at the time*; at other times, the trait may not confer an advantage. Darwin called this process of selecting the "fittest" *natural selection* because it is nature (the environment) that "selects" the favorable variants and preserves them in later generations.

Natural selection, the differential reproductive success of genotypes, is the engine and organizer of evolution because it continuously adjusts populations to their environments. Biologists call these adjustments *adaptations*. Adaptations may be structural (anatomical), functional (physiological), or behavioral. It is important not to fall into the trap of thinking that traits are selected *in order* to make organisms more adapted to their environments. Such thinking implies purpose. Evolution has no "purpose"; it cannot look into the future to divine some plan for optimal adaptation of organisms. Natural selection is very much a trial-and-error process. Environmental conditions set evolution on a particular adaptive trajectory, but if environments change drastically, former adaptations may become maladaptive and may even drive a species into extinction.

Neo-Darwinism

Darwin knew all about trait variation, but he had no idea what the source of that variation was or how it was passed on. He was unaware of the existence of genes and of the work of Gregor Mendel, which would eventually lead to the field of genetics. Today we know that trait variation among organisms is caused by genetic recombination (reshuffling) during the division of sex cells (meiosis) and by mutation. (The vast majority of mutations are harmful and are removed by natural selection.) Today's evolutionary theory is *gene-based* and is a synthesis of Darwin's theory of natural selection and genetics (the so-called *modern synthesis*).

The marriage of genetics to natural selection filled in many blanks in Darwin's theory. In addition to understanding the genetic source of trait variation, we now view evolution as changes in the genetic composition of a population from generation to generation and reserve the term *fittest* to mean the most prolific reproducers. Survival means nothing in evolutionary terms if survivors do not pass on the traits that helped them to survive. The most reproductively successful organisms, regardless of the reasons for their success, leave behind the largest number of offspring and, hence, the greatest number of genes. This is what *fitness* means. The genes underlying traits that contributed to reproductive success will thus be found more frequently in subsequent generations. Evolutionary theory has thus converged on a simple but powerful idea: To the degree that a particular type of behavior is prevalent in a population, that behavior is likely to have contributed to the reproductive success of the ancestors of the individuals displaying the behavior.

THINKING IN EVOLUTIONARY TERMS

As noted previously, the uncommon logic of evolutionary thinking makes its acceptance difficult among the general public and social scientists alike. Evolutionary theory is not shy about revealing the "dark" side of human nature. It talks about reproductive success as the ultimate goal of life, and it lays bare our aggressiveness, deceptiveness, and selfishness as evolved strategies that have proved useful in pursuing it. It is not pleasant to think of ourselves in this light, and some of us would rather burn the message than try to decipher it. However, other more positive human characteristics, such as altruism, nurturance, and empathy, have also evolved because they equipped us with parental and social skills. After all, having offspring does little to perpetuate the parental genes of those offspring who do not themselves survive to reproductive age in the company of relatively caring and trustworthy others. Let us briefly explore the major concepts of evolutionary theory about which there are a number of misunderstandings that have led critics to accuse evolutionary psychology of being tautological and deterministic, and of ignoring cultural variables.

Adaptations versus Exaptations

The adaptation concept is sometimes accused of being tautologous, as in: "Mechanism X is an adaptation because it was useful in assisting ancestral organisms to survive and reproduce." "How do we know it is an adaptation?" "Ancestral organisms obviously survived and reproduced because their progeny are everywhere." This criticism is a red herring. Concepts must certainly be defined in falsifiable, noncircuitous ways, and evolutionary theory does this elegantly in defining *adaptation* independently of "the fittest survive because they are the fittest" (see Ridley, 1993, for extensively documented evidence for the validity of the assumptions of adaptationism). In general, we may say that to identify an adaptation we first must identify a mechanism that is clearly currently functional in terms of the evolutionarily relevant goals of survival and reproduction. Secondly, we determine if the properties of this mechanism solved a recurring adaptive problem present in ancestral environments in a nonrandom way. John Tooby (1999:4) casts the issue of what constitutes an adaptation in hypothesis-testing terms: "To establish something as an adaptation, all one needs to do is to collect evidence that justifies the rejection of the hypothesis that the structure arose by chance (with respect to function)."

It is necessary to differentiate those things that arose by chance and those that arose and promoted their own frequency via an extended period of selection. Chance alterations of the genome occur all the time via mutations, the vast majority of which are disadvantageous. Because they do not promote fitness, they are soon culled from the gene pool by natural selection. Evolutionary psychologists do not assume that everything that is currently useful is an adaptation. All functional features of organisms need not be adaptations per se, but rather features that have been coopted by characteristics built by natural selection for quite different purposes. Features that are useful but that did not arise as adaptations for their present roles have been called *exaptations* (Gould, 1991) or *preadaptations* (Pinker & Bloom, 1992).

To give a readily understandable example of distinction between an adaptation and an exaptation, consider automobile engines and heaters. Automobile engines were designed to move pistons and wheels so that automobiles may convey their occupants from one place to another. A by-product of the activity of engines is heat. Engines were not designed for producing heat, but this by-product was seized upon by engineers to design mechanisms for defrosting the car's windshield and warming the car's interior. The engine's function—that of moving pistons and wheels—is analogous to an adaptation because it solved some environmental problem—that of getting from one place to another. The heat generated by the engine (a by-product of an "adaptation") was seized upon and utilized to make moving from place to place both safer and more comfortable. Safety and comfort also solved environmental problems, but they were not the problems engines were designed to solve. The heater mechanism that provides comfort and safety is thus a mechanical analog of a biological exaptation.

We should not think of adaptations as optimal solutions to all evo-lutionarily relevant problems. Biologists and engineers could doubtless dream up better solutions to our survival and reproductive concerns than those with which evolution has presented us. Natural selection, however, does not have the luxury or foresight or access to compara-tive models; it can only work algorithmically with the genetic varia-tion existing at the time a given environmental problem presents itself. Nor can natural selection anticipate the future. Behavior that was adaptive in the past may not be today, or may even be maladaptive, and behaviors that may be adaptive (fitness-promoting) today may not be adaptations in the sense that they have an evolutionary history (Daly, 1996; Mealey, 1995). "Adaptiveness is always a variable" (more or less adaptive) "and always relative" (Lopreato & Crippen, 1999:119). To claim that something is an adaptation, then, is to make a claim about the past, not the present, and definitely not about the future.

Direct versus Indirect Motivation

Another common misunderstanding of evolutionary logic is that behaviors alleged to be adaptive are *directly* and consciously motivated by concerns of reproductive success. They are not: "Evolutionary psychology is not a theory of motivation. . . . Fitness consequences are invoked not as goals in themselves, but rather to explain why certain goals have come to control behavior at all, and why they are calibrated in one particular way rather than another" (Daly & Wilson,1988:7). No behavior can be considered to result from conscious motives to increase fitness, and even vigorous attempts to start a family are hard-ly driven by the conscious concerns about pushing our genes into the future. We are adapted to seek the immediate means of achieving spe-cific goals, not ultimate ends (Symons, 1992; Tooby & Cosmides, 1992). Reproduction is not even the motivation for the vast majority of copulations in bonded relationships. It is the highly pleasurable means by which reproductive success may be achieved that we are moti-vated to seek, and there was certainly a tighter fit between conscious means and mindless evolutionary goals in ancestral environments. This is why evolutionary psychologists prefer to use the phrase *adap-tation executors* (acting in ways that would have maximized fitness in ancestral environments but do not necessarily do so today) rather than *fitness maximizers* to refer to the evolved behavior of modern humans.

To give another example, parents do not nurture and love their chil-dren because a subconscious "selfish gene" whispers to them that if they do they will have greater genetic representation in future generations. Parents nurture and love their children because, well, they love them.

They do so because ancestral parents who loved and nurtured their children saw more of them grow to reproductive age and pass on the genes underlying the traits we now define as love and nurturance. The neurohormonal properties underlying nurturing behavior are adaptations because they solved a recurring adaptive problem—the survival of offspring. Parents who did not love and nurture their children compromised the viability of their offspring and, thus, the probability of pushing their genes into the future. The love and nurturance of offspring greatly increases the probability that parental genes will survive, but in no sense can this consequence be construed as parents' motivation for lavishing love and care on their children.

Fitness, Inclusive Fitness, and Adaptation Execution

Evolutionary psychology is often accused of emphasizing competition and egoism over cooperation and altruism, and of not being able to explain the latter. This criticism is untrue, but it is easy to see how one could think it true, especially in the case of altruism. Fitness is a quantitative measure of reproductive success, and reproductive success is the spoils of an unconscious competition to contribute more of one's genes to subsequent generations than other members of the breeding population. Altruism, or the extending of some evolutionarily relevant benefit to others at a cost to the altruist, was often viewed, even by some biologists, as a fly in the ointment of evolutionary logic. If altruism reduced fitness, why should an animal engage in altruistic behavior? It simply did not make sense that an organism would risk its own fitness for the benefit of others, especially after group-selection thinking (the thinking that organisms behave "for the good of the group") all but disappeared.

The apparent paradox was solved by William Hamilton's (1964) theory of *inclusive fitness* (the perpetuation of one's genes and those of close genetic relatives). Consider the behavior of the eusocial insects of the order *hymenoptera,* such as bees, ants, and termites. Specialist organisms in this order (e.g., soldiers and workers) have an evolved strategy that literally requires them to sacrifice their lives for the good of the group. How can such utterly selfless behavior possibly contribute to the fitness of such "heroes"? It does so because male specialists are sterile, so the only way that their genes can attain immortality is to help their sisters (with whom they share 75 percent of their genes), one of whom will eventually become the queen and pass those genes on (Lykken, 1995). There is obviously no conscious component to this adaptation. Any insect species in which the majority of males were sterile that did not evolve a strategy of self-sacrificial defense of the colony simply would not be with us today. The driving force of evolution is reproduction. If sacrificing one's life to protect a fertile organism sharing one's genes is the only way of perpetuating the genes of the sacrificial organism, then that behavior will be favored by natural selection. Human altruism is obviously not like this, but inclusive fitness theory does explain how altruism could have been selected for in any species.

The concept of fitness has itself been criticized on the grounds that we do not observe people striving to maximize their fitness. Not only that, we observe that high status is negatively related to number of offspring today, which is the exact opposite of what naive evolutionary thinking would lead us to expect. It is quite true that in modern societies fertility tends to decline with increased social status, thus reversing the age-old positive correlation between social status and reproductive success. Doesn't this prove that culture is more important than any evolved propensities to maximize fitness?

The first criticism was partially addressed in the discussion of direct-versus-indirect (or proximate-versus-ultimate) motivation above. As for the second, evolutionary psychology considers the environments (either physical or cultural) in which an evolved trait is expressed to be of the utmost importance. Acting in ways that maximized reproductive success in ancestral environments but that do not do so today does not constitute evidence against evolutionary logic. Perusse (1992) found that high-status males in modern environments are executing adaptations in that they enjoy more copulations (or *number of potential conceptions*, to use Perusse's terminology) with more partners than lower-status males, particularly as they grow older and acquire more resources. High-status males, living under culturally enforced monogamy and utilizing evolutionarily novel contraceptive technology, are obviously not striving to maximize their fitness, but they are nevertheless executing an adaptation as they "go through the motions" of making babies without actually doing so. These high-status men would have been fitness maximizers in preindustrial and precontraceptive societies, and most especially in environments of evolutionary adaptation, but now they are apparently content to enjoy the pleasures of being mere adaptation executors.

THE ENVIRONMENT OF EVOLUTIONARY ADAPTATION

Evolutionary psychologists often refer to conditions as they existed in the *environment of evolutionary adaptation* (EEA). There is an unfortunate singularity to *the* EEA that implies to critics that evolutionary psychologists believe that there was only one EEA and that evolution no longer takes place. There was no one EEA, either in terms of time or geography. Most adaptations that are uniquely human (e.g., language, culture) evolved in the 1.6 million-year-long Pleistocene epoch during which we observed dramatic increases in hominid brain size (Bromage, 1987). For the adaptations that we share wholly or partially with other primates (e.g., bipedalism, nurturing behavior), the relevant EEA is the approximately 5- to 6-million-year period before the present. Other adaptations (e.g., aggression, egoism) go back to the very beginning of animal life on the planet. Thus, although it is conventional to speak of *the* EEA, evolutionary psychologists are aware that it should be EEAs—one for each of our adaptations (Crawford, 1998a:281).

NATURAL IS GOOD?

The term *natural* is often used synonymously with the terms *good* or *desirable* ("Try the *natural* way to good health"; "She has a *natural* beauty"). Scientists should not conflate these two terms, for what is natural is not always good. To conflate the terms is to commit what philosophers of science call the *naturalistic fallacy.* The naturalistic fallacy is the fallacy of confusing *is* with *ought* (Beckstrom, 1993:2). Nature simply *is*; what *ought* to be is a moral judgment. For example, when evolutionary psychologists claim that forced copulation is a natural phenomenon (i.e., a product of natural selection), they are accused of dignifying or justifying it (Brownmiller & Mehrhof, 1992) or of implying that it is inevitable or even morally acceptable (Dupre, 1992).

These critics have not made the distinction between establishing facts and morally evaluating them. To claim that forced copulation is a natural phenomenon is no more a moral statement than to claim that disease and death, which are likewise unwelcome facts of life, are normal and natural phenomena. A number of morally reprehensible traits have been selected for because of their contribution to reproductive success, but this fact does not constitute a moral argument for or against any of those traits; it is simply an empirical statement. Evolution is morally blind in that it "allows" for the selection of traits to the extent that they enhance fitness regardless of how morally repugnant we may consider them. The powerful logic of evolution helps to illuminate the ultimate reasons why these traits and behaviors exist, and perhaps even suggest ways to control them. It is incumbent upon us to control immoral behaviors regardless of whether scientists show them to be products of natural selection, because just as *natural* does not mean *desirable*, it does not mean *inevitable*.

THE EVOLUTION OF CRIMINAL BEHAVIOR

Crime is Normal

In common with Emile Durkheim (1982), evolutionary psychologists view crime as normal (albeit, regrettable) behavior engaged in by normal individuals engaged in normal social processes (Cohen & Machalek, 1994). If criminal behavior is in fact normal, it follows that the potential for it must be in us all and that it must have conferred some evolutionary advantage on our distant ancestors. But how can such heterogeneous acts as murder, theft, rape, burglary, and assault be conceived of as adaptations when they are typically maladaptive in modern environments? As explained earlier, the fact that a behavior is apparently maladaptive today (it can land a person in prison for a long time, which is not very conducive to reproductive success) does not mean that the mechanisms underlying it are not evolved adaptations. Modern environments are so radically different from the hunter/gatherer environments *Homo sapiens* evolved in that many traits selected for their adaptive value at the time may not be adaptive at all today. Further, it is the traits underlying criminal behavior, not the specifics of criminal behavior (or of any other social behavior for that matter), that are the alleged adaptations. As David Rowe (1996:285) has pointed out, "Genes do not code themselves for jimmying a lock or stealing a car . . . the genome does not waste precious DNA encoding the specifics."

Criminal behavior is a way to acquire valued resources from others by exploiting and deceiving them. Deceptive and selfish behavior clearly provides evolutionary advantages to a wide variety of animal species (Alcock, 1998; Ellis, 1998; Ellis & Walsh, 1997). The general tendency of organisms to seek their own interests above those of others is the adaptation, not any specific manifestation of it. Evolutionary psychologists refer to an exploitive strategy as a *conditional* strategy. It is conditional because the assumption is that although preparedness to engage in it is genetically universal in the human species (Figueredo, 1995), it is employed only if environmental conditions are deemed appropriate for its use by those who use it. In a species such as ours, it is more useful to have genes turned on and off by environmental cues rather than to have genetically distinct behavioral types following strategies fixed at birth regardless of the environments in which they find themselves (Tooby & Cosmides, 1990).

This is not to say that evolutionary psychologists deny different individual thresholds for the emergence of exploitive (including criminal) behavior; they simply deny that exploiters constitute an alternative adaptation such that they are genetically different with regard to that strategy than noncriminals (but see the discussion of psychopathy below). Evolutionary psychologists tend to think of individual traits associated with the exploitation of others, such as impulsiveness, aggression, and low empathy, in terms of normal distributions dispersed around adaptive means. Whether such behavior is manifested depends on evolutionarily relevant environmental triggers (typically, perceived threats to resource and mate acquisition and/or opportunities to gain them with minimal effort) interacting with individual differences in facilitative traits and with cultural practices constraining it. These threshold distributions are not fixed; they can shift to the left or right in response to changes in the sociocultural environment.

Although we all have the potential to exploit and deceive to the extent of committing criminal acts, we are also a highly social and cooperative species with "minds [that] are exquisitely crafted by evolution to form cooperative relationships built on trust and kindness" (Allman, 1994:147). Cooperative and altruistic behavior is probably the defining characteristic of almost all social species. Because altruism is viewed as behavior ultimately designed to serve the purposes of the altruist, unless directed at close genetic kin, it is typically contingent on reciprocal behavior on the part of the recipient (Machalek, 1996). Altruism and cooperation are thus tit-for-tat strategies favored by natural selection because of the benefits they confer. Again, this does not mean that we are genetically urged to give unto others and cooperate with them "in order" to maximize our fitness. We cooperate and act altruistically because we tend to feel good when we do, expect to be rewarded in kind, and because such behavior confers valued social status on us by identifying us as persons who are kind, reliable, and trustworthy. In the ultimate sense, we do so because our distant ancestors who were altruistic and cooperative enjoyed greater reproductive success than those who were not, thus passing on the genes for the brain structures and neurotransmitters that presumably underlie the traits (Barkow, 1997). Although individual organisms are adapted to act in ways that tend to maximize their own fitness in evolutionary environments, not to behave "for the good of the group," their fitness goals are best realized by adhering to the rules of cooperation and altruism, that is, by "being nice."

Cooperation Creates Niches for Cheats

Social living is characterized by conflict as well as by cooperation and reciprocal altruism. Because cooperation occurs among groups of reciprocal altruists, it creates a niche for cheats to exploit (Alexander, 1987; Mealey, 1995; Trivers, 1991). Cheats are individuals in a population of cooperators who signal their cooperation but fail to reciprocate after receiving benefits. If there are no deterrents against cheating, it is in an individual's fitness interests to obtain resources from others under the assumption of reciprocity and then to default, thus gaining resources at zero cost. This "social parasitism" has been observed among a variety of nonhuman animal species (Alcock, 1998; E. Wilson, 1975), and its ubiquity across species implies that it has had positive fitness consequences (Machalek, 1996). In the human species, criminal behavior may be viewed as an extreme form of defaulting on the rules of reciprocity (Lykken, 1995; Machalek & Cohen, 1991). However, cheating comes at a cost, so before deciding to default, the individual must weigh the costs and benefits of cooperating versus defaulting. This has been nicely illustrated in the "prisoner's dilemma" of game theory (Axelrod, 1984) described below.

Suppose two recently acquainted criminal accomplices—Bill and Frank—are being held in jail for an alleged crime. They have both sworn that each would never "rat" on the other. The evidence against them is weak, prompting the prosecutor to approach each man separately and offer him a deal. If Bill testifies against Frank, Bill will be released and Frank will get 20 years, and vice versa. If both testify, both will be convicted and receive a reduced five-year sentence because of their cooperation with the prosecutor. If neither testifies (i.e., they cooperate with each other as they had sworn to do), both will be convicted of a minor crime carrying a sentence of only one year in prison. The dilemma is that Bill and Frank are being held in separate cells so that they cannot communicate with one another and cement their agreement not to default on their promise. Under these circumstances, Bill's best strategy is to testify regardless of what Frank does because it will either get him released (if Frank does not testify) or five-years (if Frank does). Both outcomes are far better than the 20 years he will receive if he remains true to his promise but Frank does not. The same holds true for Frank. Each man, following his own best interests, testifies against the other, and receives a sentence of five years. The paradox is that although the payoff for cheating is high when the other actor does not cheat, if both cheat, they are both worse off than if they cooperate.

By defaulting on his promise, each man behaves entirely rationally (I define rationality as a positive fit between one's ends and the means used to achieve them). However, if cheating behavior is so rational, how did cooperative behavior come to be predominant in social species? The answer is that cheating is really only rational in circumstances of limited interaction and communication. Frank and Bill were recent acquaintances who might never see each other again. Thus, they did not fear any repercussions arising from their cheating. Had Bill and Frank been brothers, good friends, or members of a long-standing gang, they most likely would not have testified against each other, and each would have benefited by receiving one year rather than five. Frequent interaction and communication breeds trust and bonding between organisms with sufficient intelligence to recognize one another (Crawford, 1998a). Under such circumstances, cheating becomes a far less rational strategy because cooperators remember and retaliate against those who have cheated them. Cheating ruins reputations, costs cheaters future cooperation, and can result in punishment, which is why most career criminals either die early or end up destitute (Shover, 1985). The punishment of cheating conspecifics (referred to as *moralistic* or *retaliatory aggression)* is noted among a wide variety of non-human animal species (Clutton-Brock & Parker, 1995).

Cheats can prosper only in a population of unconditional altruists (game theorists call them *suckers*). Suckers are individual organisms who continue to cooperate with, and extend benefits to, those who have cheated them. Any sucker genotype would soon be driven to extinction by cheats, leaving only cheats to interact with other cheats. Evolution logic predicts that a population of cheats could not thrive any more than could a population of suckers, and selection for cooperation would occur rapidly (Machalek, 1996). Pure suckers and cheats are thus unlikely to exist in large numbers, if at all, in any social species. The vast majority of social animals, including human beings, are *grudgers*. Grudgers are susceptible to being suckered because they abide by the norms of mutual trust and cooperation and expect the same from others. However, if suckered, they retaliate by not cooperating with the cheat in the future and perhaps even by repaying the cheat in kind (Raine, 1993). Cheaters interact with grudgers in a *repeated* game of prisoner's dilemma in which players adjust their strategies according to their experience with other players. Cooperation rather than cheating becomes the rational strategy under such circumstances because each player reaps in the future what he or she has sown in the past (Machalek, 1996; Wright, 1994).

As predicted by evolutionary logic, in computer simulations of interactions between populations of cheats, suckers, and grudgers, cheats are always driven to extinction (Raine, 1993; Allman, 1994). Why do we continue to see cheating behavior despite threats of exposure and retaliation then? The problem with such simulations is that players are constrained to operate within the same environment in which their reputations quickly become known. Cheats are not constrained to remain in one environment in the real world; they can move from location to location, meeting and cheating a series of grudgers who are unaware of the cheater's reputation. This is exactly what many career criminals do. They move from place to place, job to job, relationship to relationship, leaving a trail of misery behind them before their reputation catches up to them (Hare, 1993; Lykken, 1995; Raine, 1993). Cheats are much more likely to prosper in large cities in modern societies than in small traditional communities where the threat of exposure and retaliation is great (Ellis & Walsh, 1997; Machalek & Cohen, 1991).

Raine (1993) cautions us against forming an overly simplistic view of cooperating and cheating from tit-for-tat computer models. Real-life strategies are not automated binary strategies—cheat/don't cheat—based only on the value of the preceding binary code. As alluded to in the previous paragraph, environmental factors such as the stability of the group and cultural dynamics must be considered, as must the fact that there are individual differences in traits underlying cooperative behavior. Two behavior-genetic studies found heritability factors of .56 and .68 for altruism and empathy, respectively (Rushton et al., 1986; Rushton, Littlefield & Lumsden, 1986). Although life is more like a poker tournament than a single game of blackjack, game theory simulations are nevertheless invaluable for fleshing out the basic logic of evolutionary processes.

Detecting Cheats

In order for grudgers not to become suckers, mechanisms for detecting cheats had to evolve. The social emotions, such as empathy, shame, and guilt, are the primary mechanisms of cheater detection (Griffiths, 1990; Mealey, 1995; Nesse, 1990). Social emotions have evolved as integral parts of our social intelligence that serve to provide clues about the kinds of relationships (cooperative vs. uncooperative) that we are likely to have with others. They also serve as "commitment devices" and "guarantors of threats and promises" (Mealey, 1995:525). Barkow (1989:121) describes them as involuntary and invasive "limbic system overrides" that serve to adjust our behavior in social situations. In other words, emotions animate, focus, and modify neural activity in ways that lead us to choose certain responses over other possible responses from the streams of information we constantly receive. Emotions move us to behave in ways that enhanced our distant ancestors' reproductive success by overriding neocortical decisions suggesting alternatives to cooperation (i.e., cheating) that may have been more rational in the short term but that were ultimately fitness-reducing.

This view contradicts the bias shared by many social scientists that emotion and rational cognition are antagonists. However, emotion and cognition are two inextricably linked components of all that we think and do: there can be no Kantian "pure reason" (Wilson, 1998). It has been well known in cognitive neuroscience for some time that cognition is always suffused with emotions to various degrees and that they play "a central role in both associative learning and memory" (Masters, 1991:307). It is worth noting that one of the defining characteristics of psychopaths (the quintessential cheats) is their inability to "tie" the brain's cognitive and emotional networks together (Hare, 1993; Mealey, 1995; Patrick, 1994).

The social emotions cause positive and negative feelings when we survey the consequences of our actions. Mutual cooperation evokes a deepened sense of friendship, a sense of pride, and a heightened sense of obligation and gratitude that enhances future cooperation. Mutual cheats feel rejected and angry, and when one party cooperates and the other cheats, the cooperator feels angry and betrayed and the cheater feels anxiety and guilt (Nesse, 1990). We find the emotions accompanying mutual cooperation rewarding and perceive those accompanying defection from the norm as punishing. As a result, the more intensely we feel the emotions, the less likely we are to cheat. Conversely, the less we feel them, the more likely we are to prefer the immediate fruits of cheating over concerns of reputation and its effects on future interactions. Emotions thus function to keep our temptations in check by overriding rational calculations of immediate gain.

Is the Psychopath an Obligate Cheater?

The continued presence of chronic cheats among us indicates that we have less-than-perfect ability to detect and punish them, and that the strategy must have had positive fitness consequences occasionally. Perhaps under certain evolutionary conditions the strategy proved to be so successful that we have a certain proportion of the human population today whose cheating behavior is obligatory rather than contingent. According to Linda Mealey (1995), the traits conducive to cheating are normally distributed in the population, but there is a small but stable percentage of individuals at one extreme of the distribution for whom cheating is an obligate strategy. These individuals are the few *primary sociopaths*, or psychopaths (3 to 4 percent of males, and less than one percent of females [Mealey, 1995]), who presumably have always existed in every society.

Such an obligate cheater strategy is likely to evolve alongside the more typical grudger strategy (in which cheating behavior is environmentally dependent rather than obligatory) when its fitness gains are *frequency-dependent*. Frequency-dependent selection occurs when an alternative mating strategy enjoys high reproductive success when few practice it but low success when it becomes more common. The strategy eventually results in organisms that are genotypically, not just phenotypically, different. The cheating strategy may be sustained as a low-level, frequency-dependent strategy in statistical equilibrium with the grudger strategy that will coexist with it as an *evolutionarily stable strategy* (ESS) (Mealey, 1995). An ESS is a strategy that, when adopted by a large enough fraction of the population, cannot be invaded and eliminated by another.

The greatly fluctuating levels of reproductive success attending a frequency-dependent strategy, combined with the evolution of counterpressures against cheating in the population as a whole, assures that obligate cheaters are rare in any population (Lykken, 1995; Moore & Rose, 1995). That is, when there are few cheats in a population, each cheat enjoys numerous opportunities to exploit its unwary members, but when many follow a cheater strategy, not only are there fewer "suckers" per cheat, there is a greater awareness of the strategy in the population and thus a lowered probability of its success (Dugatkin, 1992; Machalek, 1995). However, as cheats become fewer in a population, more opportunities arise for those who remain to prosper, and the whole process recycles.

This process is a coevolutionary "arms race" similar to the coevolution of predator and prey in which the adaptations of one species are molded by the adaptations of the other. The continual competition between cooperators and cheats has molded the sensibilities of both. Just as cooperators have undergone evolutionary tuning of their senses for detecting cheats, cheats have evolved mechanisms that serve to hide their true intentions (Alexander, 1987; Mealey, 1995; Trivers, 1991). The probable adaptation aiding cheats is a muting of the neurohormonal mechanisms that regulate the social emotions so that cheats have little real understanding of what it is like to feel guilt, shame, anxiety, and empathy. Selection for self-deception would even better enable the cheater to pursue his interests without detection (Alexander, 1987; Dugatkin, 1992; Drake, 1995). We all have this capacity for self-deception (think of some of the defense mechanisms in psychoanalytic theory that serve to protect our egos), but most of us are not all that good at maintaining the fiction (Nesse & Lloyd, 1992). Because chronic cheats operate "below the emotional poverty line" (Hare, 1993:134), they do not reveal clues that would allow others to judge their intentions. Lacking an emotional basis for self-regulation, chronic cheats tend to make social decisions exclusively on the basis of rational calculations of immediate costs or benefits (Mealey, 1995; Trivers, 1991).

There is wealth of evidence that psychopaths have a greatly diminished capacity to experience the social emotions (Hare, 1993, 1996; Lykken, 1995; Patrick, 1994). However, the proposition that there is a distinct behavioral type in human populations for which deception and exploitation is an obligate rather than a conditional strategy is probably the most difficult evolutionary proposition for criminologists to accept. Many evolutionary scholars disagree with the proposition, but many others do not (see commentaries following Mealey's [1995] article).

It is notable that obligate and conditional cheater reproductive strategies, each with its own distinct genetic basis, do exist collaterally in numerous animal species as ESSs (Alcock, 1998). There is also some human evidence that psychopathy constitutes a discrete taxonomic class (a categorical rather than continuous variable) *phenotypically* (Harris, Rice & Quinsey, 1994), but this evidence does not mark psychopaths as distinct from nonpsychopaths *genotypically*. Absent the kinds of genetic experiments conducted with nonhuman animals, we may never know with certainty if there is a distinct genetically based human cheater morph.

An interesting piece of purely circumstantial evidence supporting the claim that psychopathy is an obligate strategy is the fact that the percentage of chronic offenders, at least in Western cultures, is remarkably consistent. The famous 1945 Philadelphia birth cohort studies of boys born in 1945 (Wolfgang, Figlio & Sellin, 1972) and 1958 (Tracy, Wolfgang & Figlio, 1990) showed that very few boys (6% in the first cohort and 7.5% in the second) committed the vast majority of the crimes among the cohort. The 6 percent (18% of the subset of delinquents in the cohort) in the 1945 cohort committed 71 percent of the homicides, 73 percent of the rapes, 82 percent of the robberies, and 69 percent of the aggravated assaults. The corresponding percentages in the 1958 cohort were 61, 75, 73, and 65. Similar cohort studies in other United States locations and in other Western countries have found almost identical figures, which may indicate that psychopathic behavior is an evolutionary stable strategy.

The vast majority of criminals are not psychopaths, and the cheater strategy they employ is conditional rather than obligate. Conditional strategies are evolutionarily more advantageous because of the flexibility they offer. In most nonhuman animal species, cheater strategists (variably labeled as *sneakers*, *mimics*, *floaters*, and *satellites*) are typically males who are reproductively disadvantaged in some way (Alcock, 1998). The most disadvantaged are the young, who have not yet established themselves in the social hierarchy, have limited resources, and cannot contend physically with older and more powerful conspecifics. Although it is not the most profitable way of acquiring copulations, the cheater strategy is marginally adaptive because it does provide more reproductive opportunities than would be the case if disadvantaged males simply waited passively for their situation to improve, which may never happen. Because a conditional cheater strategy has some fitness consequences, genes governing the neurohormonal mechanisms that allow us to respond to environmental conditions by changing our behavior (cooperator to cheater, and vice versa) have survived in us all. In a very real sense, then, the antisocial impulse is universal but is constrained by rules that most of us profit from following most of the time.

Violence and Status

The vision of *Homo sapiens* as an essentially nonviolent species moved to violence only by extreme circumstances is popular in anthropology and sociology (Tiger, 1990). Yet, our bloody history attests to how easily we "nonviolent" creatures are moved with alarming frequency to create situations that lead to violence. Our species is not alone in its penchant for violence; violent acts, including infanticide, siblicide, lethal male fights, rape, xenophobia, and rudimentary warfare, have been documented in a wide variety of nonhuman species ranging from insects to chimpanzees (Alcock, 1998; Pater, 1990; Wrangham & Peterson, 1996). The ubiquity of such acts across species, and across human cultures and historical periods, strongly implies that violence has served important evolutionary purposes.

It is a central tenet of evolutionary theory that the human brain evolved in the context of overwhelming concerns for resource and mate acquisition. When food, territory, and mates are plentiful, the use of violent tactics to obtain them is a risky and unnecessary waste of energy, but when resources are scarce, acquiring them any way one can, including the use of violence, may be worth the risk (Barkow, 1989). Among the most successful of our ancestral males in acquiring resources were probably those who were willing and able to use violent tactics on occasion. The acquisition of resources brought prestige and status to those who acquired them. Because females have evolved mechanisms that incline them to favor high-status males, high-status males have access to a disproportionate number of females (Buss, 1995).

Status is not necessarily associated with aggressive and violent tactics (often it is, quite the opposite today in most social contexts), but it almost certainly was more so in our ancestral environments (Chagnon, 1996; Wrangham & Peterson, 1996). Because status brought more copulation opportunities, genes inclining males to pursue their interests aggressively (which sometimes meant becoming violent) enjoyed greater representation in subsequent generations. From the evolutionary point of view, violence is something human males, as well as males in numerous other species, are designed by nature to do (another statement of fact, not moral approval). Wherever we look in the world, males are far more likely than females to be both the victims and the perpetrators of all kinds of violent acts (Barak, 1998; Campbell, 1999).

Gratuitous violence among humans in ancestral environments (at least within the kinship group) was probably rare compared to that which existed in many other species. Violence may be *in* the nature of human males, but it is not *the* nature of human males. Natural selection has not strongly favored violent aggression over access to females in long-lived species such as ours because males in long-lived species have plenty of time to move up status hierarchies and acquire mates via courtship rather than risking their lives in desperate mating battles early in life (Alcock, 1998). High-risk battles over access to females take place mostly in polygynous and short-lived species.

Sexual dimorphism (the ratio of female-to-male body size) is an indicator of a species' mating history. The selection for size and strength among males, resulting in males who are much larger (up to 100 percent or more larger in some species) than females, reflects a polygynous mating history in which dominance is established by physical battles among males. The fossil record shows that males of early hominid species (*Australopithecus anemensis* and *Australopithecus afarenis*) were also 50 to 100 percent larger than females (Geary, 2000). The fairly low degree of sexual dimorphism among modern *Homo sapiens* (males are only 7 to 10% larger than females, on average) indicates an evolutionary shift from violent male-male competition for mates to a more monogamous mating system and an increase in paternal investment (Plavcan & van Schaik, 1997). In cultures in which polygyny and low paternal investment still exist, we find homicide rates greatly exceeding those of any modern society, such as the Agta rate of 326 per 100,000 and the Yanomamo rate of 166 per 100,000 (Ellis & Walsh, 2000:71). Homicide translates directly into reproductive success among the Yanomamo. Males who have killed the most in intervillage warfare are the most respected and have about three times as many wives and children than those who have killed the least or not at all (Chagnon, 1988).

Because high status has contributed to human reproductive success, and because a capacity for controlled aggression has contributed to attaining it, selection for aggression, which sometimes might mean violent aggression, is an evolutionary given (Daly & Wilson, 1988b). Killing rival suitors and rival claimants to resources doubtless conferred a reproductive advantage on their killers, but this does not mean that there is an evolved adaptive mechanism dedicated to homicide in the human brain. However, adaptations such as male sexual propriety, jealousy, and status striving, which do have mechanisms dedicated to them, would have occasionally manifested themselves in homicide. Thus, although there are genes governing psychophysiological processes that facilitate violence, their expression is contingent on cultural and situational factors. Competition between human males is rarely in the form of brute physical combat; rather, it is in culturally prescribed ways of achieving power, wealth, esteem, and status, the acquisition of which draws females to the most successful competitors (Barkow, 1989). Within human and nonhuman primate groups with established dominance hierarchies, social rules restrain the emergence of widespread violent conflict (Raleigh et al., 1991).

SPECIFIC EVOLUTIONARY THEORIES OF CRIME

We have thus far explored the logic of evolutionary theory is it pertains to criminal and antisocial behavior in general. We now briefly explore specific evolutionary theories of criminal and antisocial behavior. The four primary evolutionary theories are *cheater theory, conditional adaptation theory, adaptive strategy theory*, and *r/K theory*. All four theories focus on reproductive strategies (mating effort versus parenting effort) and the tactics that flow from them as their foundation.

Cheater Theory

We have already encountered aspects of cheater theory in the discussion of psychopathy. The theory rests ultimately on the broad asymmetry between the reproductive strategies of males and females. Females have a much lower reproductive ceiling than males, although almost all females will probably reproduce. The major factor in female reproductive success has been to secure and hold on to the assistance of a mate to raise her offspring. There is much more variability in male reproductive success, with some males leaving no offspring and others fathering large numbers. This is particularly so in polygynous species and polygynous human cultures, and probably so in human EEAs. Given lower variation but greater reproductive certainty, females have evolved a mating strategy inclining them to be far choosier about with whom they will mate than are males (Buss, 1994; Wright, 1994).

Male reproductive success is potentially greater the more females a male can mate with, and males have an evolved desire for multiple partners. Males can respond to the more reticent female strategy in one of two ways: They can comply with female preferences and assist a single female raise their offspring, or they can either trick or force a female to have sex and then move on to the next female. Almost all males have probably falsely proclaimed love and fidelity and used some form of coercion to obtain sexual favors, but the vast majority will eventually settle down and assist a female in raising their young. This strategy is facilitated by the social emotions, particularly love (Fisher, 1998; Walsh, 1995a). The second strategy is likely to be followed by males who are deficient in the social emotions, such as chronic criminals and psychopaths, well after adolescence (Hare, 1993; Lykken, 1995). The basic point of cheater theory is that criminal activity is facilitated by the same traits that make for the successful pursuit of a cheater's sexual strategy. It is important to stress that cheater theory does not, nor does any other theory presented here, postulate that criminal behavior reflects a defective genome; rather it reflects a normal, albeit morally regrettable, alternative.

Conditional Adaptation Theory (CAT)

CAT proposes that people adopt different reproductive strategies for environmental rather than genetic reasons, although the possibility of genetic variance influencing the selection of a strategy is not denied (Belsky & Draper, 1991). According to the theory, individuals will tend to adopt an unrestricted (promiscuous) sexual strategy if they learned during their childhood that interpersonal relationships are ephemeral and unreliable (as indexed by such things as parental divorce and witnessing others engaging in short-term relationships). Individuals who learned the opposite will tend to adopt a more restricted strategy. Neither strategy is consciously chosen, but rather flows from subconscious expectations based on early experiences of the stability/instability of interpersonal relationships.

Unlike other evolutionary theories of crime, CAT includes features that allow for predictions about the involvement of women in antisocial behavior as well as men. Thus, in addition to the "*cad* vs. *dad*" dichotomy to describe male mating strategies, we have the "*whore* vs. *Madonna*" dichotomy to define female mating strategies. A large amount of evidence shows that both male and female criminals and serious delinquents have significantly more sex partners and begin sexual activity earlier than do persons in general. A review of 52 studies from seven different countries found a significant positive relationship between number of sex partners and a variety of criminal/antisocial behaviors, one study found a nonsignificant relationship, and no study found a negative relationship. Regarding age of onset of sexual activity, all 31 reviewed studies found that the earlier the onset of sexual activity, the greater the involvement in criminal behavior (Ellis & Walsh, 2000:227).

Alternative Adaptation Theory (AAT)

AAT proposes that, largely for genetic reasons, humans are arrayed along a continuum regarding where they have a tendency to focus their reproductive efforts (Rowe, 1996). At one extreme is mating effort (effort devoted to seeking multiple sex partners) and at the other is parenting effort (effort devoted to rearing young). The best demographic predictors of where effort is focused are gender and age, which are also the best demographic predictors of crime and delinquency. Males and the young emphasize mating effort, and females and older persons emphasize parenting effort. In terms of individual traits, the suite of traits useful for focusing on mating effort, such as deceitfulness, impulsiveness, and hedonism, are also useful in pursuing criminal activity. Conversely, traits useful for parenting effort, such as empathy, conscientiousness, and altruism, are also useful for noncriminal, or prosocial, activity.

AAT makes the same predictions CAT does regarding early onset of sexual behavior and number of sexual partners but would explain the relationship by indicating that both criminal activity and a high level of mating effort is sustained by the same suite of heritable traits. In addition, unlike proponents of CAT, Rowe (1996:290) places little emphasis on childrearing, pointing out that behavior-genetic studies consistently show that common rearing environment (which is stressed by CAT) has little or no lasting influence on an individual's personality or intelligence. The relationship between childhood experiences and the adoption of a particular reproductive strategy could be the result of the genes children share with the parent(s) providing those experiences rather than the experiences per se (Walsh, 1999).

Anthropological evidence supportive of aspects of both CAT and AAT is provided by Harpending and Draper (1988), who contrasted reproductive strategies in two cultures located in drastically different ecological environments. The first group is the !Kung bushmen, who inhabit the inhospitable Kalahari Desert in South Africa, and the second is the Mundurucu, who inhabit the resource-rich Amazon basin. Because conditions are harsh in the Kalahari, life is precarious, cooperative behavior is imperative, and parenting effort is favored over mating effort. The Mundurucu's rich ecology frees males for fighting, raiding other groups, and engaging in competition for females. Mating effort is favored over parenting effort among the Mundurucu. What is most interesting from a criminological perspective is that cultures emphasizing mating effort exhibit behaviors that would be considered antisocial in Western societies, such as low-level parental care, aggressiveness, "protest masculinity" (hyper masculinity), and transient bonding (Ember & Ember, 1998; Harpending & Draper, 1988). These behaviors, however, are adaptive in such cultures and may be adaptive in certain subcultures of modern industrial societies as well.

r/K Theory

The final theory, r/K theory, is both more complicated and more controversial than the other theories because it makes predictions about race, as well as about age and gender. Specifically, it predicts that blacks will commit more crimes than whites who will in turn commit more crimes than Asians. This racial pattern of crime rates is consistently found worldwide (Ellis & Walsh, 2000; Eysenk & Gudjonsson, 1989; Rushton, 1990). The r/K theory originated in the mathematics of population biology and refers to a continuum of reproductive strategies ranging from r to K. The extreme r strategy (r stands for the intrinsic rate of population growth) is characterized by maximum egg production and no parenting effort. The r strategy is most characteristic of short-lived creatures such as insects and fish, whose extreme fertility ensures genetic continuity even if the vast majority of offspring perish before reaching reproductive age. The K strategy (K stands for the carrying capacity of the environment) emphasizes parental care over number of offspring to ensure genetic survival. This is characteristic of long-lived species, particularly humans.

The r and K strategies covary with many heritable traits that are helpful in maintaining them (Ellis, 1987; Rushton, 1988, 1995). For instance, Ellis (1987) showed that traits used to identify r-selection were more typical of criminals and that traits used to identify K-selection were more typical of noncriminals. His review of numerous studies revealed that persons with serious delinquent/criminal histories appeared to have the following six r-selected traits to a greater extent than persons in general: (1) shorter gestation periods; (2) earlier onset of sexual activity; (3) greater sexual activity outside bonded relationships; (4) less stable bonding; (5) lower parental investment (high rates of abuse, neglect, and abandonment of offspring); (6) shorter life expectancy.

This is where the controversy and the charges of racism appear. If criminals in general are higher on traits used by biologists to define r-selection species, and if the black-over-white-over-Asian pattern of crime prevalence is consistently found, does it imply a black-versus-white-verus-Asian gradient of r-selection? An examination of this question requires that we rank-order large samples from each population on as many indicators of r- and K-selected traits as possible and their mean scores be compared. Rushton (1990) did this by placing 26 traits associated with r or K selection into five higher-order concepts—social organization, personality/temperament, maturation rate, intelligence, and reproductive effort. Socialization is heavily involved in social organization, achievement, and sexuality, but minimally, if at all, in other traits such as morphology, speed of physical maturation, and gamete production. If racial differences are random with respect to r/K indicators, then most research results will be null and the remainder will be about equally split between negative and positive results. Reviews of the literature have shown this has not been the case across the hundreds of studies that have examined these characteristics and traits in a variety of contexts (Ellis, 1987; Rushton, 1995).

It is important to note that although population differences on these indicators are demonstrably there, they are not large and there is considerable overlap across the races. We also need to realize that r/K theory, when applied within species, is not an example of "genetic determinism," as Rushton (1994:42) made clear: "Although genes provide the initial set point, environmental factors move individuals up or down the continuum of reproductive strategies." Environmental factors inclining individuals to behaviors associated with more r- than K-selected behaviors will be examined in Chapter 8.

The primary strength of r/K theory is that it weaves a network of meaning that joins diverse phenomena and their correlates in ways that order the data consistent with evolutionary theory. Although scientists have long admired theories able to incorporate previously unrelated phenomena into a coherent explanatory scheme, many find the theory objectionable when applied to criminal behavior because of the race connection (Roberts & Gabor, 1990). Besides charges of racism and insensitivity (recall Freeman's concern cited in Chapter 1), criticism generally centers on problems of research design, definitions of race, the validity of certain trait measures, and the applicability of r/K theory to within-species differences. The real crux of the matter, however, is the consistent black-over-white-over-Asian ordering on r-selected traits. No critic has been able to supply aggregate data indicating a different gradient, so unless all measures of the traits utilized in hundreds of studies are hopelessly invalid, critics will have to come up with theories of their own to explain the observed gradient. Unless or until this occurs, criminologists should at least view r/K theory as a useful heuristic.

BEHAVIOR GENETICS AND EVOLUTIONARY PSYCHOLOGY

As previously noted, evolutionary psychology and behavior genetics are animated by two separate concerns: the former by the central tendency of traits, and the latter by their variation. Evolutionary psychologists explore how behavior we now define as criminal may have been adaptive in EEAs. Because adaptations apply to all members of a species, some evolutionary psychologists may view the substantial heritability of important traits linked to criminality as challenging the tenets of adaptationism (Daly, 1996). This is because natural selection drives heritability of the most vitally important traits in a species to zero. Observations such as this lead some evolutionary psychologists to distance their discipline from behavior genetics. According to behavior geneticist David Rowe (in Horgan, 1995), some evolutionary psychologists disavow behavior genetics because it makes their work both politically and scientifically easier. If all differences in human behavior can be ascribed to the environment, and all similarities to genes, then model construction is simplified and political correctness is maximized. These are very poor reasons for ignoring such a closely related discipline. Evolution is the domain of population genetics more so than of psychology, and certainly we cannot apportion behavioral differences and similarities into separate disciplinary specialties so simply.

What of the claim that substantial heritability of traits associated with criminality challenges the tenets of adaptationism? Most evolutionary psychologists appear to see no contradiction in viewing behaviors designed to solve adaptive problems as also being heritable. As we have seen, it is true that there can be no heritability for the presence or absence of morphological structures or species-defining characteristics, but in terms of cognitive traits, such as temperament, personality, and behavior, natural selection in fluctuating human environments would have almost certainly favored genetic variation over fixity in these characteristics (Bailey, 1997; Segal & MacDonald, 1998). Indeed, the Hardy-Weinberg Equilibrium (the foundational law of the genetic basis of evolution) informs us that there is always a reservoir of genetic variation (Woodward, 1992). This reservoir is a necessary requirement for evolution to occur if future conditions dictate it. Thus, I am in agreement with a number of scholars who have worked in both disciplines that evolutionary and behavior-genetic explanations are complementary explanations that together provide a deeper understanding than either provides separately (Bailey, 1997; Crawford, 1998a; Scarr, 1995; Segal & MacDonald, 1998). After all, the much-heralded "modern synthesis" is the synthesis of Darwinian and Mendelian thought.

The most recent evolutionary addition to the brain is the cerebrum, which forms the bulk of the human brain. The cerebrum is divided into two complementary hemispheres, each with its own specialized functions, that are connected at the bottom by the corpus callosum. It is generally accepted that the right hemisphere is specialized for perception and the expression of emotion (particularly negative emotions), and that the left hemisphere is specialized for language and analytical thinking. The outer layer of the cerebrum is the cerebral cortex. The cerebral cortex is the "thinking" brain, organizing and analyzing information from other structures and formulating and relaying back to them the appropriate responses.

From the perspective of the behavioral scientist, the most important part of the cerebral cortex is the prefrontal cortex (PFC). The PFC occupies approximately one-third of the human cerebral cortex, a proportion greater by far than in any other species. This is the last brain area to fully mature (Grafman, 1994). This vital part of the human cortex has extensive connections with other cortical regions, as well as with deeper structures in the limbic system. Because of its many connections with other brain structures, and because it is involved in so many neuropsychological disorders, it is generally considered to play the major integrative, as well as supervisory, role in the brain. The PFC is also vital to the forming of moral judgments, the mediation of affect, and for social cognition (Grafman, 1994; Sowell et al., 1999). Given these functions, it is no surprise that biosocial scientists interested in antisocial behavior have given a lot of attention to the PFC.

Making up all these anatomical structures are hundreds of billions of nerve cells called neurons. All our thoughts, feelings, emotions, and behavior are the result of communication networks composed of these neurons. Each neuron consists of the cell body (soma), an axon, and a number of dendrites. The cell body contains the nucleus that carries out the metabolic functions of the neuron. The axon originates in the cell body, and the dendrites are branch-like extensions of the cell body. Axons serve as transmitters sending signals to other neurons, and dendrites serve as receivers picking up information from neighboring neurons. Each of the more than 100 billion communicating neurons makes up to an average of 1,000 connections with other neurons, which makes the potential combination of connections in the human brain "hyper-astronomical" (Edelman, 1992:17). Many lower-level brain structures, such as the brain stem, come with neural connections more or less complete at birth (in the parlance of neuroscience, they are "hard-wired"), but development of the higher brain areas in the cerebrum, and to a lesser extent in the limbic system, depends on making connections between neural networks after birth.

These communicating structures are not actually physically connected. The receiving and sending of messages takes place in microscopic fluid-filled gaps between axons and dendrites called synapses. Information from the cell passes along the axon electrically until it reaches the synaptic knob, at which time it is translated into chemistry as tiny vesicles burst open and spill out one or more of a variety of chemicals. These chemicals (neurotransmitters) cross the synaptic gap to make contact with postsynaptic receptor sites, where the message is translated back into an electrical one either for further transportation or inhibition of the message. Once neurotransmitters have passed on their messages, excess amounts are pumped back up into the presynaptic knob or destroyed by enzymes. Neurotransmitters (either excitatory or inhibitory transmitters) that have been linked to the probability of antisocial behavior include norepinephrine, serotonin, and dopamine, as well as the enzyme monoamine oxydase that degrades (destroys) them after they have performed their tasks. The anatomical and chemical systems and circuits described above are fully interactive entities, each affected by and affecting the others to various extents.

NEURAL SELECTIONISM AND CONSTRUCTIVISM

There are nature/nurture arguments in the neurosciences surrounding the issue of brain development (albeit, not about naive dichotomies). The debates are about contributions to brain development of processes intrinsic to the brain (in the genome) relative to extrinsic (environmental) contributions: "To what extent does the information needed to build an organism reside in the genome of the fertilized egg, and how much does neural development depend on interaction between the growing organism and its environment?" (Ribchester, 1986:166). Neuroscientists who come down most strongly in favor of innateness are generally called *selectionists* or *nativists*, and those more in favor of the power of extrinsic factors to mold the brain are generally called *constructivists* or *connectionists*. Both positions agree that the environment is of the utmost importance in the development of the brain; the argument is not "*whether* the environment thoroughly influences brain development, but *how* it does" (Quartz & Sejnowski, 1997:579; emphasis in original).

Selectionists are strongly influenced by evolutionary theory and by artificial intelligence theory. The evolutionary argument boils down to the assertion that the brain cannot have evolved as a general all-purpose computing machine, because there was never any general problem in environments of evolutionary adaptation that our ancestors had to solve. Selectionists maintain that the human brain was cobbled together piecemeal over evolutionary time in response to a series of problems (all subproblems of the one central problem all living things share—

how to survive and propagate their genes) faced by our ancestors (Geary, 1998). The neurophysiology underlying each brain function is thus seen as an adaptation designed to solve some *specific* problem. These adaptations are neural circuits that subserve specific functions. We know this because damage to those circuits produces specific impairments of cognitive functioning, not an overall impairment (Dellarosa-Cummins & Cummins, 1999; Gazzaniga, 1998). A popular metaphor for this discrete yet functionally integrated collection of specialized modules (sets of neural networks) is that of a Swiss army knife (Cosmides, Tooby & Barkow, 1992). For the evolutionary neuroscientist, the mind is a series of specialized modules with a basic logic specified by genes.

We should not take this to mean that selectionists are "genetic determinists" claiming that our minds are preprogrammed to respond stereotypically to everything it will encounter, that there is a gene for every trait, or that learning is not important. On the contrary, Nobel Prize-winning neuroscientist Gerald Edelman (1992) has claimed that his theory of neural Darwinism (to be discussed later in this chapter) permits and predicts human free will, a position that not many strict environmentalists would be comfortable defending from a scientific point of view. But how can we reconcile the assertion that the mind has a genetically programmed logic with the claim that the environment thoroughly influences brain development? To answer this question, we have to turn to the so-called *frame problem* of artificial intelligence theory.

The human mind is not a blank slate that must learn everything through experience; it is fertile with specific built-in assumptions (call them by the old-fashioned term *instincts* if you like) about the nature of the species-relevant environments that it will encounter. We selectively attend to some kinds of information more readily than to others because we possess such built-in assumptions. This was not fully appreciated until researchers in robotics and artificial intelligence tried to program "common sense" into their computers, "the ultimate tabula rasa" (Pinker, 1997:15). Without highly detailed and specific instructions, robots tend to respond to novel encounters with the environment with bizarre and often self-destructive responses, such as trying to push their hands through their own bodies (Spelke, 1999).

There are an enormous number of ways that an organism can respond to a specific environmental stimulus, some of which are advantageous and some of which are highly disadvantageous. Think of how members of different animal species (including humans) respond to insects, heights, snakes, water, cats, temperature, dung, dead carcasses, open/closed spaces, or any number of other environmental features. What makes a spider or a frog perceive a buzzing fly as a potential meal, while humans swat at it as a potential disease carrier? What makes the dung beetle view a pile of excrement as a great place to raise its young, while humans view it as definitely something to avoid? Members of each species respond to environmental stimuli in species-specific ways with built-in assumptions (neural algorithms) that "frame" the response problem for them (hence the term *frame problem*). Nature simply cannot leave responses to many aspects of any species' typical environment to the vagaries of experiential learning. Responses are certainly strengthened and fine-tuned with experience, but the general response pattern was framed by natural selection. As Elizabeth Spelke (1999:1) put it, "The frame problem precludes the possibility of bootstrapping oneself up from a position of no assumptions." Unlike robots, animals have epigenetic rules exquisitely crafted by natural selection to perceive and respond to the environment by sorting stimuli into positive and negative categories according to their potential for harming or assisting them in their survival and reproductive goals. We categorize so effortlessly and automatically that the process is referred to in the vernacular as "common sense."

Constructivists reject both the image of the brain as a general-purpose computational machine with generic learning procedures, and the extreme view of domain-specific modules embedded in the brain carrying a priori predispositions. The essence of the constructivist position is that evolution has shaped our minds by providing us with a highly plastic (malleable) brain able to construct itself from the experience rather than providing us with innate modules that are finely tuned for specialized tasks. They point to studies demonstrating that the brain can recruit supposedly specialized areas to perform tasks usually assigned to other areas when those areas have been damaged. The most dramatic example of this is the ability of one brain hemisphere to assume the functions of the other in children who have had a hemisphere removed if surgery is performed during the period of the brain's maximal plasticity (reviewed in Elman et al., 1996). However, constructivism is not a return to a *tabula rasa* view of the mind or a total denial of selectionist principles. Indeed, major proponents of this view explicitly state that "assumption-free learning is impossible" (Quartz & Sejnowski, 1997:584).

The argument between these two schools of thought with respect to this issue is thus one of degree only. It is not inconceivable that natural selection has provided both selectionist and constructivist solutions to adaptive problems (Hurford et al., 1997). It is certainly not necessary for criminologists to understand and appreciate the arcane subtleties that separate these two positions to understand and appreciate the message that brings them together. The message is that genes have surrendered much of their control over human behavior to a more plastic, complex, and *adaptive* system of control called the human brain, and that the development of the brain depends greatly on environmental input. The message is that *we and the experiences we encounter will largely determine the patterns of our neuronal connections, and thus our ability to successfully navigate our lives.* Genes do play a crucial part, but only a part, in specifying the trillions of connections that exist among the brain cells of human beings. The environment provides the other, equally crucial, part.

THE BRAIN AND ITS ENVIRONMENT

About 50 to 60 percent of all human genes are involved in brain development (Shore, 1997). The genes specify basic brain architecture, build the cells, synthesize the various neurotransmitters and enzymes, and provide the framing assumptions. The process of neuronal birth, migration, and differentiation are also genetically determined, but they can be adversely affected by environmental events such as maternal substance abuse, malnutrition, or exposure to radiation and other noxious substances (Shore, 1997). However, while genes carry an immense amount of information, they are task-specific and few in number (only 30 to 40 thousand according to initial reports from the International Human Genome Sequencing Consortium [2001]) relative to the billions of neurons and the trillions of connections they will eventually make with one another. If genes alone had been assigned the task of specifying neuronal connections, we would all be hard-wired drones incapable of adapting to novel situations, just like the robots who tried to push their hands through their bodies. The more varied and complex the environment, the more organisms inhabiting them must change and adapt. Human environments are much too varied and much too complex for hard-wired brains.

Neuroscientists distinguish between two brain-developmental processes that *physically* capture environmental events in the organism's lifetime in the same way that genes capture environmental events in the genome during the lifespan of the species. These two processes are called *experience-expected* and *experience-dependent* (Black & Greenough, 1997; Edelman, 1987, 1992; Greenough, Black & Wallace, 1987). Both processes utilize environmental input to facilitate synaptic proliferation, the former less so than the latter. Experience-expected mechanisms are hard-wired and reflect the phylogenetic (species-wide) history of the brain; experience-dependent mechanisms reflect the brain's ontogenetic plasticity (concerning the development of the individual). Otherwise stated, every member of a species inherits species-typical brain structures and functions that are produced by a common pool of genetic material, but individuals will vary in brain functioning as their genes interact with the environments they encounter to construct those brains (Depue & Collins, 1999).

Experience-expected processes have evolved as neural preparedness to incorporate environmental information that is vital to an organism and ubiquitous in its environment. Experience-expected processes most fully support the specialized-module model of the brain. With respect to these modules, natural selection has recognized that certain processes, such as sight, speech, depth perception, affectionate bonds, aversion to insects and waste products, mobility, and sexual maturation, are vital—and has provided for mechanisms (adaptations) designed to take advantage of experiences occurring naturally within the normal range of human environments. Pre-experiential rudimentary brain organization (built-in assumptions) frame our experiences so that we will respond consistently and stereotypically to vital stimuli (Black & Greenough, 1997; Kalil, 1989). Natural selection has removed heritable variation for these processes (their alternatives failed evolutionary selection tests long ago), making them stable across all members of a species.

Experience-dependent brain development depends on experience acquired in the organism's developmental environment. Much of the variability in the wiring patterns of the brains of different individuals depends on the kinds of physical, social, and cultural environments they will encounter. It is not an exaggeration to say that "experience-dependent processes are central to understanding personality as a dynamic developmental construct that involves the collaboration of genetic and environmental influences across the lifespan" (Depue & Collins, 1999:507). These processes best reflect the constructivist argument that the brain literally constructs, or wires, itself in ways that directly reflect its experience. Although brain plasticity is greatest in infancy and early childhood, a certain degree is maintained throughout the lifespan so that every time we experience or learn something, we shape and reshape the nervous system in ways that could never have been preprogrammed.

The process of wiring the brain is known as *synaptogenesis*, a process that occurs according to both a genetic program and the influence of the environment. The neonate's cerebral cortex consists of small and underdeveloped neurons with few dendrites. During the first few months, dendrites proliferate and axons begin the process of *myelination*. Myelin is a fatty substance that coats the axons and makes for speedier transmission of electrical impulses—nerve conduction velocity increases from about two meters (6.5 feet) per second to about 50 meters (164 feet) per second when an axon becomes fully myelinatated (Casear, 1993). The process of dendritic growth and axonal myelination continues to some degree throughout life but proceeds at an explosive rate during infancy and toddlerhood. Because they are the most vital brain regions in terms of sheer survival, the experience-expected "lower" brain regions (reptilian and limbic regions) are the first to be myelinated, and some "higher" brain areas (especially the PFC) are not fully myelinated until adulthood (Paus et al., 1999; Sowell et al., 1999). This observation has important consequences for criminological theory, as we shall see.

The most important issue relating to synaptogenesis is not so much the genesis of a particular synapse or set of synapses composing a neuronal module, but whether it will survive the competition for synaptic space and functional viability. The most active period of synaptogenesis is infancy and early childhood, with the number and density of synaptic connections being higher than they will ever be at eight months of age (Rakic, 1996). About one-half of these connections will eventually be eliminated. Although the brain creates and eliminates synapses throughout life, creation exceeds elimination in the first two or three years. Production and elimination are roughly balanced thereafter up until adolescence, after which elimination exceeds production (Shore, 1997; Sowell et al., 1999).

This process of selective production and elimination has been termed *neural Darwinism* (Edelman, 1987, 1992). Edelman posits a selection process among competing cortical modules (populations of synapses). In order for neuronal natural selection to take place, there must be an excess of synapses available, just as natural selection requires a large excess of genetic variation. Neuronal connections are selected for retention or elimination according to how functionally viable (adaptive) they prove to be in the organism's environment. Just as environmental challenges select from a population's repertoire of genetic variation those traits that help it and its progeny to meet those challenges, the brain's repertoire of excess connections are selected for retention or pruning according to the input pattern provided by the environment. The brain's neuronal populations thus evolve in somatic time very much like species evolve in geological time by selective elimination and retention.

Retention of synapse networks is very much an activational, or use-dependent, process. In the competition for scarce synaptic space, strength and frequency of experience will determine which connections will survive and which will not. This competition "is biased in favor of the [neuron] populations that receive the greatest amount of stimulation during early development" (Levine, 1993:52). Experiences with strong emotional content are accompanied by especially strong nerve impulses, and if these impulses are both frequent and strong, the neurons involved become more sensitive and responsive to similar stimuli in the future (Kandel & Hawkins, 1992). Frequently activated neurons are thus primed to fire at lower stimulus thresholds once voltage-dependent neurological tracks have been laid down (Llinas, 1989).

Experience-dependent neuronal organization has been experimentally tested in the lab. It has long been known that animals raised in stimulus-enriched environments have significantly greater neurological development than animals raised in stimulus-deprived environments. Cloned (thus genetically identical) animals have been subjected to different environmental experiences and their dendritic density and branching patterns compared. If genes alone were responsible for synaptogenesis, then branching patterns would be identical in cloned animals regardless of the environments to which they had been exposed. What researchers actually find, however, is that the branching pattern is usually more variable between pairs of cloned animals subjected to different environments than between the left and right sides of the brain of the same individual animal (Changeux, 1985; Molenaar, Boomsma & Dolan, 1993).

It is safe to say that the evidence is unequivocal on two major points about brain development: (1) the brain is always a "work in progress," and (2) development is "use-dependent." However, although synaptic selection does depend on the strength and frequency of activation, all cortical modules are not *equal* candidates for selection. Recalling the studies from Chapter 2 showing that monozygotic twins reared apart assess their affectual experiences with their adoptive parents significantly more similarly than do dizygotic twins reared together, the concept of gene/environment correlation assures us that some modules have a greater probability of selection than others. Temperamentally pleasant infants evoke responses (cuddling, playing, kissing) from others that will lay down neuronal pathways to the infants' pleasure centers. Temperamentally unpleasant infants are at risk for evoking responses (infrequent holding, neglect, and possibly abuse) that may lay down pathways leading to displeasure centers. Because the temperaments of parents and their biological children are positively correlated, the probability of pleasant stimuli evoking pleasant responses and unpleasant stimuli evoking unpleasant responses is increased. Brains are wired in a probabilistic epigenetic way, and this pattern of development has been invoked as an explanation for why nonshared environment is consistently found to be more powerful in accounting for variation in most human traits than shared environment (Molenaar, Boomsma & Dolan, 1993; Smith, 1993).

WHY BONDING AND ATTACHMENT
ARE NEUROLOGICALLY IMPORTANT

It has been pointed out that "the affection dimension of child rearing appears to pull in more correlates with child behavior than any other dimension" (Rowe, 1992:402). Humans appear to have powerful neurological and endocrine structures that demand the formation of affectual bonds. As one researcher put it, "Human newborns, and altricial animals in general, are adapted to receive support for physiological homeostasis and motivation from the contact stimuli of an affectionate caretaker in a protected environment" (Trevarthen, 1992:225). The literature lists many negative outcomes associated with the failure to form these bonds, including the relative inability to form lasting and positive adult bonds (Perry & Pollard, 1998; Shore, 1997; Walsh, 1995b; Zeifman & Hazan, 1997). But why should this be? What evolutionary advantage does the acquisition of affectual bonds confer, and what might be the neuropsychological consequences relevant to criminal behavior of not forming them?

We might begin by noting that hominids (erect bipedal primate mammals) experienced a rapid rate of selection for intelligence after separating from the apes. From the approximate 1.5 million years that separated *Australopithecus afarenis* and *Homo erectus,* hominid cranial capacity doubled from a mean of 450 cubic centimeters to a mean of 900 cubic centimeters (cc), and by another 70 percent to about 1,350 cc, from *Homo erectus* to modern *Homo sapiens* (Bromage, 1987). This selection for intelligence, and the cranial capacity to store it, placed tremendous reproductive burdens on females. The human female birth canal could not accommodate the birthing of an infant whose brain was 60 percent of its adult weight, as it is in newborn macaques, or even 45 percent, as in newborn chimpanzees (Shore, 1996). The pelvis of *Australopithecine* females was probably shaped by natural selection to satisfy upright posture and bipedalism (which has the effect of narrowing the birth canal) more than for increased fetal brain size, thus precipitating a conflict between our ancestral female's obstetric and postural requirements (Abitol, 1987; Buck, 1999). Evolutionary conflicts such as this are not uncommon; natural selection works on trajectories already in motion, and it cannot anticipate future needs. Selection for larger pelvises may have been one strategy tried, but pelvises large enough to allow the passage of human infants as developmentally advanced as other primate infants may have severely hindered locomotion and placed both mother and infant at the mercy of predators.

The evolutionary mechanism that partially solved the obstetrics/posture conflict (human females still have more difficulty giving birth than other species because of this problem) was for human infants to be born at earlier and earlier stages of development as cerebral mass increased. Human infants experience 25 percent brain growth inside the womb, and 75 percent growth outside the womb. Developmental neuroscientists call these two neural growth periods *uterogestation* (gestation in the womb) and *exterogestation* (gestation outside the womb). Such a high degree of developmental incompleteness of the human brain assures a greater role for the extrauterine environment in its development than is true of any other species.

If a species is to have extremely altricial young (that is, young who will require care for some time), then there must have been strong selection pressures for neurohormonal mechanisms among those who bore them, pressures that were designed to assure the young would be nurtured for as long as is necessary. These mechanisms ensure that there will be a "continuous symbiotic relationship between mother and child" (across the two gestation periods) (Montagu, 1981:93). Ashley Montagu calls these mechanisms by their popular name—*love*. He goes on to add, "It is, in a very real and not in the least paradoxical sense, even more necessary to love than it is to live, for without love there can be no healthy growth or development, no real life. The neotenous principle for human beings—indeed, the evolutionary imperative—is to live *as if to live and love were one.*" (1981:93, emphasis in original).

The concept of neoteny further helps us to understand why *Homo sapiens* is a species exquisitely adapted to fine-tune itself in response to problems and opportunities present in its environment. *Neoteny* literally means *holding youth*; and conceptually, it means "the retention of embryonic or juvenile characteristics by retardation of development" (Bjorklund, 1997:155). Human beings are highly neotenous, losing far fewer embryonic and juvenile features (both morphological and behavioral) than other animals, including, as Montagu suggests, the need for love. Neoteny is an adaptation resulting from perhaps only a few minor mutations at genetic loci involved with developmental timing, and may have been all that it took for our ancestors to branch off the evolutionary line we shared with the apes (Feder & Park, 1989). The analysis of hominid skeletons from *Australopithecines* to modern humans has led many evolutionary scientists to conclude that neoteny has been a major, perhaps *the* major, determinant of human evolutionary direction (Gould, 1977; Groves, 1989).

Neoteny has many important evolutionary advantages. Because human development is so delayed and prolonged, we are given more time to become adaptively affected by environments in flux to a far greater degree than any other animal. Developmental retardation means that unlike, for example, snakes or alligators, we do not need hard-wired brains to make us respond appropriately (instinctively) to environmental exigencies. What is "appropriate" in human environments varies so much that we have to learn what it is, and that takes time. (This in no way gainsays what was said earlier about built-in assumptions that bias learning in certain directions.)

There are two major disadvantages of neoteny from the criminologist's point of view. The first is that the most neotenous feature of *Homo sapiens* is the associative areas of the neocortex, a point that shall be returned to in Chapter 6. The second disadvantage is that we all do need Montagu's "continuing symbiotic relationship" in order to take full advantage of the opportunities of neoteny, but some of us fail to get it. Those who fail to form this relationship often fall prey to many developmental and behavioral problems, including criminal behavior. The relationship between criminality and childhood abuse and neglect is one of the best documented in the literature (Heck & Walsh, 2000), although this literature rarely addresses the possible neurological mechanisms by which childhood abuse and neglect affect the probability of later antisocial behavior. The next section discusses what neuroscience has discovered about the effects of abuse and neglect on the developing brain.

ABUSE, NEGLECT, AND THE DEVELOPING BRAIN

In discussing the effects of abuse and neglect on the developing human brain, this book will rely heavily on Gary Kraemer's (1992) seminal laboratory work with rhesus monkeys, a review of the literature by Danya Glaser (2000), and the research findings and opinions of 150 leading brain experts presented and discussed at the Brain Development in Young Children: New Frontiers for Research, Policy and Practice (BDYC) meeting held in Chicago in 1996 (Shore, 1997). There are those who balk at extrapolating findings derived from monkeys (as in Kraemer's work) to human beings, although such extrapolations have never been a problem in the medical sciences. Evolution is parsimonious; it does not discard mechanisms that work and start all over again as species branch off from the parental line. Mechanisms might need additional tuning as they cross species lines, but evolution can only work with what is in the gene pool. Kraemer's work deals with how affective and attachment failure affects neurohormonal mechanisms, and how these mechanisms, in turn, affect behavior in one primate species. Such failures can be expected to influence humans also. Perhaps they affect human primates even more so because we possess brains that are much more plastic than monkey brains, "even more primed to respond to the environment" (Shore, 1997:25).

Neuronal pathways forged from the early experiences among experimentally deprived monkeys have been identified via aberrant electrophysiological activity for decades. It has also been known for some time that chronic stress can produce neuron death via the frequent production of corticosteroids (stress hormones) (Teicher et al., 1997), and that children with chronic high levels of these hormones have been shown to experience more cognitive, motor, and social development delays than other children (Gunnar, 1996). Kraemer's work spans decades and was built on the earlier work done at the Harlow Primate

Laboratory at Madison, Wisconsin. Harry Harlow's work (1962) focused on the behavioral aberrations of monkeys raised in isolation. Advances in theory and technology since Harlow's time enabled Kraemer to explore the effects of such rearing (nonattachment) in terms of brain structure and functioning. Among his many findings were the following:

- Reductions in cortical and cerebellar dendritic branching.

- Altered electrophysiology in the cerebellar and limbic regions.

- Disregulation of biogenic amine systems, particularly a reduction in norepinephrine concentrations in cerebrospinal fluid.

- A neurobiological and behavioral "supersensitivity" when exposed to pharmacological agents or novel stimuli that act on biogenic amine systems.

- Changes in brain cytoarchitecture (the cellular structure).

- The failure to organize emotional behavior in response to stressors.

What all this boils down to is that the lack of attachment experiences during early development may cause permanently altered neurophysiological systems that will adversely affect the organism's ability to interact with its world adaptively. We should not be too alarmist about slightly negative or dysfunctional environments, however. Studies such as Kraemer's elucidate mechanisms by which normal development may be diverted, but they also show that for diversion to occur among genetically normal animals the deprivation must be quite severe. Among genetically normal individuals, adaptive behavior will develop within a wide range of "average expectable environments" (Scarr, 1992, 1993). Humans are fairly resilient creatures, and neoteny affords children reared in negative or dysfunctional environments the opportunity to learn positive ways of responding to the world (to rewire their brains) in spite of early experiences (Bjorklund, 1997).

This observation should not divert our attention away from rearing environments that are truly horrendous and do leave permanent psychophysiological scars. As Perry and Pollard (1998:36) point out, "Experience in adults *alters* the *organized* brain, but in infants and children it *organizes* the *developing* brain" (emphasis added). In brains that are organized in response to stressful and traumatic events, future events—even neutral or positive ones—will tend to be relayed along the same negative neural pathways etched out by those events. For better or for worse, well-grooved synaptic pathways established in early life are more resistant to pruning than pathways laid down later in life. These pathways have been stabilized, and thus they subconsciously intrude into our transactions with others across the lifespan. Next we will explore the possible neurological sequelae (aftereffect) of infant/childhood nonattachment and abuse and neglect in the context of neurologically specific theories of antisocial behavior and criminality.

Reward Dominance Theory

Reward dominance, or BAS/BIS theory, is a neurological theory based on the proposition that behavior is regulated by two opposing mechanisms, the *behavioral activating* (or *approach*) *system* (BAS) and the *behavioral inhibition system* (BIS). The BAS is sensitive to signals of inherent reward or cessation of some aversive stimulus, and the BIS is sensitive to threats of punishment (Kruesi et al., 1994). The BAS can be likened to an accelerator motivating a person to seek rewarding stimuli, and the BIS can be likened to a brake, which in response to punishment cues from the environment, inhibits a person from going too far in that pursuit. The BAS motivates us to seek food, drink, and cognitive, physical, emotional, and sexual pleasures, and the BIS tells us when we have had enough for our own good. A normal BAS combined with a faulty BIS, or vice versa, may lead to a "craving brain" that can get us into all sorts of physical, social, moral, and legal difficulties, such as obesity, gambling, and alcohol and drug addiction (Ruden, 1997).

The anatomical and chemical substrates of the BAS and BIS have been roughly identified. The BAS is primarily associated with dopamine and with mesolimbic system structures such as the nucleus accumbens, a structure particularly rich in neurons that produce and respond to dopamine. The BIS is primarily associated with serotonin and with limbic system structures such as the hippocampus that feed into the prefrontal cortex (Pinel, 2000). Dopamine and serotonin act both as neurotransmitters and neuromodulators, depending on where in the brain they are working. Neurotransmitters influence the intensity of messages from sensory receptors; neuromodulators filter the information to be processed (Ruden, 1997). Regardless of where it operates, dopamine facilitates goal-directed behavior, and serotonin generally facilitates neural processes subserving the inhibition or modulation of that behavior (Depue & Collins, 1999).

Most people are more or less equally sensitive to both reward and punishment because their BAS/BIS systems are biobalanced (in a state of dopamine/serotonin equilibrium) most of the time (Ruden, 1997). For others, one system might dominate the other most or all of the time. Reward dominance theory asserts that criminals, especially chronic criminals and psychopaths, have a dominant BAS, which means that they tend to be overly sensitive to reward contingencies and relatively insensitive to punishment cues (Lykken, 1995). The opposite profile—a relatively strong BIS and/or a relatively weak BAS—is associated with obsessive compulsion disorder (OCD). OCD individuals are characteristically wracked with unreasonable guilt and self-doubt, whereas psychopaths exhibit little of either (Kruesi et al., 1994).

It has been proposed that individual differences in the number of neurons in brain areas associated with the BAS, and thus the structural capacity to release high levels of dopamine, develop during sensitive periods in experience-dependent fashion (Depue & Collins, 1999). This proposition is consistent with Kraemer's (1992) psychobiological theory pertaining to the effects of nonattachment on various neurological systems previously discussed. Serotonergic mechanisms, however, seem to be more affected by immediate rather than distal environmental events. For instance, poor parenting is correlated with low serotonin levels in children, although the causal direction is unclear (Pine et al., 1997). Poor parenting could be a reaction to children's impulsive behavior induced by low serotonin, rather than a cause of their children's low serotonin. It could also be a mutual relationship, with each feeding on the other.

Jeffrey Gray (1987, 1994), one of the pioneers of reward dominance theory, adds a third system of behavior control to the BAS/BIS model: the fight/flight system (FFS). The FFS is a generalized response system sensitive to *unconditioned* aversive stimuli, such as pain and extreme frustration. The BIS, on the other hand, responds to stimuli associated in the past with aversive consequences; that is, *conditioned* aversive stimuli. Although the fight/flight system is part of the autonomic nervous system (ANS), Gray wants to distinguish its specific fight/flight function from the more basic general "housekeeping" functions of the ANS. However, because most researchers continue to use the term autonomic nervous system rather than fight/flight syndrome when referring to arousal, this book will do so also.

The ANS has two complementary branches, the sympathetic and the parasympathetic. The sympathetic branch is the peripheral nervous system's analog of the central nervous system's BAS in that it mobilizes the body's endocrine system to pump out epinephrine (adrenaline) so that it can more actively and more efficiently confront an environmental threat. In other words, the ANS responds to fear and mobilizes an organism to meet the challenge by changing its physiology from its normal balanced state. The parasympathetic branch is analogous to the BIS in that it restores the body to equilibrium after the threat is over.

Just as individuals differ in terms of BAS/BIS functioning, they differ in their threshold of ANS arousal. Thresholds for ANS arousal can be thought of as roughly normally distributed, with most individuals clustered around the mean and a small minority of individuals on each tail (Leverson, 1994). Individuals with a *hyper*arousable ANS are very fearful and condition very easily, because arousal produces punishing visceral feelings associated with anxiety and fear. Acquiescing to the conformity demands of socializers (both specific others and the "generalized other") prevents ANS arousal. Persons who become easily aroused and who contemplate actions contrary to the expectations of others find that not acting on the impulse quickly restores his or her ANS to homeostasis. This powerfully reinforces conforming behavior via the reduction of fear and anxiety. A hyperarousable ANS is a protective factor against criminal behavior, even among males at high environmental risk for criminality (Brennan et al., 1997).

Individuals with a *hypo*arousable ANS are relatively fearless and difficult to condition. They do not receive visceral reinforcement for conforming behavior, because they are not aroused to fear in the first place and thus cannot receive positive reinforcement for conforming behavior in the form of a return to ANS homeostasis (Raine, 1993). Because the acquisition of a conscience is fundamentally about classical conditioning (Trasler, 1987), and classical conditioning relies on ANS arousal, individuals deficient in conscience may be that way partially because they have an unusually unresponsive ANS. Individuals with a relatively unresponsive ANS will be relatively fearless, an attribute that can be quite useful when engaging in criminal activity (Lykken, 1995; Raine, 1997), as well as a number of prosocial activities such as police officer, firefighter, or members of special forces regiments. A review of 40 studies of ANS activity (measured by skin conductivity and/or heart rate) and criminal and antisocial behavior found 38 studies that supported the link and two (both for childhood conduct disorder) that had nonsignificant results (Ellis & Walsh, 2000:282).

Prefrontal Dysfunction Theory

As previously noted, the frontal lobes, and in particular the prefrontal cortex (PFC), are prominent and important features in the human brain. The PFC is responsible for a number of uniquely human attributes, such as making moral judgments, planning for the future, analyzing, synthesizing, and modulating emotions, all of which are collectively referred to as *executive functions*. These executive functions are quite clearly involved in prosocial behavior; if compromised in some way, they can result in antisocial behavior. Because many of these functions are uniquely human, neocortical components of the BAS and BIS should be more extensive and influential in humans than in nonhuman animals (Sutton & Davidson, 1997).

Consistent with this claim, Adrian Raine (1997), the major figure in prefrontal dysfunction (PFD) theory, claims that the theory can account for some of the physiological arousal factors observed in antisocial individuals by relating physiological functioning with psychological processes. He bases his claim primarily on EEG and brain imaging studies that indicate a moderate to strong correlation between measures of physiological arousal and arousal of the PFC (i.e., reduced physiological arousal is associated with reduced arousal in certain areas of the PFC). In samples of normal individuals, it is consistently found that experimentally manipulating skin conductance orienting (a physiological measure of attention allocation) also changes blood flow in the frontal lobes. Other studies have found that individuals with lesions to the PFC have reduced anxiety and fear and are less reactive to stressors of all kinds (reviewed in Raine, 1997).

The association between the frontal lobes and prosocial and antisocial behavior is often illustrated by the dramatic case of Phineas Gage, a railroad construction foreman in the nineteenth century who suffered a terrible wound to the frontal lobes (he had a tamping iron blasted through his skull) that drastically changed his personality. This case gave early neuroscientists their first clues about the specialized functions of the PFC, although it is important to realize that it was an extreme example. Damage does not have to be massive, or even anatomically discernible, in order to impact behavior negatively. PFC damage could be at the cellular level and be the result of genetic factors that affect neuron migration during the earliest stages of frontal lobe development, or maternal substance abuse during pregnancy (Pihl & Bruce, 1995). Even slight damage to the PFC, particularly to the left hemisphere, has been linked to a number of cognitive deficits (Reiss et al., 1996).

An abundance of neurological evidence from electroencephalograph (EEG), positron emission tomography (PET), and magnetic resonance imaging (MRI) studies links the PFC and antisocial and criminal behavior. As expected, the evidence is most sound for criminals convicted of impulsive crimes. A PET study comparing nine impulsive murderers with 15 murderers whose crimes were apparently planned found that impulsive murderers showed significantly lower prefrontal and higher subcortical (limbic) activity than the nonimpulsive murderers and control subjects (Raine et al., 1998). The nonimpulsive murderers had prefrontal functioning similar to the control subjects, but they also showed excessive right subcortical activity. An MRI study (Raine et al., 2000) found that males diagnosed with antisocial personality disorder (APD) had 11 percent less prefrontal gray matter volume than subjects in two control groups (a "healthy" group and a substance-dependent group) matched for SES, ethnicity, IQ, and head circumference. This prefrontal deficit was not attributable to any discernible brain trauma. The antisocial group also evidenced reduced ANS activity during exposure to stress, which supports Raine's (1997) earlier suspicions based on EEG data. The APD group self-reported a significantly greater number of violent crimes than either control group. The observed prefrontal cortex and autonomic nervous system deficits predicted APD versus non-APD status independently of 10 psychosocial risk-factors, and they were by far the most powerful predictors.

Reward Dominance and PFD Theories and Child Abuse/Neglect

Although the "set points" of BAS/BIS and PFC functioning are genetically influenced, the plasticity of the human brain leads most neuroscientists to believe that early experience may be more important than genetics in this regard. The limbic system's hippocampus and amygdala are among the most plastic areas of the brain, and the PFC is the most plastic of all (Teicher et al., 1997). Recall that plasticity essentially refers to the physiological calibration of the brain in response to environmental experience, especially early experience. Thus, the activation "set points" for the various neurological structures can be altered for better or for worse. Traumatic events may alter them in the many brain areas that respond to threats. Although the evidence for trauma-induced alteration of brain function is strongest in controlled animal experiments, given the greater human reliance on learning to navigate life, abuse and neglect may be more strongly associated with dysregulation of various neural structures in abused children (McBurnett et al., 2000).

The possible effects of abuse and neglect on limbic system structures such as the hippocampus and amygdala have particular relevance for the BIS. The hippocampus is a crucial component of the BIS. Protracted abuse and neglect can alter its threshold setting (possibly via the effects of excess corticosteroids secreted in response to stress) so that it often fails to perform its appropriate inhibitory role (Teicher et al., 1997). Similarly, frequent "kindling" (arousal, excitation) of the amygdala (the most seizure-prone area of the brain) in response to abuse and neglect may eventually lead to subconvulsive seizures (van der Kolk & Greenberg, 1987). Subconvulsive seizures are the result of kindling that often may not have any immediate environmental derivation. The term *episodic dyscontrol* is used to describe behavior resulting from these seizures (Suchy, Blint & Osman, 1997). Ellis and Walsh (2000) reviewed 111 studies pertaining to the relationship between subconvulsive seizures and criminal behavior and found the relationship to be invariably significant for impulsively violent and acting-out behaviors, but not for any kind of planned criminal behavior.

In terms of the effects of abuse and neglect on PFC functioning, Perry (1997) suggests that children who spend a great deal of time in a low-level state of fear tend to focus consistently on nonverbal cues of imminent danger because the brain has been habituated to do so. This tendency has been referred to as "frozen watchfulness" (DeLozier, 1982:98). Both Perry and DeLozier suggest that a cognitive profile in which performance IQ (P) is significantly greater than verbal IQ (V) (P>V) is a marker of this tendency. A significant (12-point) P>V discrepancy has been consistently linked with chronic criminal offending (Miller, 1987; Moffitt, 1996; Walsh, 1991), and a significant V>P profile has often been found to be a marker of prosocial behavior (Cornel & Wilson, 1992). One study found that P>V males were 29 times more likely to be found in prisons than V>P males, although both IQ profiles are found to be about equally represented in the general population (Barnett, Zimmer & McCormack, 1989). A study of 513 juvenile delinquents found that boys who were born illegitimate and raised by a single mother had higher abuse/neglect scores, higher delinquency scores, and a greater P>V discrepancy than boys born and reared under other circumstances (Walsh, 1990).

Other lines of evidence support Perry's insight. Teicher and his colleagues (1997:197) write that childhood memories may be preferentially stored in the right hemisphere because abuse and neglect may be "associated with greater left-hemisphere dysfunction, which may lead to greater dependence on the right hemisphere. Increased right frontal function, in turn, may lead to enhanced perception and reaction to negative affect." They further note that the right hemisphere plays a particularly significant role in the perception, processing, and expression of negative emotions. This is supported by an EEG study that found that right PFC activation is related to BIS strength, and left PFC activation is related to BAS strength on the BAS/BIS scale (Sutton & Davidson, 1997). Sutton and Davidson (1997:209) conclude that "individuals with tonically active right prefrontal regions may be predisposed to become vigilant for threat-related stimuli [DeLozier's "frozen watchfulness"], concurrently inhibiting behavior, organizing resources for behavior withdrawal, and experiencing negative affect (i.e., BIS activity)."

The most difficult data to reconcile are those concerning trauma and changes in arousal patterns and the data linking abuse/neglect to later criminal behavior. There is evidence that the abuse of children and adolescents does lead to increased ANS responsiveness (Hill et al., 1989), and that chronic stress and/or acute trauma can result in post-traumatic stress disorder (PTSD) and hyper ANS responsiveness among adults (Pitman & Orr, 1993). If abuse/neglect can lead to a hyper-arousable ANS, and if a hyperarousable ANS has been linked to a lower probability of antisocial behavior, then abuse and neglect could be naively construed as protective factors against antisocial behavior. There is contrary evidence, however, indicating that abuse and neglect may result in *hypo*responsivity of the ANS. Raine (1997) reconciles these two lines of evidence by speculating that an important factor is when the stress is experienced. If the organism experiences chronic stress during the organizational phase of brain development, as opposed to acute traumatic stress experienced as an adult or adolescent, then that stress should lead to hyporesponsivity as an "inoculation" to stress. Experiments have shown that repeated aversive stimuli (e.g., electric shock) administered to laboratory animals has a steadily decreasing effect on ANS arousal until the animals become almost completely unreactive to stimuli that initially produced extreme symptoms of fear and anxiety (Lykken, 1995; Solomon, 1980).

We can conclude that there is abundant evidence that a significant association exists between child abuse/neglect and the kinds of neurophysiological abnormalities that have been associated with criminal behavior, but it is difficult to determine the direction of the causal relationship in any absolute sense. Given the growing awareness of gene/environment correlation processes among researchers, many of them now voice their awareness of the equally plausible hypothesis that congenital neurophysiological abnormalities may lead to acting-out behavior on the part of children. Acting-out behavior, in turn, may increase the likelihood of maltreatment on the part of caregivers (Heck & Walsh, 2000; Perry, 1997; Teicher et al., 1997).

Many of us are reluctant to entertain the painful notion that certain infants and children could be somehow responsible for their own abuse by evoking negative responses from their caregivers. For practical purposes (policy recommendations), it is not necessary to do so, for we know that infants and children are adversely affected by maltreatment and lack of attachment that has nothing at all to do with their behavior. It has been estimated that as many as 375,000 infants born each year have been exposed to cocaine in utero, and that in some inner-city hospitals as many as 50 percent of pregnant women test positive for crack or powder cocaine (Mayes et al., 1995). Children in orphanages around the world have long been known to suffer a numerous physical and psychological problems (reviewed in Frank et al., 1996). These children had no opportunity to influence their mother's drug habits or their own orphan status.

Neglected children as well as those in orphanages may lack something as basic as tactile stimulation, the importance of which is made palpable by the fact that the infant can only experience and express love or its absence through its body. We are programmed to secrete the brain's own opiates (the endorphins) in situations of social comfort, and a lack of frequent bodily contact between mother (or other caregiver) and child has to be interpreted as abandonment, because the infant can only "think" with its skin. The infant's contact comfort experienced from the sensitive responses of others during times of duress tells it that everything is all right, "She's there for me," I'm safe," All is right in my world." Ashley Montagu summarizes the relationship between tactile stimulation and human development when he writes, "The kind of tactuality experienced during infancy and childhood not only produces the appropriate changes in the brain, but also affects the growth and development of the end-organs in the skin. The tactually deprived individual will suffer from a feedback deficiency between skin and brain that may seriously affect his development as a human being." (1978:208).

Similarly, children born into poverty have an increased risk of neurological developmental delays because of malnutrition, less access to medical attention, low levels of physical and mental stimulation, a greater probability of abuse and neglect, and a generally unsafe environment. None of this, of course, has been evoked by the child's own behavior. The neurological evidence, then, strongly supports liberal calls for nurturant strategies to crime control, such as paid maternal leave, nutrition programs, home visitation programs, Head Start-type programs, and so forth (Shore, 1996; Vila, 1997; Walsh, 1991; Walsh & Ellis, 1997). Methwin (1997) provides a number of examples of cost-efficient child development programs yielding good results that could be implemented on a national scale. Data like these, plus the relatively hard data from the neurosciences, doubtless has more power to influence tightfisted lawmakers and a skeptical public than do heartstring appeals from humanists, and as Vila (1997:18, emphasis in original) points out, "Keeping adequate resources flowing toward child development programs is a *social investment strategy that pays compound interest.*"

Chapter 5

Anomie/Strain Theory and Status

THE SOCIAL STRUCTURAL TRADITION

All criminological theories contain a view of human nature, whether explicit or implicit. The first half of the twentieth century saw the beginning of sociology's dominance of criminology, which has taken on its parent discipline's assumptions about human nature. In a very general sense, sociology assumes that human nature is socially constructed; that is, it has no (or very little) essential content beyond that which has been imparted during the process of socialization into a specific culture. This is the meaning of the comment heard often in existential and social science circles: "Man has no nature, he only has a history" (Ruffie, 1986:297). Much of sociology also implicitly assumes that human beings are naturally good (Rousseau's "noble savage") until corrupted by society. The contradiction in assuming no essential human nature and assuming that humans are "naturally" good appears to escape those who hold both views. Nevertheless, given these assumptions, the task of sociological criminology is to arrive at an explanation for why inherently good social animals commit antisocial acts. If crime is alien to social impulses, its causes must be sought outside of the individual. This searching often takes the form of looking for flaws and defects in society, such as a discriminatory class system, racism, value conflicts, and capitalism, and largely discounts the existence of any flaws or defects in the individual criminal. If any such individual flaws are posited, their origin is typically declared to lie in some cultural or social structural defect.

Almost all sociological theories of crime emphasize social structure to various degrees. By social structure, we mean how society is organized by social institutions, the family, and educational, religious, economic, and political institutions, and how it is stratified on the basis of various roles and statuses. Social structure is the framework that shapes the patterns of relationships that members of society have

97

with one another. Structural theories favor external "out there" reality as being of primary importance in determining human social behavior; that is, they tend to work from assumptions made from a general model of society and to deduce the everyday experiences of individuals from them. These kinds of theories have a tendency to slip into ways of thinking that render the individual almost irrelevant. An extreme example of this sort of thinking is Rodney Stark's (1996:140) defense of environmental explanations over what he calls "kinds of people" explanations: "Surely it is more efficient and pertinent to see dilapidation, for instance, as a trait of a building rather than as a trait of those who live in the building." The absurd implication of this statement is that buildings are maintained or trashed by forces acting independently of the values and behavior of those who inhabit them.

The first traditional criminological theory examined here is anomie/strain theory. This theory has been chosen for three reasons: (1) It is the most long-lived of all existing criminological theories; (2) it began as the most macro of criminological theories, with its emphasis on whole societies; and (3) it illustrates the epidemiological method of continually reducing levels of analysis as the lessons learned at one level are exhausted. The theory began with Durkheim's (1982) and Merton's (1938) analysis of whole societies and has gone through subcultural (A. Cohen, 1955) and social psychological (Agnew, 1992) phases, and may be on the verge of entering a behavior-genetic phase (Walsh, 2000a).

Emile Durkheim

Emile Durkheim is arguably the most influential sociologist of all time. Despite his reputation among his contemporaries as a metaphysician, and unlike many sociologists after him, Durkheim had a view of human nature—and it was a naturalistic one at that (Lopreato & Crippen, 1999:17). His view was very close to the classical view that humans first and foremost seek to maximize their pleasures and minimize their pains. Although Durkheim never used evolutionary terminology, he viewed human nature as something that "is substantially the same among all men, in its essential qualities" (1951a:247). He also saw humans as clearly adapted to attend to their self-interest and to live in social groups (which mitigates self interest). The balance between these two adaptations is a central feature of Durkheim's thought.

Although Durkheim viewed humans as similar in their "essential qualities," he realized that "[o]ne sort of heredity will always exist, that of natural talent" (1951a:251). Thus, although everyone is more or less equal in their desires, not everyone is equally capable of achieving them.

This presents a problem for the individual (and by extension for society) because, for Durkheim, human appetites are insatiable, and "[n]o living thing can be happy or even exist unless his needs are sufficiently proportioned to his means" (1951b:246). Because all persons do not possess the same means to accomplish the things necessary to satisfy their appetites, "[a] moral discipline will therefore still be required to make those less favored by nature accept the lesser advantages which they owe to the chance of birth" (1951:151). This moral discipline is provided by society, which "is the only moral power superior to the individual," for "it alone has the power necessary to stipulate law and to set the point beyond which passions must not go" (1951a:149).

According to Durkheim, society does not exist simply by rational agreement, as many so-called contractual theorists such as Hobbes and Rawls assert, but rather it exists by virtue of a "pre-contractual solidarity" based on an emotional sense of belonging to a community and a moral obligation to it. Evolutionary psychology would again find much to agree with in Durkheim's vision, for all indications are that *Homo sapiens* evolved over millions of years living in small hierarchically structured social groups with strong attachments to one another and have probably always been more emotional than rational (deWaal, 1996; Krebs, 1998). Durkheim referred to this sense of belonging and moral obligation that was the basis for social solidarity as the "collective conscience."

Durkheim was preeminently concerned with the effects of modernization on social solidarity as well as with how individuals respond to these effects. Modernization essentially involves the progression from traditional societies characterized by uniformity, primary group interactions, strong normative agreement, and mechanical solidarity, to modern industrialized societies characterized by mostly secondary group interactions, weak norms, and organic solidarity. Societies characterized by mechanical solidarity possess a strong collective conscience and exert strong pressure on individuals to conform to it. Primarily because of an extensive division of labor, people in modern societies have less common "social likeness," the collective conscience is weakened, and it thus exerts less pressure for social conformity. The greater degree of social integration enjoyed by members of mechanical societies cushions them to a great extent from the trials and tribulations of life. Conversely, the looser bonds experienced in organic societies provide little support, which may result in greater stress and frustration—and in a greater probability of deviant responses to it.

Modern societies are characterized by a great deal of social change. Each change tends to detract from shared social likeness and weakens the collective conscience. Rapid social change leads to a state of affairs Durkheim referred to as *anomie*. Anomie is a condition of social deregulation and a relative collapse of social solidarity. Anomic social conditions result in diminished feelings of participating in a shared community and of a sense of obligation to fellow citizens, which tends to release egoistic self-interest. Under such conditions, we can expect a rise in all sorts of deviant behavior, including crime, as people seek to satisfy their appetites unrestrained by a sense of shared belonging and morality. The 300 percent increase in crime in Hungary over the three-year period immediately following the demise of communism (Gonczol, 1993), and the similar figures reported from Russia over the same period (Dashkov, 1992), provide strong support for Durkheim's insight regarding the anomic effects of rapid social change and deregulation.

Udry (1995) is probably correct in his assessment that Durkheim was not the thoroughgoing "social factist" that sociologists have made him out to be. Durkheim was careful to distinguish between social facts and biological and psychological facts, and between crime and criminality: "From the fact that crime is a phenomenon of normal sociology, it does not follow that the criminal is an individual normally constituted from the biological and psychological points of view. The two questions are independent of each other" (1982:106). There is no doubt that crime is sociologically normal in that it occurs in all societies (even in societies characterized by mechanical solidarity) and at all times. There is also no doubt that crime rates fluctuate with social conditions and are thus firmly in the category of social facts, because there is no existing theory capable of deriving shifting crime rates from the properties of individuals.

Criminality, on the other hand, is a property of individuals and is a continuously distributed trait (which is itself an amalgam of other continuously distributed traits) succinctly defined as the willingness to use and abuse others by any means for personal gain. As social bonds weaken and norms break down in response to social, political, and economic changes, the threshold for this "willingness" is lowered; as a result, increasingly more people succumb. Anomic conditions serve as "releasers" of criminal behavior, which occurs at lower thresholds for some individuals than for others. This is where biosocial theories are needed, because just as individual-level theories cannot explain crime rates, macro-level theories cannot explain why some individuals commit crimes while others in the same environments do not. Durkheim himself seemed to make this point when he remarked, "Thus, since there cannot be a society in which the individuals do not diverge to some extent from the collective type, it is also inevitable that among these deviations some assume a *criminal character*. What confers upon them this character is not the intrinsic importance of the act but the importance which the common consciousness ascribes to them" (1982:101, emphasis added).

According to Durkheim, then, there are a number of individuals in any society that possess a character that motivates them to act in ways that society defines as criminal. Cohen and Machalek interpret Durkheim's position as follows: "Thus, although the definition of a behavior as criminal is strictly a matter of social labeling, the *root causes of the behavior itself* are to be traced to individual character traits" (1994: 293, emphasis in original). It is not clear whether it is Durkheim's position that all criminal definitions are arbitrary, or that he recognized that there are crimes that are inherently (*mala in se*) criminal. These are the crimes that militate against evolutionary imperatives to survive and reproduce, such as murder, rape, and the theft of resources (Walsh, 2000b). Furthermore, people can and do use and abuse other people for personal gain regardless of whether the means used have been defined as criminal, and it is this propensity that defines criminality, quite independent of the social labeling of an act as criminal.

Durkheim sounds very much like an evolutionary psychologist here. He was clear that it is humanity's insatiable appetite for resources (wealth, status, prestige) that underlies both crime and criminality. Resources have been the coin of reproductive success throughout the evolutionary history of the species, and we should thus expect our appetite for them to be insatiable (although surely the satiation threshold varies greatly from person to person) were it not for some mechanism to hold it in check. Because we are a social species, we have evolved tit-for-tat strategies (reciprocal altruism) in social exchange and a set of moral norms based on the social emotions to support them and to constrain self-interest within acceptable boundaries. Whenever events occur that tend to weaken these moral norms, selfish appetites are released to flood society with crime and other forms of deviance. As an evolutionary psychologist might paraphrase Durkheim, in an evolutionarily novel environment such as industrial and postindustrial capitalism, with the enormous degree of social change it generates, a vast number of niches are created in which individuals can pursue conditional cheater strategies.

Durkheim also sounds very much like an evolutionary psychologist writing about the coevolution of cheating and cooperative behavior in his belief that crime (cheating) is necessary for the evolution of social solidarity (cooperation). Although crime and deviance beyond a certain level is socially harmful, Durkheim characterized it at "normal levels" as "a factor in public health, an integrative element in any healthy society" (1982:98). Crime and other forms of deviance, particularly those forms that undermine norms of reciprocal altruism, serve to define the boundaries of right and wrong. Punishment of such acts reinforces those norms and strengthens the collective conscience. Although Durkheim saw punishment primarily as a social ritual, he recognized that the urge to punish is inherent in human nature and that it serves an expiatory role for the individual (Walsh, 2000b).

Robert Merton

Robert Merton extended Durkheim's concept of anomie in his famous paper *Social Structure and Anomie* (1938). Because Merton was writing in mid-twentieth-century America and Durkheim was writing in late-nineteenth-century France, we can expect some discontinuity of thought. However, although some have criticized Merton for his theoretical departures from Durkheim, Passas (1995:93) argues that Merton presents "significant lines of continuity" and is an "appropriate extension of Durkheim's ideas." A major difference between the two theorists is that Merton's theory limits itself to the role of culture and social structure and ignores individual differences altogether. The "root" cause of crime (no distinction is made between crime and criminality in Merton's theory) is not to be found within individuals whose insatiable appetites must be kept under control by strong normative controls, but rather in sociocultural contradictions. Merton argued that being unable to attain resources legitimately generates frustration (strain) and sometimes leads to efforts to obtain them illegitimately.

Unlike Durkheim, Merton viewed selfishness and acquisitiveness as characteristics generated by a culture driven by an overweening concern with monetary success rather than as an intrinsic property of human nature. He argued that American culture feeds the notion that all citizens should aspire to the "American dream," the attainment of which symbolizes a person's character and self-worth. He maintained that at the same time these cultural goals are being touted as goals toward which everyone should strive, social structure restricts access to legitimate means of attaining them to certain segments of the population. Also, unlike Durkheim, for whom anomie was an occasional condition that rises and declines according to levels of social stability, Merton viewed anomie as a permanent condition of capitalist American society that is generated by this disjunction between cultural goals and structural impediments to attaining them (Merton, 1968).

The metatheoretical essence of Mertonian anomie/strain theory is that people are social animals who desire to follow social rules and will only resort to breaking them when placed under great pressure or strain. In this view (and it is a view that is a 180-degree turn away from Durkheim), society serves as a motivator rather than a restrainer of criminal behavior. Crime is woven into the fabric of American society because it arises from *conformity* to its values—a way disadvantaged people get what they have been taught to want—not from deviation from its values due to social deregulation. While for Durkheim, greed, acquisitiveness, egoism, deviance, and crime are *consequences* of anomie, for Merton, they are *causes* of anomie (Passas, 1995).

Merton considered American culture to be fairly uniform as it pertained to success goals across class lines, thus all members of a society share the strains of attempting to achieve common cultural goals. However, because of limited access to legitimate means of achieving these cultural goals, some—particularly those in the lower classes—will be more strained than others. Thus, Merton used the cultural argument to explain why crime rates are high in the United States in general, and the structural argument to explain the concentration of crime in the lower classes (Bernard, 1987).

Merton provided a comprehensive typology (conformity, ritualism, retreatism, rebellion, and innovation) of people's adaptations to strain. But what sorts members of society into these different modes of adaptation? People do not, of course, consciously decide that they are going to follow one mode rather than another, but tend to slip almost subconsciously into them over time. According to generations of anomie/strain theorists, they tend largely to adopt a particular mode based on their SES and race/ethnicity rather than their individual characteristics. The upper and middle classes have access to legitimate means of attaining desired success goals, but the lower classes and some racial/ethnic groups do not. Even people who are successful may feel strain as they compare themselves to others who are more successful, but it is the lower classes that feel the bite most strongly.

Given the emphasis on the attainment of monetary success and middle-class status as the overweening goal stressed by American culture, and on the modes of adaptation to the strain it engenders, it is curious that strain theorists have not explored the correlates of occupational success and of the different ways people have of coping with strain. Merton's (1938) famous "plus or minus" table of adaptations merely states that people "accept" or "reject" cultural goals and institutionalized means of obtaining them. It is easily deducible from Merton's writings, however, that people sort themselves into one mode or another based on their perceptions of, and attitudes about, their chances of achieving middle-class success goals legitimately. These perceptions and attitudes are assumed to be class-linked, and class is assumed to be both given and relatively static. This is circular reasoning in that it essentially means that social class is the cause of social class. Unless they want to adopt the position that SES is an uncaused "first cause," anomie/strain theorists have to come to terms with the notion that SES is as much a dependent variable as it is an independent variable.

Anomie/strain theorists also had to come to terms with the fact that people handle strain differently. By definition, most people adopt the conformist mode, many others adopt the ritualist mode, and only a comparative few adopt the retreatist and innovative modes. Among those who do, most will do so only temporarily during adolescence (Moffitt, 1993). Even among the lower classes, where strain is felt most acutely, most [as Merton (1968) acknowledged] will adopt ritualist rather than criminal lifestyles. Thus, some people cope with frustration and pressure poorly and destructively, while others cope with it well and constructively. Those who cope poorly are not likely to achieve middle-class status, regardless of the SES of their parents, while those who cope well have at least a sporting chance, regardless of their class origins.

Robert Agnew

Early extensions of Merton's theory by Cohen (1955) and Cloward and Ohlin (1960) noted the individual's lack of interest in and/or inability to pursue the legitimate means of attaining middle-class success as causes of crime and delinquency as much as sociocultural barriers. Cloward and Ohlin (1960: 96) wrote of the inability of lower-class youths to defer gratification, their impulsivity and sensation-seeking, and their preference for "big cars," "flashy clothes," and "swell dames." Writing about the status frustration lower-class youths experience, Cohen (1955:66; emphasis in original) states that these youths come to define as meritorious "the characteristics they *do* possess, the kinds of conduct of which they *are* capable."

These individual characteristics, not being consistent with the social factist paradigm, were deemphasized by others with a desire to defend criminals and persistent delinquents from any allegations of being different (Hirschi & Hindelang, 1977). Cloward and Ohlin (1960:117) also fall back on the more traditional sociological tactic of denying that delinquents are any different from nondelinquents in the abilities required for occupational success: "There is no evidence . . . that members of delinquent subcultures are objectively less capable of meeting formal standards of eligibility [for middle-class occupations] than [nondelinquents]. . . the available data support the contention that the basic endowments of delinquents, such as intelligence, physical strength, and agility, are the equal of or greater than those of their nondelinquent peers."

The equality of delinquents (especially of persistent delinquents) with their nondelinquent peers on the first of these "endowments" is empirically false, as we shall see. It is probably true that delinquents are equal or superior to nondelinquents on the second and third endowments, for a number of studies have found delinquents to be more mesomorphic (muscular) than nondelinquents (reviewed in Eysenck & Gudjonsson, 1989; Wilson & Hernnstein, 1985). However, unless one aspires to be an athlete, acrobat, lumberjack, or some such occupation, strength and agility, without the temperament and intelligence to match, have little relevance for occupational success in modern society.

Robert Agnew's (1992) general strain theory (GST) resurrects individual differences and is thus more faithful to Durkheim than to Merton (Barak, 1998). Traditional strain theory was concerned only with the strain that resulted from being prevented from achieving positively valued goals, or more specifically, from achieving monetary success legitimately. Agnew (1992) expands strain beyond that generated by failure to achieve positively valued goals to include strain resulting from the removal of valued stimuli and from the presentation of negative stimuli. Every imaginable source of strain is included in GST, and its magnitude varies with social location. For Agnew, the important factor is not strain per se, but rather how one copes with it.

Agnew (1992) recognizes this in his discussion of negative affect (the tendency of persons to subjectively experience strain negatively and to react to it with frustration and anger) as an important intervening variable. Negative affect, or *negative emotionality* as it is referred to in psychology, has been found to have heritability coefficients of between .50 and .60 in various populations (McGue, Bacon, & Lykken, 1993; Tellegen et al., 1988). Thus, Agnew pushes the theory into the realm of person-environment interaction and thus into the realm of gene-environment interaction. The personal characteristics that Agnew cites as important insulators against the negative consequences of strain are "temperament, intelligence, creativity, problem-solving skills, self-efficacy, and self-esteem" (1992:71). Temperament and intelligence were the two individual-level factors that were found to insulate boys at environmental risk for antisocial behavior in Werner and Smith's (1992) Hawaiian cohort study. In addition to being insulators against strain, these variables also have obvious applicability to achieving occupational success and thus to the adoption of one of Merton's adaptations.

Agnew (1995, 1997) has taken further reductionist steps in the epidemiological process, citing criticism that anomie/strain theory does not speak to developmental aspects of delinquency. In particular, he asserts that the theory should predict an increase in antisocial behavior in late adolescence because that is when individuals seriously enter the job market. What we actually observe, though, is a decrease in antisocial behavior during this period (1997:101). Just when the central issue of the theory (perceptions about the possibility of achieving the American dream via occupational success) becomes most salient, instead of a dramatic increase in delinquency as people begin to perceive Merton's "disjunction," delinquency actually decreases.

Responding to this potentially fatal criticism, Agnew reflects on the fact that developmental theorists (mostly psychologists) talk about two general types of offenders, those who begin offending before adolescence and continue long into adulthood, and those who limit their offending to adolescence (1997:103). He wants to differentiate the reactions to strain between the two types of offenders by adding aggressiveness, which he views as an umbrella term covering hyperactivity, attention deficit disorder, impulsivity, and insensitivity, to his previous list of individual differences affecting delinquency and criminality. Agnew indicates that individuals high on these traits are likely to evoke negative reactions from others and are "less likely to form close attachments to conventional others—such as parents, teachers, and spouses; learn prosocial beliefs and behaviors; do well in school; and obtain rewarding jobs" (1997:106). These are also the individuals most likely to continue their criminal activity across the life course.

Agnew hints at reactive gene/environment correlation in the above passage, but faithful to his discipline, he appears to claim these traits are exclusively products of early childhood socialization (1997:107), although he does indicate that others have pointed out that they are heritable (1997:109). The next logical step in anomie/strain theory is to review the genetic and environmental contributions to the development of the traits important to the theory. Agnew does not do this, but his work over the past two decades points to the necessity of reducing the level of analysis in any science as new issues arise. Anomie/strain theory began as a structural/cultural theory, and performs well as an explanation at that level (Messner & Rosenfeld, 1994), but from Durkheim to Merton to Agnew, the trajectory has been toward lower levels of analysis. The next logical step is to frame the remaining issues in behavioral genetic terms.

All the characteristics Agnew lists as important for understanding antisocial behavior will be addressed in future chapters, but for now let us briefly review the literature on the two major individual-level factors (temperament and intelligence) that he identifies as important to successful coping.

Agnew remarks on a number of occasions that: (1) temperament and intelligence bear a strong relationship to problem-solving skills, and (2) the lower classes feel strain most acutely (1997:111-114). Unfortunately, even though SES is central to anomie /strain theory, he never attempts to make the connection between SES and the temperamental and cognitive correlates of problem-solving (assuredly an important coping resource), though he is more than willing to state that such traits are a function of both biological and social factors (1997:105).

Making a connection between individual traits and SES would be resisted by many sociologists, who tend to treat SES as a variable that explains all sorts of other things but that needs no explanation itself. The various measures of SES are viewed in terms of broad structural influences that impinge on the individual, such as unemployment rates, availability of schooling, and discriminatory wage patterns (Rowe, Vesterdal & Rodgers, 1999). In effect, SES is generally viewed in sociology as self-perpetuating, so if offspring's SES is caused by anything other than an unfair social system, it is caused by parental SES, presumably by mechanisms such as modeling and the transmission of values and attitudes. Any attempt to change a person's SES from his or her parental SES, however, is hopelessly confounded by genetics. As we shall see, in an open society, offspring's IQ predicts offspring's SES more strongly than parental SES does (or any other single variable, for that matter.)

INTELLIGENCE AND SES

Given the depth and breadth of research findings (twin studies, adoption studies, EEG, MRI, PET, and molecular genetic studies) touched on in Chapter 2, few scientists familiar with the literature seriously doubt the importance of genes in explaining IQ variation. Intelligence, as operationalized by IQ tests, is an obvious determinant of both a person's occupational success and coping strategy, yet it is one that is conspicuously absent in sociological discussions of social status. For instance, a densely packed 750-page book of readings on social stratification (Grusky, 1994) amazingly does not even have the terms *IQ* or *intelligence* listed in the index. Lee Ellis (1996:28) has also commented on this strange absence of any discussion of intelligence in sociological theories of the origins of SES: "Someday historians of social science will be astounded to find the word intelligence is usually not even mentioned in late-twentieth-century text books on social stratification." Ellis is aware of the possible inflammatory effects of making the obvious link between SES and IQ, but also that the link is in desperate need of dispassionate consideration.

The litmus test for any assessment tool is its criterion-related validity—its ability to predict outcomes. IQ tests do a particularly good job in this regard. An examination of 11 meta-analyses of the relationship between IQ and occupational success found that IQ predicted success better than any other variable in most occupations, particularly in higher-status occupations, and that it predicted equally well for all classes and racial or ethnic groups (Gottfredson, 1986). One study of more than 32,000 workers in 515 different occupations revealed that the correlations between IQ and job performance rose from .23 for "low-complexity" jobs (e.g., cannery worker) to .58 for "high-complexity" jobs (e.g., circulation manager) (Gottfredson, 1997). Correlations would doubtless be higher for even more complex occupations not included in the study, such as engineer or physician.

Intelligence is particularly important in technologically advanced societies in which low-complexity occupations become mechanized and high-complexity occupations become more prevalent. Industrial and postindustrial economies are incompatible with a closed caste-like society in which occupations are assigned by accident of birth. Rather, modernization requires open competition for the choicest occupations, with class, gender, and race/ethnicity very much playing second fiddle to talent, the engine driving any modern economy. Employers compete for talented employees, and IQ testing has been *the* major tool in capitalist (and surreptitiously, in communist societies) to locate them from all segments of society (Eysenk, 1982). This is not to deny that IQ has been a tool of exclusion also. For instance, because of high training costs and levels of failure, the United States Army is forbidden by law to enlist anyone with an IQ below 80 (Gottfredson, 1997). Whether we choose to view the role of intelligence and intelligence testing in modern societies positively or negatively, the fact remains that "in open societies with high degrees of occupational mobility, individuals with high IQs migrate, relative to their parents, to occupations of higher SES, and individuals with lower IQs migrate to occupations of lower SES" (Bouchard & Segal, 1985:408).

This was true even in the 1930s. Coincidentally, the article immediately following Merton's "Social Structure and Anomie" in the *American Sociological Review* examined the relationship between IQ and occupational choice (Clark & Gist, 1938). This study found that IQ was highly correlated with occupation and that it served to funnel people into their various occupations, not Merton's "social structure." Clark and Gist were not saying that IQ is the only cause of SES any more than this book is (although they did conclude that it was perhaps the most important cause). It is without question that being born into an upper- or middle-class family confers many advantages, and that being born into a lower-class family brings with it many disadvantages, but let us not forget that those advantages and disadvantages are both genetic and environmental (Gordon, 1997).

Although there is no such thing as a totally open society, unlike the rigid caste-like societies of the past, modern "class attainments do not represent environments imposed on adults by natural events beyond their control" (Rowe, 1994:136). In the rigid and aristocratic caste societies of the past, genes played almost no role in determining social class, but as previously noted, they play an increasingly important role in more modern, competitive, and egalitarian societies. Genes, and the individual differences they underlie, become important to determining SES in roughly direct proportion to equalization of environments. Although this may seem paradoxical at first blush, as we saw in Chapter 2, it is a basic principle of genetics. The more homogeneous (or equal) the environment, the greater the heritability of a trait; the more heterogeneous (or unequal) the environment, the lower the heritability of a trait (Plomin et al., 1997). High heritability coefficients for socially important traits tell us that the society is doing a good job of equalizing the environment with respect to the traits in question (Lykken, 1995).

But just how mobile is the American occupational structure? According to one major study, it is quite substantial (Hurst, 1995). This study found that 48 percent of sons of upper-white-collar-status fathers had lower-status occupations than their fathers, with 17 percent falling all the way to "lower manual" status, and that 51 percent of sons of lower-manual-status fathers achieved higher status, with 22.5 achieving "upper-white-collar" status (Hurst, 1995:270). Hurst (1995:276) concluded, "There was a great deal of movement both within and between generations. Well over half of the sons moved out of the occupational strata of their fathers and out of the strata of their own first jobs." Given this degree of upward and downward social mobility and the degree to which IQ predicts it equally for all races and social classes, it is difficult to maintain that any group is systematically denied (i.e., denied by "the system") access to legitimate opportunities to attain middle-class status.

Indeed, far from being denied by a discriminatory and racist socioeconomic system, recent studies have found that because of programs such as affirmative action, the occupational mobility of African-Americans (the group most often considered discriminated against) into the most prestigious positions has increased at a more rapid rate than it has for whites (R. Farley, 1996; Wilson, Sakura-Lemessy & West, 1999). As Vold, Bernard, and Snipes (1998:177) conclude, "It is not merely a matter of talented individuals confronted with inferior schools and discriminatory hiring practices. Rather, a good deal of research indicates that many delinquents and criminals are untalented individuals who cannot compete effectively in complex industrial societies."

When compelled to confront the correlation between IQ and SES, social scientists are more prone to consider IQ to be an effect of SES rather than the other way around (or more precisely, to be an effect of parental SES). A large number of studies have found the correlation between parental SES and children's IQ to be within the .30 to .40 range (which is predictable from polygenetic transmission models). The real test, however, is not the correlation between parental SES and the individual's IQ, but rather the correlation between the individual's IQ and his or her attained adult SES. This correlation has been found across a number of studies to be in the .50 to .70 range (Jensen, 1998a). As Jensen remarks, "If SES were the cause of IQ [rather than the other way around], the correlations between adults' IQ and their attained SES would not be markedly higher than the correlation between children's IQ and their parents' SES" (1998a:491). As we see, offspring IQ accounts for about three times the variance (25 to 49 percent) in offspring SES than does parental SES (9 to 16 percent). Even the upper-level estimate of 49 percent leaves plenty of variance in SES remaining to be explained by other individual and environmental factors.

IQ and Criminality

If differential IQ predicts differential adult SES, and if the lack of success leads to a mode of adaptation that includes criminal activity, then IQ must itself be a predictor of criminal behavior. When evaluating the relatively small (8 to 10 IQ points) difference said to separate criminals and noncriminals (Wilson & Herrnstein, 1985), we must remember that researchers do not typically separate what Moffitt (1993) calls *adolescent-limited* (AL) from what she calls *life-course-persistent* (LCP) offenders. As statistically normal individuals temporarily responding to the contingencies of their environments in antisocial ways, we would not expect AL offenders to be significantly different from nonoffenders on IQ, and they are not. Moffitt (1996) reports a one-point mean IQ deficit between AL offenders and nonoffenders but a 17-point deficit between LCP offenders and nonoffenders. Other studies (e.g., Stattin & Klackenberg-Larsson, 1993) find similar results. Aggregating temporary and persistent offenders on IQ creates the erroneous perception that IQ has minimal impact on antisocial behavior.

While these studies separated temporary and persistent offenders, they did not separate IQ subtest scores. This also leads to an underestimation of the effects of IQ by pooling verbal IQ (VIQ), which uniformly shows a significant difference between offenders and nonoffenders, and performance IQ (PIQ), which typically does not (Herrnstein, 1989). As indicated in Chapter 4, the most serious and persistent criminal offenders tend to have a PIQ score exceeding their VIQ score by about 12 points. Low verbal IQ (about one standard deviation below the mean) indexes poor abstract reasoning, poor judgment, poor school performance, impulsiveness, and low empathy. These traits are not conducive to occupational success, but they are conducive to antisocial behavior, especially if combined with a disinhibited temperament (Farrington, 1996).

The most frequently heard explanation for the IQ/delinquency relationship is that low IQ impacts delinquency and criminality via poor school performance (Ward & Tittle, 1994). However, a national cohort study found that IQ scores at age four, long before the children could accumulate school experiences, predicted later delinquency (Lipsitt, Buka & Lipsitt, 1990), and other research has shown that early childhood conduct problems predict adolescent delinquency better than school performance per se (Fergusson & Horwood, 1995). In other words, poor cognitive skills and antisocial behavior are evident before children enter school, and poor school performance is just another manifestation of this disability. As Terrie Moffitt and her colleagues put it:

Children who have difficulty expressing themselves and remembering information are significantly handicapped. Dysfunctional communication between a child and his parents, peers, and teachers may be one of the most critical factors for childhood conduct problems that grow into persistent antisocial behavior in young adulthood (1994:296).

Another interpretation of the relationship between IQ and crime is that it is a spurious consequence of the "fact" that only the less intelligent criminals get caught. Hirschi and Hindelang (1977) surveyed the available evidence pertinent to this "differential detection hypothesis" and concluded that it was not empirically supported. Moffitt and Silva (1988) also tested the hypothesis with an elegantly designed study of a birth cohort. Dividing the cohort into three groups (self-reported delinquents with police records, self-reported delinquents unknown to the police, and self-reported nondelinquents), they found that the first two groups (detected and undetected delinquents) did not differ from one another; that is, undetected delinquents are no more intelligent than detected delinquents. Both delinquent groups, however, differed significantly from the nondelinquent group on verbal IQ but not performance IQ.

TEMPERAMENT AND SES

Temperament is the second phenotypical characteristic identified by Agnew (1992) as important to understanding criminal versus non-criminal responses to strain. Intelligence alone is not sufficient for occupational success; one must also have the requisite temperamental qualities, such as perseverance, patience, and sense of responsibility. Temperament is a phenotypical trait identifiable early in life that constitutes an individual's habitual mode of emotionally responding to stimuli. Temperamental variation is largely a function of heritable variation in central and autonomic nervous system arousal patterns (Kochanska, 1991; Rothbart & Ahadi, 1994). Heritability coefficients for the various components of temperament range from about .40 to .80, which also indicates a substantial contribution of the environment (Gottesman & Goldsmith, 1994). These heritabilities indicate that although it is reasonably stable across the life course, environmental input can strengthen or weaken innate temperamental propensities, and different temperamental components emerge at different junctures as neurological and endocrine arousal systems are fine-tuned by experience. In other words, "Temperament develops, that is, emotions and components of emotions appear at different ages" (Rothbart, Ahadi & Evans, 2000:124).

It is largely temperamental differences that make children differentially responsive to socialization via reactive gene/environment correlation. Temperamental unresponsiveness to socialization is exacerbated by the fact that the temperaments of parents and children are typically positively correlated. Parents of children with difficult temperaments tend to be inconsistent disciplinarians, irritable, impatient, and unstable, which makes them unable or unwilling to cope constructively with their children, thus saddling their children with both a genetic and an environmental liability (Lykken, 1995:11; Moffitt, 1996:93). Temperamental irritability may also adversely affect the quality of parent-infant interactions regardless of parent temperament, and thus lead to a situation of nonattachment and all the negative consequences that implies (Rothbart, Ahadi & Evans, 2000). Numerous studies have shown that children with difficult (disinhibited, irritable) temperaments are responded to negatively not only by parents but also by teachers and peers, and that these children find acceptance only in association with peers with similar dispositions (reviewed by Ellis, 1996b; Moffitt, 1996; Raine, 1993). Caspi (2000:170) summarizes this literature:

> In the early years of life, person-environment covariation occurs because of the joint transmission of genes and culture from parents to offspring. Given that parents and children resemble each other in temperamental qualities, children whose difficult temperament might be curbed by firm discipline will tend to have parents who are inconsistent disciplinarians, and the converse is also true: Warm parents tend to have infants with an easy temperament. Later in life, person-environment covariation occurs because people choose situations and select partners who resemble them, reinforcing their earlier established interaction style.

Conscientiousness

Temperament is the foundation upon which personality is built. Personality refers to the relatively enduring, distinctive, integrated, and functional set of psychological characteristics that results from an individual's temperament interacting with his or her culture and personal experiences. These characteristics can help or hamper the individual in the world of work. Conscientiousness, one of the "big five" factors of personality, is particularly important to success in the workforce and is thus important to our discussion of crime (Brand, 1995; Lykken, 1995; Lynn, 1996). Conscientiousness is a dimension ranging from well-organized, disciplined, scrupulous, responsible, and reliable at one end of the continuum, and disorganized, careless, unreliable, irresponsible, and unscrupulous at the other. The trait has been labeled the "will to achieve" and is highly linked with upward mobility (Kyl-Heku & Buss, 1996:49). Employers can be strongly expected to favor high levels of conscientiousness in their employees and perspective employees, and they do. In an intergenerational study following subjects from early childhood to retirement, Judge and his colleagues (1999) found that conscientiousness predicted occupational success better than any other factor they examined, and it did so controlling for general mental ability.

As we might expect, variance in conscientiousness is heritable. An analysis of 21 behavior-genetic studies of conscientiousness found a median heritability of .66 (Lynn, 1996), which still leaves considerable room for environmental influences on the trait. In short, individuals with certain types of temperament tend to develop certain types of personalities, but this innate tendency may be sidetracked one way or another to some degree by cultural and experiential variables. Persons with disinhibited and irritable temperaments do not typically develop the personal qualities needed to enable them to apply themselves to the long and arduous task of achieving legitimate occupational success. They will become "innovators" and/or "retreatists" not because a reified social structure has denied them access to the contest, but rather because they find the race intolerably boring and choose to busy themselves with more "exciting" pursuits instead.

An interesting longitudinal study having to do with the influence of temperament on occupational success was conducted by Caspi, Bem, and Elder (1989). This study identified males with a history of temper tantrums in late childhood and traced them for 30 years investigating multiple areas of their lives. The majority of bad-tempered boys from middle-class homes ended up in lower-status occupations than their fathers, had erratic work histories, and experienced more unemployment than other males with more tranquil temperaments. They were also more than twice as likely than other men to be divorced by age 40, which illustrates the heterogeneity of negative outcomes that can arise from a single temperamental dimension.

Crime as a Cause of Low SES

The link between SES and crime often boils down to the assertion that poverty causes crime. Many criminological theories either implicitly or explicitly assume that poverty, or "poverty in the midst of plenty," as one sociologist put it (Farley, 1990:217), is the major cause of crime. While it is true that the vast majority of jail and prison inmates are from lower-class backgrounds and that growing up poor increases a person's exposure to criminogenic forces, it does not necessarily follow that poverty causes crime. The majority of poor people do not become criminals, and many of their children with good cognitive skills and a normal temperament achieve a middle-class lifestyle.

An argument could be made that the relationship between poverty and crime is more likely to be the reverse of the typical sociological argument; that is "crime causes poverty." Individuals who drop out of school, do time in a juvenile detention center, and acquire a criminal record severely compromise their opportunities to gain meaningful employment, to form prosocial networks, to become attractive as marriage partners to prosocial females, and to lead a "straight" life. Although there are perhaps a few exceptionally talented career criminals who enter middle- and old-age financially secure, and a few who manage a decent life despite their bad starts, the great majority live their lives in poverty (Raine, 1993:285).

The typical culmination of a life of crime is summed up by a 52-year-old ex-con: "Look at me. I'm 52 years old, I don't have anything. I don't have a car. I don't have a place to stay. Have very few clothes, you know? And I have no job. How in the hell can I be anything but ashamed?" (Shover, 1985:134). Another offender contrasts his life with that of a person who grew up in similar poor circumstances but stayed straight: "I say, a dude I went to school with—my age—you know—so he's got his own house out there, you know. He's got a family, he done raised a family. . . . I look at him, you know, and say, 'Goddamn, this old nigger hasn't been nothing but an old square nigger, but look what he done accomplished. Hey, I ain't got a m..... f...... thing. So who's the square?" (Shover, 1985:135). The proposition that SES is caused by individual characteristics leads to what is for some the unpalatable conclusion that poverty (at least as it appears among offenders) is caused by those same characteristics. It is mainly for this reason that SES will probably never be viewed as a dependent variable by radical criminologists.

As well as foreclosing on personal opportunities for middle-class monetary success, crime may also cause poverty by stripping the communities in which crime is most prevalent of their businesses and jobs. Why would a small business want to stay in an area where robberies, thefts, break-ins, and muggings are an everyday occurrence? When teachers and children are more concerned about rapes, dope dealing, and assaults, how can any meaningful learning take place in schools serving high-crime areas? How can people be proud of their homes and hope to accrue equity when all other houses around them are run down and bullet marked? "Poverty is endemic where crime is endemic" is just as plausible a proposition (and I would argue more so) than the proposition that "crime is endemic where poverty is endemic." Democratic Congressperson John Lewis sums up this argument well: "It is not only poverty that has caused crime. In a very real sense it is crime that has caused poverty, and is the most powerful cause of poverty today" (cited in Walinsky, 1997:11).

Arousal Theory and Status Striving

How does temperament impact the probability of antisocial behavior? We have already discussed one interpretation of low arousal in terms of fearlessness in Chapter 4. The interpretation discussed now is that of sensation seeking. These two interpretations are not mutually exclusive, because sensation seeking is aided by fearlessness (Raine, 1997). Arousal theory (sometimes known as *suboptimal arousal theory*) is based on the well-established finding that different levels of physiological arousal correlate with different personality and behavioral patterns. In identical environmental situations, some people are suboptimally aroused, and other people are superoptimally aroused. Suboptimal and superoptimal arousal levels are opposite tails on a normal distribution, with most people, by definition, being optimally aroused under the normal range of environmental conditions (neither too constant nor too varied). What is an optimal level of environmental stimulation for most of us will be stressful for some and boring for others.

As we saw in Chapter 4, the vital regulator of neurological arousal is the reticular activating system (RAS), the brain's filter system that determines the stimuli to which higher brain centers will pay attention. Some individuals are *augmenters*, that is, they possess an RAS that is highly sensitive to incoming stimuli (more information is taken in and processed); others are *reducers,* possessing a RAS that is unusually insensitive. No conscious attempt to augment or reduce incoming stimuli is implied. Augmentation or reduction is solely a function of the differential physiology of the RAS, which itself appears to be related to different levels of exposure to androgens *in utero*. Males, who receive higher levels of androgen *in utero*, tend to be reducers and females tend to be augmenters, although there is a great deal of overlap (Ellis & Coontz, 1990). Augmenters prefer more constancy than variety in their world and seek to tone down environmental stimuli that most of us find to be "just right." Such people are rarely found in criminal populations. Suboptimally aroused people, on the other hand, are reducers who are easily bored with "just right" levels of stimulation, and continually seek to boost stimuli to levels that are more comfortable for them (Raine, 1997; Zuckerman, 1990).

A number of studies have shown that relative to the general population, criminals, especially those with the most serious records, are chronically underaroused as determined by EEG brain wave patterns, resting heart rate, skin conductance, and histories of hyperactivity and attention deficit disorders (reviewed by Ellis, 1996b; Raine, 1997). Individuals who are chronically bored and continually seeking intense stimulation are not likely to apply themselves to school or endear themselves to employers, regardless of their IQ. Yet these individuals have the same needs for status as their less frenetic peers, and this is what may lead them into trouble.

Status Striving and Evolutionary Theory

Anomie/strain theory shares its deep interest in social status with evolutionary psychology. Both perspectives view status concerns as a fundamental motivating factor behind much of human behavior. They differ, however, on the origins of status striving. For anomie/strain theory, it is simply learned behavior, conformity to a particular set of cultural values. Evolutionary psychology does not view status as socially constructed in the sense that there could be cultures in which status is not something sought and valued, because status *is* sought and valued in every culture. Desiring dominance and status is an inborn universal feature of all social animals because of its role in reproductive success in ancestral environments. Evolutionary psychologists do view the specific actions and activities that confer social status as being socially constructed, however. That is, status means different things in different ecological and cultural environments, but whatever form it takes, status is very much something that social animals, particularly males, are designed by nature to seek.

It has been alleged that sociology in general has ignored indicators of status other than education, income, and occupation and has been "insensitive to context" (Lopreato & Crippen, 1999:232). Just how important are these "middle-class" mainstream indicators to young males relative to other indicators, particularly young males in economically deprived environments? Specifically addressing himself to anomie/strain theory, David Rowe denies that young males compare themselves with "distant middle-class standards" and further asserts that the "main source of strain is an attempt by males to win in male-male encounters a high level of social prestige in local peer groups" (1996:305). Antisocial behavior and a life of crime are not merely the default options of those unable to meet the intellectual and temperamental demands of occupational success. Chronic criminals not only lack the requisite characteristics for middle-class success, but their personalities are such that they do not want to live a straight life and probably would not even if offered one "ready made; no effort required." For instance, studies of criminals in the witness protection program show that even when provided with such a ready-made straight life and the resources to go with it, approximately 21 percent of them are arrested under their new identities within two years of entering the program (Albanese & Pursley, 1993:75). It is obvious that criminal activity has intrinsic as well as extrinsic rewards.

Jack Katz's (1988) phenomenological study of inner-city criminals draws the same conclusion: chronic criminals are seduced by a life of action and they value their "bad ass" reputations—and the dominance and status that comes with them—more than any middle-class "American dream." Katz also uses anomie/strain theory, which he feels is too materialistic, as a foil to his theory. Katz maintains that the primary appeal of antisocial and criminal behavior is the intrinsic rewards that accompany it—the thrills, the euphoria, the rush of taking risks and getting away with it—not the frequently negligible material rewards of such activities. Katz's view is reminiscent of Cohen's (1955), who saw delinquency as motivated by short-run hedonism rather than material gain and as malicious and destructive rather than instrumental. More recent versions of anomie/strain theory ignore the expressive and nonutilitarian nature of much of delinquency.

Although Katz's work hints at concepts from arousal theory, he never attempts to explore the neurobiology of the subjective thrills accompanying criminal behavior. Gove and Wilmoth (1990) have suggested that the risky, low-payoff types of crimes that Katz and Cohen write about produce positively reinforcing neurological events that are intrinsically pleasurable. These endogenous reinforcing events involve dopamine arising in the ventral tegamentum area and terminate in the nucleus accumbens, an important "pleasure center" in the brain. According to Gove and Wilmoth (1990:262), the stress and anxiety accompanying the anticipation and commission of high-risk crimes activates the endogenous opiates in the ventral tegamentum. The activation of these opiates, in turn, results in activation of dopamine synapses in the nucleus accumbens to induce the neuropsychological high after the successful completion of the act. The high is more intense the more arduous and risky the behavior is.

But why would humans (and other animals) have evolved a neurological reward system for engaging in arduous and risky behavior that affords them little or no tangible reward? Gove and Wilmoth suggest that the major function of the endogenous opiates is to counteract the negative effects of environmental stress. If stress (such as the anxiety accompanying burglarizing a house) were not negated somewhat by these opiates, then we may never engage in any kind of risky behavior, legal or otherwise. Noting that sensation-seeking is much more prevalent in males than in females, and that much of sensation-seeking involves risky behavior, it has been speculated that sensation-seeking, despite its many dangers, may have contributed to male reproductive success in ancestral populations (Crawford, 1998b; Zuckerman, Buchsbaum & Murphy, 1980). Risky behavior must have frequently been necessary for survival in ancestral environments, even though it may not have always paid off in terms of immediate external rewards. In other words, sensation-seeking, and the neurochemistry underlying it, may be the proximate mechanism that aided immature and disadvantaged males in ancestral environments to pursue contingent cheating strategies that improved their reproductive success (Crawford, 1998b). In modern environments, the search for amplified excitement often leads the underaroused person into conflict with the law, particularly if the person lacks the resources to pursue socially acceptable ways of seeking thrills.

Risky violent confrontations among males over issues ultimately related to reproductive success are most often observed in environments lacking firmly established dominance hierarchies and in which social restraints have largely dissolved. These environments have been termed "subcultures of violence" or "honor subcultures," in which taking matters into one's own hands is seen as the only way to obtain the all-important "juice" (status) on the street (Anderson, 1999; Mazur & Booth, 1998). Official statistics and victimization surveys consistently show that violent behavior is highly concentrated among the uneducated, unmarried, unpropertied, and unemployed young males in our society (Barak, 1998). Serious assaults and homicides among such groups are generally the result of seemingly trivial altercations over matters of honor, respect, and reputation in the context of a culture where the violent defense of such intangibles is a major route to status (Bernard, 1990a; Mazur & Booth, 1998). Assaults and homicides in these subcultures tend to take place in front of an audience composed of friends of both the killer and the victim, thus squeezing the maximum amount of "juice" from the incident (Wilson & Daly, 1985). Reacting violently to even minor threats to one's status lets others know that "You can't push *me* around!"

Because status has positive fitness consequences, it will be sought after in different ways depending on the cultural context. The cost/benefit ratio attending the violent behavior of culturally disadvantaged males, while seeming to defy rational choice assumptions, is quite understandable when viewed by the light of evolutionary theory. According to Daly and Wilson (1988a:129), killing has been "a decided social asset in many, perhaps most, prestate societies," and dueling over trivial matters of "honor" was ubiquitous among the aristocracy of Europe and the American South until fairly recently. Status, prestige, and respect are so highly valued by males because these things mattered socially more than just about anything in ancestral environments in terms of reproductive success. We should not be too surprised that similar duels over trivial matters of honor still occur in subcultures where there is not likely to be much respect for laws forbidding it and where alternate forms of status-striving are perceived to be unavailable.

Although seeking status through violence is maladaptive in modern societies, our psychological mechanisms were crafted to solve status problems faced by males in environments far different from those faced by young males in the inner cities of the modern world. From an evolutionary perspective, the more young males come to devalue the future, the more risks they are willing to take to obtain their share of street status. The male brain has been finely calibrated to seek status in social groups because status led to increased mating opportunities— and, ultimately, to greater fitness in evolutionary environments. Enhanced mating opportunity is not normally the *conscious* motivation for seeking status in most subcultures (although Chagnon [1996] states that most fights and wars among the Yanomamo start over women). Status-seeking evolved as a means to an evolutionary end, but like the pleasures of sexual copulation, status among one's peers offers such powerful psychic rewards that it is sought as a highly desirable end in itself.

Experiments with nonhuman primates have shown that mechanisms involving the neurotransmitter serotonin underlie status hierarchies (Zuckerman, 1990). Artificially augmenting serotonin activity in male vervet monkeys typically results in their attaining high dominance status in the troop (Raleigh et al., 1991). In naturalistic settings, the highest-ranking males typically have the highest levels of serotonin (which, among other things, promotes confidence and self-esteem), and the lowest-ranking generally have the lowest levels. In established dominance hierarchies, low-ranking males usually defer without much fuss to higher-ranking males over access to females and other resources. When the hierarchy is disrupted or is in flux, which it frequently is, these same lower-level males may become the most aggressive in the competition for resources. The males rising to positions of status in the new dominance hierarchy tend to be those who most aggressively seek it, which includes, above all, successfully forming alliances with other high-status males and females (Raleigh et al., 1991; Wrangham & Peterson, 1996). Serotonin levels of newly successful males rise to levels commensurate with their new status (Brammer, Raleigh & McGuire, 1994), which indicates that although serotonin level is heritable (between .55 and .66), environmental events strongly influence its secretion patterns (Hur & Bouchard, 1997; Tellegen et al., 1988).

The same kinds of relationships between serotonin levels and self-esteem, status, impulsivity, and violence are consistently found among human males, indicating a common set of fitness concerns among all primates (Raine, 1993; Virkkunen, Goldman & Linnoila, 1996; Virkkunen & Linnoila, 1990). As previously noted, rising to a dominant position in a status hierarchy among primates is not simply a matter of individual combativeness. Confident and ambitious individuals in nonhuman primate species form alliances, coalitions, and "gangs" within the troop to help them to achieve their aim, just as aspiring human leaders do (Raleigh et al., 1991). Given the bidirectional relationship between social status and serotonergic mechanisms, it may well be that natural selection has equipped us with these mechanisms to adjust ourselves to the social statuses in which we find ourselves within well-ordered groups. This is not social Darwinism asserting that the status quo exists because it is naturally ordained, and therefore good. These same serotonergic mechanisms also equip those with little to lose with the necessary mechanisms to attempt to elevate their status by taking violent risks when social restraints are weak (Brammer, Raleigh & McGuire, 1994; Wright, 1994).

Chapter 6

Differential Association / Social Learning Theories and Adolescence

The focus of this chapter is the differential association/social learning (DA/SL) tradition and adolescent offending. The DA/SL tradition is a social process perspective that has its theoretical home in symbolic interactionism. Unlike social structural theorists, who sometimes write about social structures as if they exist apart from human activity, symbolic interactionists focus on how people interpret their social reality, and how they create, sustain, and change it. The perspective is summed up in the *Thomas theorem*: "If men define situations as real, they are real in their consequences" (cited in Nettler, 1978:272). The DA/SL tradition is thus about defining social reality and how people learn these definitions as they are socialized into the groups of which they are a part. Although formulated in the 1930s, differential association theory remains popular with modern criminologists (see Table 1.1 on page 15) and is still guiding empirical research in essentially its original form (e.g., Costello & Vowell, 1999; Mears, Ploeger & Warr, 1998).

THE BASICS OF DIFFERENTIAL ASSOCIATION THEORY

Differential association theory is the brainchild of America's best known criminologist, Edwin Sutherland, who is credited with single-handedly making the sociological perspective the dominant one within criminology (Matsueda, 1988). Sutherland's ambitious agenda was to develop a theory that could simultaneously explain individual criminality and aggregate crime rates by identifying conditions that must be present for crime to occur and that are absent when crime is absent; that is, a necessary and sufficient cause. This general theory of crime had to be developed without reference to "psychologizing" or "biologizing," to which Sutherland was openly hostile (Laub & Sampson,

1991). Although Sutherland often used the terms *crime*, *criminality*, and *delinquency* interchangeably, his theory is clearly couched in terms of juvenile delinquency. This chapter therefore concentrates on antisocial behavior in childhood and adolescence. It is important to understand the mechanisms associated with antisocial behavior surrounding the adolescent years, because it is so prevalent during this period that youths (particularly males) who do not become antisocial are considered statistically abnormal (Moffitt, 1993). Almost all adults arrested for felony crimes have juvenile records [longitudinal studies show very low (1% to 4%) rates of adult-onset criminal behavior (Elliot, Huizinga, & Menard, 1989)], and adult-onset crime tends to be nonviolent and less frequent (Blumstein & Cohen, 1987).

Differential association theory asserts that humans, like chameleons, take on the hues and colors of their environments, blending in and conforming with natural ease. Most Americans may like baseball, hot dogs, apple pie, and Chevrolets, as a Chevrolet commercial used to remind us, but do we prefer these things over, say, soccer, bratwurst, strudel, and Volkswagens because the former are demonstrably superior to the latter, or simply because we are Americans rather than Germans? We view the world differently according to the attitudes, beliefs, and expectations of the groups around which our lives revolve; it could hardly be otherwise, particularly in our formative years. Sutherland's basic premise is that delinquent behavior is learned as effortlessly and as normally in certain subcultures as all of us learn to play the games, eat the food, and drive the cars that are integral parts of our cultural lives.

If different subcultures within the dominant culture hold different values and attitudes about what constitutes proper behavior, there will be cultural, or normative, conflict. The conditions said to be conducive to normative conflict mirror those in the anomie/strain tradition. That is, a capitalist economy leads to ambition, competition, the division of labor (as well as its accompanying diversity of attitudes and values), the loosening of social bonds and social controls, and a social structure that blocks access to success goals for large segments of its population (Sutherland & Cressey, 1974:93-110). Thus, the two major criminological perspectives of the period were in basic agreement regarding the criminogenic nature of American society, or of any capitalist society for that matter.

Sutherland was more interested, however, in the process of learning delinquent attitudes than in their alleged structural origins. His theory takes the form of nine propositions outlining the process by which individuals come to acquire attitudes favorable to criminal or delinquent behavior. His first three propositions assert that criminal behavior is learned in the process of social interaction, particularly within intimate personal groups. They also assert that criminal and delinquent behavior is not biologically inherited, the result of psychological abnormalities, invented anew by each criminal, nor learned from impersonal communication (i.e., from movies, television, magazines, and other such distant teachers). The learning of delinquent behavior involves the same mechanisms involved in any other learning. It includes specific skills and techniques, as well as motives, rationalizations, justifications, and attitudes.

The key proposition in the theory is "A person becomes delinquent because of an excess of definitions favorable to violations of law over definitions unfavorable to violations of law" (Sutherland & Cressey, 1974:77). Learning delinquent conduct is not a matter of simple imitation; it is a process of modeling the self after, and identifying with, individuals who hold an excess of procriminal definitions over anticriminal definitions and whom we respect and value. "Definitions" refer to meanings that experiences have for us; how we see things; our attitudes, values, and habitual ways of viewing and responding to the world (Matsueda, 1988).

Associations with others holding definitions favorable to violation of the law vary in *frequency, duration, priority,* and *intensity.* That is, the earlier in life we are exposed to criminal definitions, the more often we are exposed to them, the longer those exposures last, and the more strongly we are attached to our mentors who supply us with them, the more likely we are to internalize them. The DA/SL tradition thus shares with the anomie/strain tradition (at least in its earlier versions) and evolutionary psychology the notion that crime and delinquency are normal products of normal individuals engaging in normal social interactions.

Although Sutherland agreed that criminal behavior is to some extent an expression of general needs and values (e.g., the need for self-esteem, the striving for pleasure and status), he insisted that they are not explanations of crime, because noncriminal behavior is also an expression of the same needs and values (Sutherland & Cressey, 1974:77). Thus, Sutherland takes issue with the strain theorist's emphasis on causes of antisocial behavior. Sutherland was saying that because these needs are constants, they cannot be used as explanations for behavior that varies between criminal and noncriminal. According to Sutherland, "criminal definitions" are not only fashioned to serve the purpose of justifying the acquisition of general needs by illegitimate means, they are the "real" causes of crime and delinquency.

Sutherland is correct that goal striving per se cannot be considered a cause of crime and delinquency. However, nor can Sutherland's excess of "criminal definitions." This proposition has been criticized as both "true and trivial," because all it essentially says is that people are apt to engage in acts contrary to the law when they do not respect the law (Hirschi, 1969:15; Nettler, 1978:265). Why some people hold these definitions and others do not is a question that needs answering. The response from differential association theorists would be that people acquire such definitions through association with delinquent peers, and may point out that the correlations found between association with delinquent peers and delinquent behavior are among the strongest found in social science (Rowe & Osgood, 1984). Because antisocial definitions flourish in delinquent groups, proponents of the theory interpret these correlations to mean that association with delinquent peers *causes* delinquency, or at least precedes it. Associating with delinquent peers is certainly a very good predictor of a person's own delinquency, but it is hardly a causal explanation. What needs to be explained is why people have the associations they do, and this is where the theory can benefit from biosocial concepts.

In Proposition 5 of the 1939 formulation of his theory, Sutherland himself recognized that individual differences affect relationship patterns: "Individual differences among people in respect to personal characteristics or social situations cause crime only as they affect differential association or frequency and consistency of contacts with criminal patterns" (1939:8). Sutherland was (perhaps unintentionally) specifying a path model in this proposition in which differential association is clearly an *intervening* variable between personal characteristics and crime as follows:

Individual differences⟶ *Contact with criminal patterns*⟶ *Crime*

He continued to claim, however, that the antisocial attitudes and values learned in association with criminal peers constituted *the* cause of crime. It is difficult to see from the form of his proposition why Sutherland failed to recognize that if individual differences sort people into different relationship patterns, it may be that the characteristics (either stable or temporary) of people "cause" the activities in which they engage, that their associations merely facilitate and accentuate them, and that their "definitions" merely grant them permission. Perhaps he did realize this, and perhaps the realization became an embarrassment to his goal of developing a pure sociological theory. In any case, he dropped any reference to individual differences in later versions of the theory.

Consistent with the claim that individual differences lead to different associations, various reviews of friendship patterns (e.g., Berndt, 1982; Rodkin et al., 2000) have shown that the propensity for a given pattern of activity (including antisocial activity) precedes association with like-minded individuals. "Birds of a feather flock together"—and they become more alike on the basis of association. If this is true, then being part of a juvenile gang (*A*) and participating in its activities (*B*) are essentially the same thing, so *A* cannot be considered a cause of *B*. Furthermore, reviews of the onset of delinquent behavior find that such behavior typically *precedes* gang membership (Wilson & Herrnstein, 1985; Lewis, 1991). Association with delinquent peers acts more like a catalyst, speeding up and enhancing antisocial conduct among the predisposed, than as a stimulator of uncharacteristic behavior among the innocent. As compelling as this criticism may be, "flocking together" is of short tenure for most youths whose antisocial proclivities are temporary.

However, even those who persist in offending well past adolescence may not have joined a gang because they had an "affinity" for antisocial behavior just as those who join tennis clubs presumably have an affinity for tennis. The choice opportunities in some neighborhoods are not as varied as they are in others, nor are the consequences of those choices similar across all environments. Defenders of differential association theory insist that the concept of *differential social organization* accounts for the associations people have (Matsueda, 1988). Children and adolescents associate with, play with, and become friendly with individuals in the neighborhood environments provided by their parents. If the neighborhood is so densely populated that "good" and "bad" kids live on the same streets or in the same buildings, there is little element of choice as to the company they keep in these circumstances (Stark, 1996). In certain neighborhoods, delinquent peers may indeed "cause" delinquency among youths otherwise insulated from it, as well as facilitate and accelerate it among others who have an affinity for it.

The independent effects of neighborhood type were demonstrated in a study by Matsueda and Heimer (1987), who explored the issue of why broken homes lead to greater delinquency among blacks than among whites. They found that broken homes lead to diminished adult supervision and increased peer involvement for both races, but also that blacks are more likely to live in "troubled neighborhoods" and were thus more likely than whites to come into contact with delinquent peers and to acquire pro-delinquent definitions. Life in many inner-city areas of the United States often literally requires belonging to a gang and participating in its attitudes and behaviors. Youngsters growing up in such areas who do not take advantage of the comradeship and protection of the local gang are probably not acting in their immediate best interests. Nonparticipation in such groups leaves one naked to the preying designs of those more in tune with the reality of their existence, and perhaps friendless to boot. Thus, while the causal-order criticism may be valid for children growing up in neighborhoods with roughly equal access to both prosocial and antisocial peers, it may not be valid for kids growing up in the urban slums, where prosocial peers are rare. The issue of neighborhood influence on crime and criminality will be addressed in greater detail in Chapter 8.

LEARNING, ATTITUDES, AND BEHAVIOR

There are those who take issue with the basic assumption of differential association theory that antisocial behavior is learned. Critics stress that antisocial behavior comes naturally to the unsocialized individual: "What is there to be learned about simple lying, taking things that belong to another, fighting and sex play" asked an early critic (Glueck, 1956:94). Assuredly, individuals learn to get better at doing these things because of their associations with other like-minded individuals, but they hardly have to be taught them. What they have to be taught is how to curb these natural behaviors, what constitutes moral behavior, and how to consider the rights and feelings of others.

If the behaviors mentioned by Glueck "come naturally," it implies that behavior precedes attitudes, and thus behavior causes definitions favorable or unfavorable to law violation rather than the other way around. Although the issue of primacy of attitudes or behaviors depends to some extent on what attitudes and behaviors we are talking about, as well as the kind of people, studies have generally found that behavior has a stronger impact on attitudes than attitudes have on behavior (Bagozzi & Warshaw, 1992). This would mean that Sutherland's "definitions favorable" are really nothing more than the morality of expediency, a set of "after-the-fact" rationalizations that are caused by (rather than being the causes of) behavior. Studies examining the relative effects of peers' attitudes and behavior on subjects' delinquency have found a greater effect for peers' behavior (Nagin & Paternoster, 1991; Warr & Stafford, 1991). None were found reporting the opposite effect. Attitudes do affect delinquency to some extent, but when attitudes and behavior are incongruent, "The actions of peers . . . speak louder [2.5 to 5 times louder] than their attitudes" (Warr & Stafford, 1991:862). Thus, it is not necessary for attitudes to be transferred in intimate social groups before offending becomes probable, and the transmission of antisocial attitudes seems less important than other social learning mechanisms such as peer pressure, modeling, imitation, and vicarious reinforcement.

THE BASICS OF SOCIAL LEARNING THEORY

Differential association theory has been revised across a number of dimensions in response to the many criticisms of it, the most thorough being *differential association-reinforcement theory*, or simply *social learning theory*. The theory originated with Robert Burgess and Ronald Akers (1966) and was designed to answer the issue of what the mechanisms are (beyond looking at frequency, priority, duration, and intensity) by which definitions favorable to antisocial behavior are learned. Burgess and Akers applied the lucid and testable ingredients of *operant psychology* to the vague "definitions favorable" concept of differential association theory.

Operant (or behaviorist) psychology is a perspective on learning that asserts that behavior is governed by its consequences. *Operants* are active instrumental behaviors that operate on the environment with the intention of bringing about some positive outcome for the actor. For instance, acting like a "bad ass" is an operant. If a gang member is rewarded with the approval of other gang members for acting that way, the operant is said to have been reinforced and thus likely to be repeated. Expressed attitudes, or "definitions favorable" to acting bad, are likewise operants that are reinforced by the approval of peers who think such attitudes are "cool." Behavior may emerge initially by imitation, modeling, or even spontaneously, but how well that behavior is learned, and whether it is repeated, depends on how others in the immediate social environment react to it.

Behavior has two general consequences; it is reinforced or it is punished (Akers, 1985:45). Behavior that is reinforced is more likely to reoccur in similar situations in the future, and behavior that is punished is less likely to occur. Behavior is reinforced either positively or negatively. Positive reinforcement occurs when a reward is received, and negative reinforcement occurs when punishment (some aversive condition) is avoided or removed. Examples of positive reinforcement might be the tangible proceeds obtained in a burglary, or the intangible but immensely desired status a gang member might gain by beating up or killing a member of a rival gang. Beating up people then becomes conditioned behavior for this person due to its rewarding consequence. Examples of negative reinforcement might include the freedom from boredom a suboptimally aroused delinquent obtains by running with a gang, or the removal of an unwanted reputation (a "punk") after demonstrating some act of bravado.

Punishment, which weakens or eliminates behavior, can also be positive or negative. Positive punishment is the application of some aversive stimulus, such as a prison term or disapproval from some valued source. Negative punishment is the removal of a pleasant stimulus, such as withdrawal of parental love, or the loss of status in the gang in response to some disapproved behavior.

Social learning theorists accept that Sutherland's "definitions" are normative meanings defining behavior as right or wrong, but view them as verbal behaviors that are exhibited because they and the behaviors they refer to have been reinforced in the process of operant conditioning (Akers, 1985:49). The acquisition of definitions favorable to delinquency or conformity depends on the individual's history of reinforcement and punishment attached to his or her actions. This is not a simple process of adding and subtracting rewards and punishments. Rewards and punishments are differently valued. They are influential according to their source and according to the meaning they have for the person experiencing them (Akers, 1985:47). A dressing down by a teacher, for instance, may be experienced by some as a punishment because they value the teacher's approval, and for others it may act as a reinforcer of the behavior that elicited the teacher's response because it served as a source of levity and approval among valued classmates. Thus, the social context is an extremely important component of Akers's theory: "Most of the learning relevant to deviant behavior is the result of social interactions or exchanges in which the words, responses, presence, and behavior of other persons makes reinforcers available, and provide the setting for reinforcement" (1985:45).

It is also recognized that even if two people experience a consequence similarly as either reinforcing or punishing, they can differ or *discriminate* greatly in their evaluation of the degree to which response to a stimulus is, or may be, reinforcing or punishing. *Discrimination* refers to the progressively finer and finer distinctions people learn to make with regard to the stimuli they experience. The process of socialization is one of becoming "fine tuned" to the nuances of social life so that we can operate more efficiently in a variety of contexts. Discriminative stimuli are signals or clues transmitted by others indicating the kinds of behaviors that will be rewarded or punished in their particular social context. Consider the different social signals presented to a person stopped in the street by a little girl, a clergy member, a Hell's Angel, a police officer, an aggressive wino, or the person's mother, and then consider his or her possible responses. The chosen responses to the stimuli presented to the person represent what he or she has learned personally or vicariously about those people, or others like them. In other words, the ratio of favorable and unfavorable definitions attached to each of those persons will determine how the person will respond.

Unlike the anomie/strain tradition, which has shown a slow but steady reductionist trajectory over the decades, the DA/SL tradition has changed very little. Akers himself has written that his social learning theory is not in competition with differential association theory, but rather that it is "a broader theory that retains all the differential association processes in Sutherland's theory" (1994:94). What Akers claims to have contributed is the couching of these processes in terms of operant psychology, which did help to clarify some of the murkier aspects of differential association theory. Akers improved on Sutherland, who appeared to believe that all people are equally susceptible to learning antisocial behavior, by pointing out that the probability of learning antisocial behavior is a discriminative function of previous reinforcement. Akers did not, however, venture into the realm of individual differences.

Wilson and Herrnstein (1985) offer a theory similar to Akers's that is based on reinforcement and conditioning principles. However, this theory puts more meat on the skeleton of learning theory by identifying individual differences in the likelihood of appreciating the long-term consequences of a behavior despite any short-term rewards it may bring. In other words, people differ in the tendency to discount the negative consequences of their behavior, and thus in the probability of their antisocial behavior being experienced as reinforcing. According to Wilson and Herrnstein, people who have a tendency to discount the negative consequences of their behavior do so because they are impulsive, have learning difficulties, and lack "the bite of conscience." The addition of these variables makes for a more effective learning explanation, because it takes into account how the learning process (what is reinforcing and what is not) is influenced by individual differences. It is perhaps because of this emphasis on individual differences that the theory has been largely ignored by sociologically oriented researchers.

GANGS AND MODERNITY

Before considering individual-level aspects of adolescent antisocial behavior, it is worth exploring the environmental context in which this behavior takes place. Adolescence has always and everywhere been a period of concern for adults because of the surge in antisocial behavior that accompanies it. Plato condemned the youth of his time in the *Republic*, as did Shakespeare in *The Winter's Tale*. The situation is more serious today than it was in ancient Greece or Elizabethan England, however. If we compare the curves graphing the relationship between age and crimes per unit of population ever since such graphs have been made, we observe a steep rise in delinquent activity occurring around the time of puberty. The rise is consistent across time periods, differing only as the typical age of puberty onset has fallen. We observed an ever-increasing peakedness (kurtosis) of the curves until the mid- to late 1990s, when crime rates began to fall. Despite this welcome drop, there is something about today's socioeconomic environment that has provided a rich terrain for antisocial behavior to become more prevalent among young people in certain areas.

When gang theorists such as Cohen (1955) and Cloward and Ohlin (1960) wrote about youth gangs, they did so in a relatively crime-free decade in which the number of cities reporting a gang problem was 58 (M. Klein, 1995). In the mid-1990s, it was estimated that the United States had more than 10,000 street gangs distributed in more than

800 cities (Klein, 1995). The proliferation of gangs and gang violence over the past two decades has been attributed to the loss of
millions of low-skill manufacturing jobs in the United States over the
period (Jackson, 1991). The deindustrializing of America has hit hard-
est at our most vulnerable citizens: the young and uneducated. Factories
leaving neighborhoods cause more social disorganization than factories moving in, changing the community composition without the
compensatory benefit of providing work. Thus, the same sociological
causes of gang formation offered by the old gang theorists—that is, perceptions of blocked opportunity and social disorganization—are still
operating today, perhaps much more strongly.

Cloward and Ohlin's well-known typology of youth gangs (criminal, conflict, and retreatist) has been supported by findings of later gang
researchers. Ronald Huff's (1989) study of gangs in Columbus, Ohio,
identified *hedonistic, predatory*, and *instrumental* gangs. Jeffrey
Fagan's (1989) multicity study identified four types—*social, party, serious delinquent,* and *organized*—suggesting that gangs are still somewhat "specialized" in their activities, depending on the opportunities
available to them. Many modern gangs combine conflict, retreatist, and
criminal activities. Intense rivalry between gangs for drug profits
(particularly lucrative with the arrival of crack cocaine) brought with
it an unprecedented level of gang violence (Albanese & Pursley,
1993:203).

Keeping in mind the distinction between relatively time-stable
gangs and simple ad hoc delinquent groups that are temporarily attractive to most adolescents, we might ask why young people join gangs?
Although not limited to such areas, gangs are highly concentrated in
areas where family disruption and poverty are also highly concentrated.
For instance, the National Institute of Justice's survey of the ethnic composition of gangs found that 48 percent were African-American, 43 percent Hispanic, 5.2 percent Asian, and 4.4 percent white (Curry, Ball
& Fox, 1994:9).

In many of the socially disorganized neighborhoods in the United
States, it becomes almost a survival imperative to belong to a gang. The
gang provides a source of income, camaraderie, excitement, and protection from rival gangs, and it functions as a substitute for an absent
or dysfunctional family life (Davis, 1993). The gang is the core embod-
iment of lower-class values, affording its members opportunities for exer-
cising "hyper-masculine behavior" (Albanese & Pursley, 1993:209).
Gang members display their "specialness" through initiation rites,
"secret" gang signals, special clothing, "colors," and tattoos. Thus,
the gang often functions as (1) family, (2) friendship group, (3) play group,
(4) protective agency, (5) educational institution, and (6) employer.
Because of large-scale breakdown of social institutions in some neighborhoods, we are seeing a disturbing increase in the age range of gang

members. In many hard-core gang neighborhoods, it is not uncommon to see gang members in their twenties, thirties, or even forties, which means that "youth" gangs are increasingly controlled by more hardened and sophisticated criminals (M. Klein, 1995:230). At the structural level, then, gangs are spawned in areas lacking effective prosocial institutions, and gang membership is an adaptive response to the environmental conditions with which members are confronted.

Differential association/social learning theory is probably adequate to explain the attraction of gang life in the worst of our neighborhoods regardless of the degree of genetic risk for antisocial behavior. However, for youths who did not grow up in such neighborhoods but maintain their antisocial activities well into adulthood, and for the most intractably criminal gang members, biosocial explanations are necessary.

DIFFERENTIAL ASSOCIATION/SOCIAL LEARNING (DA/SL) AND GENE/ENVIRONMENT (G/E) CORRELATION

Although the DA/SL tradition is nested in the larger sociological tradition of symbolic interactionism, it treats groups, gangs, behavior patterns, and "definitions" as though they were freestanding entities "out there" rather than abstractions that depend on individuals for their existence. With the exceptions noted earlier, individuals join groups, accept ideas, and engage in activities because these things are attractive to them for one reason or another. Because adolescence is a time of life when rebelliousness becomes an integral part of claiming independence and agency, many youths are attracted to the most rebellious of their peers (Moffitt, 1993; Rodkin et al., 2000). Thus, age and peer influences go a long way toward explaining the prevalence of youthful offending, but they say nothing about that small proportion of offenders who commit the majority of serious crimes and continue to do so long after adolescence.

DA/SL theory is also silent about desisting from delinquency, something done by the great majority of males who offended as juveniles (Moffitt, 1993). Indeed, in common with most sociological theories, DA/SL theory suggests that criminal behavior is self-perpetuating and continuous once initiated (Gove, 1985). It is something of a mystery how a theory silent on the mechanisms that herald the end of the phenomenon it purports to explain (as well as offering a circumscribed explanation for its onset) has managed to survive for so long without major modifications. Sutherland's animus toward nonsociological explanations doubtless kept many of his followers from considering what biology and psychology may have to offer. The absence of any explanation for desisting suggests that it is a theory limited to accounting for peer influence on delinquency during the adolescent years (and it does a very limited job of that).

In common with symbolic interactionism, the concept of reactive and active G/E correlation avers that individuals react to situations according to the subjective meanings the situations have for them, and that they are active shapers of their own environments. The G/E correlation concept, however, goes beyond a mere statement of the obvious to explore the foundations of those subjective meanings. DA/SL theory presents a passive and static model of delinquency in that it essentially posits a one-way transmission of "definitions favorable to law violation" and a sociocultural environment as an independent variable that causes the behavior of the individual. There is nary a hint of reciprocal effects, or that the sociocultural environment could be the dependent variable forged by similar phenotypes selectively aggregating. In a similar critical vein, Beirne and Messerschmidt (2000:136) complain that Sutherland's image of the social actor is "that of an empty vessel" into which are poured "pro- and anti-criminal tendencies." By way of contrast to this static theory, and the view of social actors as automatons, this book focuses on the biosocial developmental model of delinquency proposed by Terrie Moffitt (1993). In common with DA/SL theory, this model has much to say about adolescence, delinquent peers, and other personal and environmental factors, but it is far more sophisticated and comprehensive in its scope.

It was previously noted that cohort studies in the United States and abroad have consistently shown that although about one-third of adolescents acquire a delinquent record, a small proportion in all cohorts commit a vastly disproportionate percentage of the offenses, particularly the serious violent offenses. It is also consistently found in these studies that high-rate offenders begin their criminal careers in childhood and continue way into adulthood. Data such as these suggest that there are at least two types of adolescent offenders, each with its own developmental history and each with its distinct causal process. In common with most other sociological theories of crime and delinquency, DA/SL groups all offenders together and applies its causal explanations to all, thus providing us with an incomplete and faulty picture of youthful offending. Moffitt, on the other hand, presents two qualitatively distinct types of offenders, which she calls *life-course-persistent* and *adolescent-limited*, and outlines a separate etiology for each.

Life-Course-Persistent Offenders

Life-course-persistent (LCP) offenders are those who begin offending early in the life course and continue well into adulthood. Studies that differentiate between prepubescent and postpubescent starters consistently find that early starters are the most frequent and serious offenders in all age categories (Caspi et al., 1995; Farrington, 1996). Moffitt proposes that neuropsychological and temperamental impairments initiate a cumulative process of negative person-environment interactions for LCP offenders that result in a life-course trajectory that propels them toward ever-hardening antisocial attitudes and behaviors. The temperamental and neuropsychological impairments most often mentioned—low IQ, hyperactivity, inattentiveness, negative emotionality, and low impulse control—are consistently found to be correlated with criminality (Moffitt, 1993:680-681) and mirror most of the traits that Agnew's (1997) developmental strain theory targets.

Moffitt proposes that these problems arise from a combination of genetic and environmental effects on central nervous system development, such as maternal substance abuse during pregnancy, poor nutrition, and birthing difficulties. These initial infant and childhood problems are exacerbated by ineffective socialization because problem children tend to have ineffectual parents, although in warm nurturing family environments early childhood problems can be corrected. Moffitt describes the antisocial trajectory of LCP offenders as one of: "biting and hitting at age 4, shoplifting and truancy at age 10, selling drugs and stealing cars at age 16, robbery and rape at age 22, fraud and child abuse at age 30; the underlying disposition remains the same, but its expression changes form as new social opportunities arise at different points of development" (1993:679). This behavioral consistency is matched by cross-situational consistency. LCP offenders "lie at home, steal from shops, cheat at school, fight in bars, and embezzle at work" (Moffitt, 1993:679).

Among the neuropsychological and temperamental deficits that can lead to a lifetime of antisocial behavior are the separate but often linked syndromes of *attention deficit with hyperactivity disorder* (ADHD), *oppositional defiant disorder* (ODD), and *conduct disorder* (CD). Despite the tendency of some sociologically trained criminologists to dismiss these syndromes as mere labels applied to childish "high spirits," they are clearly identifiable as much more than that. ADHD is consistently found to be related to a variety of antisocial behaviors. Ellis and Walsh (2000:237) found 99 studies in which ADHD was positively related and only one (for drug offenses) in which no significant relationship was reported.

ADHD is characterized by an extremely short attention span, constant moving and restlessness, low levels of inhibitory control, impulsiveness, difficulties with peers, frequent disruptive behavior, academic underachievement, and a proneness to extreme boredom. While most children manifest some of these symptoms at one time or another, in ADHD children they cluster together to form a syndrome (eight out of 14 symptoms are required for diagnosis) and are chronic and more severe (Weiss, 1991). ADHD affects somewhere between 2 and 9 percent of the childhood population and is four or five times more prevalent in males than in females (Levy et al., 1997). Although the precise etiology of ADHD is not known, 15 twin studies and two adoption studies have found evidence that genetic factors influence it, and no such study has failed to do so (Ellis & Walsh, 2000:442). The heritability of ADHD is exceptionally high compared to other behavioral disorders (reported to range between .75 to .91). The findings are robust regardless of the cutoff criteria applied or whether ADHD is considered to be a categorical or continuous trait (Levy et al., 1997).

Mechanisms associated with ADHD include suboptimal arousal and frontal lobe dysfunction. Some, but not all, children diagnosed with ADHD show EEG patterns of underarousal (slow brain waves) similar to adult psychopaths (Lynam, 1996). Such a brain wave pattern is experienced subjectively as boredom, which motivates the person to seek or create environments containing more excitement. Hyperactive children's behavior can be normalized temporarily by administering methylphenidate (Ritalin), which is a mild stimulant drug. The efficacy of Ritalin and other such stimulants gave researchers their first clues to the underlying neurochemical basis for the disorder (Weiss, 1991). Although stimulants have the effect of *increasing* activity for non-ADHD individuals, they have a calming or normalizing effect on suboptimally aroused individuals by raising the activity of the brain's sensory mechanisms (principally, the RAS) to normal levels. This relieves boredom because the brain becomes more attentive to features of the environment that it could not previously capture. Being responsive to normal levels of environmental stimuli when on medication, ADHD children are less disruptive, become less obnoxious to peers, and can focus more on schoolwork.

ADHD children engaged in delinquency are more likely than non-ADHD children engaged in delinquency to persist in their offending as adults, but this probability rises dramatically for ADHD children also diagnosed with *conduct disorder* (CD). CD is defined as "the persistent display of serious antisocial actions [assaulting, stealing, setting fires, cruelty to animals] that are extreme given the child's developmental level and have a significant impact on the rights of others" (Lynam, 1996:211). *Oppositional defiant disorder* (ODD) is a form of CD that appears earlier and is less severe. It is characterized by such behaviors as temper tantrums and lying, and it frequently develops into CD. ADHD and CD are found to co-occur in 30 to 50 percent of cases in most clinical and epidemiological studies (reviewed in Lynam, 1996).

Many of the cognitive and temperamental symptoms of CD and ADHD children are similar. CD children, unlike ADHD children, tend to score in the low-normal or borderline range of intelligence and are highly overrepresented in impoverished family environments

(Lewis, 1991). As mentioned, the comorbidity of ADHD and CD represent the greatest risk for serious delinquency and adult criminality. ADHD symptoms usually appear first, followed by ODD symptoms, and finally by CD, as the child and others in its environment are locked in a spiral of negative stimulus/response interactions. ODD and CD children are significantly more likely than children without these behavior patterns to have parents diagnosed with antisocial personality disorder (APD), which partially explains why CD children are most likely to be found in impoverished families (Lahey & Loeber, 1994). Because CD symptoms are necessary for a diagnosis of APD in adulthood, this cross-generation linkage strongly suggests genetic transmission. Although not couched in the language of G/E correlation, Lynam (1996:22) describes the trajectory from ADHD to criminality in very similar terms, stating that the co-occurrence of ADHD and CD:

> [m]ay tax the skills of parents and lead to then adoption of coercive child rearing techniques, which in turn may enhance the risk of antisocial behavior. Entry into school may bring academic failure and increase the child's frustration, which may increase his or her level of aggressive behavior. Finally, the peer rejection associated with hyperactivity may lead to increased social isolation and conflict with peers.

Adolescent-Limited Offenders

Adolescent-limited (AL) offenders have a different developmental history that puts them on a prosocial trajectory that is temporarily derailed at adolescence. They do not have to contend with the temperamental and neurolopsychological problems that burden LCP offenders. Moreover, for the most part, they are adequately socialized. These youths are statistically "normal," and we may view their offending as adaptive responses to conditions and transition events that temporarily divert them from their basically prosocial life-course trajectories. Moffitt (1993:692) agrees entirely with DA/SL theory that AL offending is a group social phenomenon and that it does not reflect any kind of stable personal deficiency on the part of offenders. Moffitt characterizes adolescent-limited offending as motivated by the widening gap between biological and social maturity, learned by mimicking antisocial peers (LCP offenders), and sustained by reinforcement principles.

According to Moffitt (1993), the route by which youths on a basically prosocial life trajectory are temporarily diverted involves biological, social, and economic vectors that are diverging as never before. Health and nutritional advances have continually lowered the age of puberty, and technological advances have continually raised the time needed to prepare for participation in today's complex economy. This divergence has resulted in about a five- to 10-year gap between puberty and the acquisition of socially responsible roles for many of today's youths, making modern adolescence a very wide strain-inducing maturity gap between childhood and adulthood. Because of this gap, many youngsters with no history of antisocial conduct suddenly become antisocial. Thus, "adolescent-limited offending is a product of an interaction between age and historical period" (Moffitt, 1993:692). Filled with boundless energy, strength, and confidence, and a strong desire to shed the restrictions of childhood, some youngsters gravitate to the excitement of antisocial peer groups led by LCP youths. Once in these groups, juveniles learn the techniques of offending via mimicry and reinforcement as outlined by social learning theory.

Adolescent antisocial behavior is adaptive, according to Moffitt, because it offers the opportunity to gain valuable resources that are otherwise temporarily unavailable. The most important of these resources is mature status, yet adolescents are still dependent on parents for almost everything, and adult independence seems to be a very distant dream. These youths may turn their envious eyes on LCP offenders, who have already declared their independence (their parents have given up on them) and have obtained a modicum of the resources (cars, nice clothes, access to sex partners) that signal mature status. Because the behavior of LCP offenders seems to bring positive results for them, novice delinquents are drawn to them and mimic their behavior. This contention is supported by a study of 59 high school classrooms in rural, suburban, and inner-city schools. This study found that the most popular boys were athletic, cooperative, and sociable, but about one-third of the most popular boys were antisocial youths who were frequently disruptive and belligerent and "central members of prominent classroom cliques" (Rodkin et al., 2000:21). Popular antisocial youths are thus rewarded with status among their peers, and their mimics receive vicarious reinforcement by identifying with them. These neophyte delinquents internalize the idea that antisocial behavior and popularity go together, and thus receive validation for their oppositional behavior.

Moffitt does not explicitly refer to the concept of G/E correlation in her work, but she has confirmed (personal communication, 1996) that this interpretation of her work "articulates the different types of G/E correlation implied by [her] writing." Figure 6.1 compares the static and generalized differential association pathway model to delinquency with Moffitt's dynamic and specific pathway models. Particular attention should be paid to the role of association with delinquent peers in the LCP and AL delinquency models. In the case of LCP offenders, *stable* antisocial characteristics precede association with delinquent peers and exemplify active G/E correlation in that like seeks like. By way of contrast, for AL offenders, association with delinquent peers precedes the development of *temporary* antisocial characteristics. This suggests that association with delinquent peers may be necessary to initiate delinquency for AL offenders, and that there is little or no genetic influence on delinquency for these temporary offenders at a time in life when peer influence is tremendously important. In other words, teens have a limited ability to choose their environments, so even those with low genetic risk for delinquency will often succumb to it under the influence of their more daring peers, whom they temporarily admire and seek to emulate.

Figure 6.1
Differential Association Theory and Moffitt's Theory

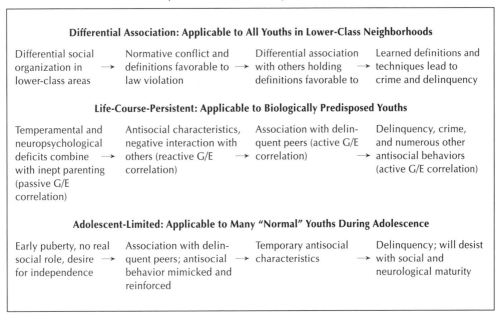

As AL offenders mature and are free to begin structuring their environments consistent with their genetic preferences, they begin to realize that an adult criminal record will severely limit their future options. They begin to "knuckle down," take on socially responsible roles, and desist from further antisocial behavior. Unlike LCP offenders, who have essentially "burned their bridges" to the prosocial world, AL offenders have accumulated a store of positive attachments (they elicit positive responses from others) and academic skills (they are intelligent) that provide them with prosocial opportunities such as a good marriage and a good job. In short, AL offenders desist from antisocial behavior because, in Moffitt's (1993:690) words, they are "psychologically healthy," and "[h]ealthy youths respond adaptively to changing contingencies."

Sampson and Laub (1999) support Moffitt's contention, showing that job stability, commitment, and attachment to a prosocial spouse are important inhibitors of adult criminal behavior among former delinquents. Sampson and Laub did not differentiate between LCP and AL offenders, but they did maintain that such positive adult social bonds are "social capital" and the result of prior "social investment." We may expect, therefore, that their findings are more salient for AL than LCP offenders, especially given the data on assortative mating (like seeking like) for antisocial behavior and characteristics (Krueger et al., 1998; Quinton et al., 1993). These studies show that the likelihood of persistent offenders securing the support of a nondeviant spouse, while not impossible, is minimal.

Moffitt and her colleagues have conducted tests of the theory with longitudinal data from a New Zealand birth cohort and found strong support for it. Overall, these studies show that LCP offenders almost always had childhood temperament problems identifiable at three years of age and were more likely to have weak family bonds, low verbal IQ, and aggressive and antisocial personalities. LCP offenders were much more likely to commit violent crimes than AL offenders, and although they constituted only 7 percent of the cohort, they were responsible for more than 50 percent of all delinquent acts committed by it (Jeglum-Bartusch et al., 1997; Henry et al., 1993, 1996; Moffitt et al., 1996). Note the consistency of these figures with other cohort data indicating that serious and frequent offending tends to be concentrated among a very small group, the vast majority of whom began offending prior to puberty.

Why do Some Adolescents Abstain from Delinquency Altogether?

Because adolescents who abstain from delinquency are statistically abnormal, their abstinence is at least as interesting as why others offend. The literature on adolescent *prosocial* conformity is extremely sparse, however. Because Moffitt views the age peak to be a function of today's long maturity gap, the most obvious reason why some adolescents do not offend is that they do not experience the maturity gap to the same degree as most young people do. That is, they may experience late puberty and/or early initiation into adult roles and responsibilities. These youngsters may be considered "throwbacks" to an age in which the crime peak was less pronounced and when puberty arrived later and less preparation was needed to enter the job market (Moffitt, 1993:689). Moffitt also speculates that abstainers may belong to religious and cultural groups in which youths are given early access to adult privileges and accountability, or that they are less well-adjusted than adolescents who experiment with delinquency. In support of the latter speculation, she cites a study that found boys at environmental risk for delinquency who did not become delinquent "seemed nervous and withdrawn and had few or no friends" (and thus no antisocial role models) (1993:689).

Another possible explanation consistent with the above observation is that abstainers are located on the "hyper" tail of the ANS arousal distribution and thus have an excessive fear of the negative consequences of any misbehavior. It has been speculated that a significant verbal-over-performance (V>P) discrepancy is a marker of superoptimal arousal because the performance scale on IQ tests relies mostly on short-term memory and is more anxiety-provoking than the verbal scale. Anxiety is hypothesized to disrupt short-term memory, leading to an inferior score on the performance IQ scale relative to the person's score on the verbal IQ scale (Walsh, Beyer & Petee, 1987). It was mentioned in Chapter 4 that V>P males have been consistently shown to be underrepresented in delinquent populations vis-à-vis P=V males and, particularly, P>V males. Across a number of studies, and compared to their expected numbers based on normative samples, V>P boys are underrepresented in delinquent populations by a factor of about 2.2 and in prison populations by a factor of about 18 (reviewed in Walsh, 1995a).

BIOSOCIAL PERSPECTIVES ON ADOLESCENT ANTISOCIAL BEHAVIOR

Adolescence, the period in which the organism no longer needs parental care but is not yet sexually mature, is a peculiarly human phenomenon. Most mammals progress from infancy to sexually active adulthood seamlessly, and only the most social and long-lived of species experience anything like a period of adolescence (Bogin, 1993). Human adolescence is thus a sort of developmental and psychological pause that is frequently stressful for persons in it. It is probably part of the general neotenous heritage of *Homo sapiens*, which must confer some evolutionary advantage, such as experimenting with social skills before having to put them into practice (Bogin, 1993).

Criminologists and other scientists have long striven to understand why adolescence is so troublesome. Age-graded crime rates, from whatever city, state, country, or time period, reveal a tremendous surge in antisocial behavior beginning at puberty, rising to a peak at around age 16 (in the modern United States) and steadily declining thereafter. Violent, destructive, and nonutilitarian crimes peak earlier and decline faster than instrumental crimes such as forgery and fraud

(Steffensmeier et al., 1989). Because most criminologists are sociologically trained, this age-related pattern tends to be explained only in terms of situational factors individuals experience at certain points in their lives. From this viewpoint, age is simply a proxy for socially generated factors, not a variable with its own intrinsic properties.

By pointing out social events associated with the rise and fall of delinquency, sociologists believe that they render nonsociological explanations impotent. In contrast to this belief, it has been pointed out that age remains a potent predictor of antisocial behavior after controlling for a host of demographic and situational variables correlated with it (Gottfredson & Hirschi, 1990; Wilson & Herrnstein, 1985). As Shavit and Rattner (1988:1457) put it, the age peak in delinquency remains "unexplained by any known set of sociological variables." Thus, we have to go beyond looking at situations associated with age, which vary immensely across cultures and time periods, and consider age as a higher-level proxy for a host of lower-level measures, such as hormonal levels and brain maturational processes. The effects of age on antisocial behavior can be more fully appreciated if we examine both biological and cultural factors that impact individuals during adolescence.

Hormones and Puberty

The major biological event of the second decade of life is the onset of puberty. During adolescence, the young find themselves at the confluence of a number of often confusing physical, social, and psychological changes. Increasing social maturation temporarily runs up against the countervailing hormonal surges of puberty. These hormonal events herald rapid increases in size and strength, as well as a general increase in novelty-seeking behavior mediated by neurotransmitter activity regulated by these same hormones (Udry, 1990; Zuckerman, 1990). Before puberty, there are only small differences in the quantity of sex hormones between the genders. At puberty, there is a huge surge of behavior-facilitating hormones, with levels of testosterone in postpubertal males approximately 10 times greater than in postpubertal females. Males also have about one-half the female level of sex-hormone-binding globulin (SHBG), which, because hormones bound to SHBG are essentially inoperative, means that males have about 20 times more "free" (activating) testosterone than females (Buchanan, Eccles & Becker, 1993; Udry, 1990). These "raging hormones" can partially account for the onset of antisocial behavior among most young men, as well as the differences in offending rates between males and females of any age.

Recall that in sociological models, no set of situational or demographic variables have been shown to render the age effect spurious. On the other hand, in biosocial models of antisocial behavior that include testosterone and SHBG levels, age drops out of the equation, leading researchers to speculate that the age effect on such behavior is "a spurious consequence of the causal relationship between age and testosterone" (Udry, 1990:7). This finding, as well as Udry's research on sexual behavior (Udry, 1988), provides excellent examples of the absorption of higher-level measures such as age and the incremental validity gained when individual measures (testosterone/SHBG ratios) are included in an analysis.

Evolutionary Considerations

We saw previously that Moffitt (1993) considers AL delinquency to be an adaptive response to temporary environmental contingencies. But what evolutionary purpose does it reflect? AL offenders are behaving similarly to young males in other primate species in that they are temporarily following a conditional cheater strategy and will desist when opportunities arise to gain status and other valued resources legitimately. As evolutionary biologists stress, natural selection has generally favored the most dominant males because such characteristics result in more mating opportunities and thus greater gene representation in subsequent generations. As is the case with other primate species, mid-adolescence and early adulthood are periods of intense competition among males, which are replete with risk-taking and some degree of violence aimed ultimately at securing more mating opportunities than the next male. As Martin Daly (1996:193) put it, "There are many reasons to think that we've been designed [by natural selection] to be maximally competitive and conflictual in young adulthood." Young males would not necessarily couch their strutting, preening, and other status-seeking behavior in terms of reproductive effort, but few of us are ever conscious of the ultimate causes of our behavior. In disadvantaged subcultures in which risk-taking and violence are endemic, there is evidence that gang membership enhances male status among young women. Just as it does within dominance alliances in other primate species, enhanced status results in gang members having more sexual partners than non-gang members in the same subculture, and in gang leaders (the alpha males) having more sexual partners than other gang members (Padilla, 1992; Palmer & Tilley, 1995).

While no one advances the position that criminality per se is an evolutionary adaptation, behaviors defined as criminal in most cultures may be maladaptive consequences of a generally adaptive mating strategy pursued by young males in ancestral environments. Certainly the neurohormonal mechanisms facilitative of dominance and aggression also promote criminal behavior in some environments, particularly in the so-called honor subcultures discussed in the previous chapter. Thus, the hormonal surges of puberty may help to explain the rapid onset of antisocial behavior, but the almost-as-rapid decline in antisocial behavior starting in the late teens/early twenties does not correspond with a similar decrease in testosterone. Thus, there must be other factors that help to explain the postadolescent decline in antisocial behavior.

Adolescence and Arousal

John Baldwin (1990) presents an arousal theory of crime that is similar to those of Katz (1988) and Gove and Wilmoth (1990) presented in the previous chapter. Baldwin (1990:212) addresses the age issue directly and states that his theory is "most compatible with social learning theories and differential association theories of crime." Rather than concentrating on differences in arousal levels among individuals, he focuses on average age-graded levels of arousal at different developmental periods and finds that these levels mirror the age/crime curve. Baldwin begins by noting that infants are easily aroused and distressed by novel stimuli and have to be soothed. They soon become habituated to increasingly more stimuli as they age, however, and begin to require higher levels of sensory input to be optimally aroused. The need for arousal is greatest during adolescence, when ratios of behavior-facilitating dopamine and the behavior-moderating serotonin favor dopamine. This is also the period when the de-aminating enzyme monoamine oxydase (MAO), which removes excess amines (a class of neurotransmitters) at the synapse, are at their lowest (reviewed by Ellis, 1991). These neurochemical fluctuations suggest that adolescence may be a period in which the brain is particularly sensitive to rewards and relatively insensitive to punishment, a combination that is facilitative of risk-taking and sensation-seeking behavior (Zuckerman, 1990). Teens drive motorcycles and fast cars, try drugs and alcohol, attend raucous rock concerts, throw themselves into mosh pits, and generally behave obnoxiously from an adult point of view. The need for stimulation is general across all adolescents, but exciting activities that are legal are either unavailable to some or are not arousing enough to satisfy their needs.

The decline in the need for novel and exciting stimuli mirrors the decline in age-related criminal activity. Habituation sets in as formerly novel occurrences become commonplace and shifting contingencies and opportunities result in decreasing reinforcements for antisocial behavior and increasing reinforcements for prosocial behavior.

Baldwin thus views delinquency much the same as Katz and Gove and Wilmoth do; that is, motivated more by hell-raising and sensation-seeking than by monetary considerations or by conformity to a set of "definitions favorable." He does not claim, however, that the neurohormonal mechanisms underlying sensory reinforcement and habituation are all that we need to know to explain age-related antisocial behavior, nor that every adolescent experiences the same level of need for stimulation. Baldwin does claim that theories of crime and delinquency must incorporate what we know about the biology of adolescence into them and to consider such information as being equal in importance to environmental variables. Although Baldwin does not mention specific variables, MAO and serotonin levels rise as we age, and testosterone levels fall, all of which contribute to less sensation-seeking, and thus placing oneself at lowered risk for antisocial behavior (Ellis & Coontz, 1990; Moir & Jessel, 1995).

The Brain and Adolescence

The view that adolescence is a period in which physical desires and abilities outrun neuropsychological maturity is supported by several studies showing generally that the earlier the onset of puberty, the greater the level of problem behavior. Juveniles who enter puberty significantly earlier than their age peers must confront their "raging hormones" with a brain that in all likelihood is no more mature than those of their peers. This brain immaturity is indexed by findings that early-maturing boys throw significantly more temper tantrums than do late-maturing boys (Buchanan, Eccles & Becker, 1993). Early-maturing girls have also been shown to engage in a number of problem behaviors more frequently and intensely than late-maturing girls (Caspi et al., 1993; Magnusson, 1988). Further evidence for the conflicting-trajectory hypothesis comes from a study that found testosterone levels predicted future problem behavior, but only for boys with early pubertal onset (Drigotas & Udry, 1993). Such findings imply that if the adolescent brain is *physically* immature relative to the adult brain, it may facilitate a tendency to assign faulty attributions to situations superimposed on an unfamiliar and diffuse state of physiological arousal. As Agnew (1997) suggests, a brain on "go slow" combined with physiology on "fast forward" may explain why many young persons find it difficult to gauge accurately the meanings and intentions of others and to experience stimuli as aversive during adolescence.

Two recent MRI studies of brain development—one a longitudinal study of the same persons (Giedd et al., 1999) and the other comparing young adolescents with a group of young adults (Sowell et al., 1999)—confirm that the adolescent brain, particularly the prefrontal cortex (PFC), is indeed immature. As noted in Chapter 4, the PFC serves various executive functions, such as modulating emotions from the limbic system and making reasoned judgments and plans. According to these MRI studies, the PFC undergoes a second wave of synaptic overproduction (the first is in infancy) just prior to puberty, which is followed by a period of pruning during adolescence and on into early adulthood. Because selective retention and elimination of synapses depend on input from the environment, Geidd and his colleagues (1999:863) suggest that adolescence is a "critical stage of development" and that it is a crucial time for adults to provide opportunities for youth to test themselves with prosocial activities that are as exciting and challenging for them as "raising hell."

To complicate things further, not only is a synaptic pruning process going on during adolescence, the adolescent PFC is less completely myelinated (recall that myelin is important to the speed and conductive efficiency of neurotransmission) than the adult PFC (Sowell et al., 1999). The fact that many syndromes associated with delinquency, such as conduct disorder/socialized type, first appear during this period (Benes, 1997) once again suggests a brain that is perhaps not developmentally up to the task of dealing rationally with the strains of adolescence and one that may rely more on raw emotion. For instance, MRI studies have shown that only the emotional limbic system is activated for many adolescents when they are shown photographs of frightened people, whereas both the limbic system and the PFC show activity among mature adults (Baird et al., 1998; Baird, personal communication, 1999). The apparently less efficient level of communication between these two brain areas among adolescents is another indication that the PFC is probably not performing its reasoning and emotion-modulating duties efficiently for at least some of them.

Perhaps partially reflective of increased brain maturation from adolescence to adulthood are findings from samples in at least five different countries that age brings with it a decrease in personality traits positively related to antisocial behavior and an increase in personality traits negatively related to antisocial behavior. According to McCrae and his colleagues (2000:183), "From age 18 to 30 there are declines in Neuroticism, Extraversion, and openness to experience, and increases in Agreeableness and Conscientiousness; after age 30 the same trends are found, although the rate of change seems to decrease." Thus, the fine-tuning of neurological and endocrine arousal systems occurs across the life span in response to both endogenous and environmental events, which results in a set of personality traits in adulthood that are conducive to prosocial behavior for most individuals.

Chapter 7

Control Theories and the Family

If society is to be possible, antisocial behavior must be kept to a minimum. To ensure that it is, mechanisms have been devised to minimize nonconformity and deviance that are collectively referred to as *social control*. Social control entails any action on the part of others, deliberate or not, that facilitates conformity on the part of those toward whom the action is directed. The first agents of social control we meet are our parents, on whose shoulders control theorists place the primary burden of producing good citizens. It is they who must teach their offspring the accepted rules of proper conduct. When we have internalized rules of conduct, we feel guilty, anxious, and ashamed when we misbehave, and happy and self-righteous when we behave well. What we call *conscience* is the sum of internalized social rules of conduct. Those who have been less than adequately socialized feel no such emotions and are thus granted permission by their consciences to do more or less as they please.

A class of theories called *control theories* focuses on mechanisms of informal control (as opposed to formal control mechanisms such as the criminal justice system). As was shown in Chapter 1, social control and self-control theories were number one and two, respectively, in popularity among contemporary American criminologists. The current discussion is limited to these two theories, both of which are associated with Travis Hirschi. These theories focus on the family and have "common sense" appeal as gauged by the results of numerous studies asking laypersons their opinions about the causes of crime. Every such study shows family factors (lax discipline and supervision, broken homes, family discord, and so on) to be uppermost in the public's mind as causes of crime and delinquency (Ellis & Walsh, 2000:79).

SOCIAL CONTROL THEORY

Most theories of crime and criminality focus on conditions within offenders or within their environments that are alleged to propel them into criminal activity. This view implicitly assumes that people naturally want to "do the right thing" and conform to conventional social rules, and that it takes some sort of negative departure from the "normal" to make them behave badly. This is akin to the discredited theory of group selection in biology (but see Wilson & Sober, 1994); that is, we have evolved to place group interests above our own individual interests and will do so unless somehow forced to do otherwise. For those who believe that crime and delinquency are behaviors learned by good people in bad environments, it make sense to ask "what causes crime?" The phenomenon to be explained for them is why essentially decent social beings get enmeshed in antisocial acts.

Control theorists believe that the "What causes crime?" question is a fundamentally flawed one and that the real question is not why some people behave badly, but why most of us behave well most of the time. Control theory shares with evolutionary psychology the assumption that humans are self-interested and will seek benefits to themselves in any way possible unless motivated to behave well (to be good reciprocal altruists). We behave well if our ties to prosocial others are strong, and we may revert to predatory self-interest if they are not. After all, human infants express little else other than concern for self-gratification, and it is only through years of socialization that they come to realize that their self-interest is bound to the self-interests of others. Children who are not properly trained (socialized) hit, kick, bite, steal, whine, scream, and otherwise behave obnoxiously whenever the mood strikes them. They have to be taught not to do these things, that, in the absence of training, "come naturally." As Freud reminded us in his *Civilization and Its Discontents* (1961), civilized society is bought at the cost of the repression of our freedom to do as we please.

The human organism must control its appetite for instant self-gratification and selfish expression and must learn right from wrong. In this view, humans are born self-centered and asocial and must learn to be prosocial, which directly contradicts the DASL tradition that asserts that we learn to be antisocial. For the control theorist, as it was for Durkheim, it is society that is "good" and human beings, in the absence of proper training, who are "bad." Crime is natural, and the criminal is just the unsocialized self-centered child grown strong. Thus, instead of asking how natural social conformists are induced to behave badly, control theorists ask how naturally selfish individuals can be induced to behave well.

Hirschi's social control theory is consistent with what we know with reasonable certainty about the demographic characteristics of typical criminals; that is, young males who grew up in fatherless homes in an urban slum and who have a history of difficulty in school and work. Having defined the typical criminal demographically, Hirschi (1977) makes a series of logical deductions, beginning with the observation that criminal activity is contrary to the wishes and expectations of others. From this he deduces that those most likely to commit crimes are least likely to be concerned with the wishes and expectations of others. Criminal activity is also contrary to the law and involves the risk of punishment. Therefore, those who commit crimes are least likely to accept the moral beliefs underlying the law and are least likely to concern themselves with the risk of punishment. Finally, criminal acts take time and are thus most likely to be engaged in by those who have the time to commit them, that is, the unemployed.

The Four Controls or Bonds

From these observations, Hirschi makes the assumptions that the typical delinquent or criminal lacks attachment to prosocial others, that he or she lacks commitment to a prosocial career and involvement in a prosocial lifestyle, and that he does not believe in the validity of the mainstream moral order. *Attachment*, *commitment*, *involvement*, and *belief* are highly interrelated social bonds or controls existing in the lives of noncriminals that restrain them from criminal activity and are assumed to be largely absent in the lives of criminals.

Attachment refers to the emotional bonds existing between the individual and key social institutions like the family and the school. Attachment to conventional others is the "master" control that lays the foundation for all other social bonds. Attachment implies strong emotional relationships in which persons feel valued, respected, and admired, and in which the favorable judgments of others in the relationship are valued. Sociologists use the concepts of *significant other* and *reference group* to refer to the people we consider important to us and whose good opinions we value. Significant others are close family members and friends, and reference groups are those groups of people who we admire and seek to emulate. These are the people to whom we look for guidance in our behavior, much of which can be seen as attempts to gain favorable judgments from our reference groups and significant others.

For many years, parents are the most important behavior-orienting significant others for us all. Children who do not care about parental reactions are those who are most likely to behave in ways contrary to their wishes. Risking the good opinion of another is of minor concern when that good opinion is not valued. Parental opinion may not be valued if parents have not earned the love and respect of their children because of physical and/or emotional neglect and abuse, the lack of intimate communication, erratic and unfair disciplinary practices, emotional coldness, or perhaps because their appearance, demeanor, or social status is embarrassing to the child (Hirschi, 1977). Lack of attachment to parents and lack of respect for their wishes easily spills over into a lack of attachment and respect for the broader social groupings of which the child is a part. Much of the controlling power of others outside the family lies in the threat of reporting misbehavior to parents. If the child has little fear of parental sanctions, the control exercised by others has little effect because parental control has limited effect.

Commitment refers to a lifestyle in which one has invested considerable time and energy in the pursuit of a lawful career, which provides a valuable stake in conformity. This is the accumulation of social capital that facilitates the transition from hell-raising to responsible adulthood for the adolescent-limited offender. Unlike the somewhat negative view of aspirations as strain-inducing that is contained in anomie/strain theory, Hirschi contended that aspirations tie individuals to the social order (1969). The person who has made this considerable investment is not likely to risk it by engaging in crime. Poor students, truants, dropouts, and the chronically unemployed do not have much of an investment in conventional behavior and, therefore, risk less in the cost/benefit comparison. The acquisition of a stake in conformity requires success in school, which requires intelligence and disciplined application to tasks that children do not relish but that they complete in order to gain valued approval. If approval is not forthcoming or is not valued, children will busy themselves in tasks more congenial to their natural inclinations, inclinations that almost certainly do not include algebra or parsing sentences. Attachment is thus the essential foundation for commitment to a prosocial lifestyle.

Involvement is a direct consequence of commitment and is part of a conventional pattern of existence. Hirschi revealed his sentiments in favor of the classical view of human nature when he wrote that "many persons undoubtedly owe a life of virtue to lack of opportunity to do otherwise" (1969:21). Essentially, involvement is a matter of time and energy constrictions placed upon us by the demands of our commitments, and involvement in lawful activities reduces exposure to illegal opportunities. Conversely, the lack of involvement in lawful activities increases the possibility of exposure to illegal activities.

Belief refers to the ready acceptance of the social norms regulating conduct. Individuals who are free of the constraints on their behavior imposed by the four social bonds evolve a belief system shorn of conventional morality. A belief empty of conventional morality contains only narrowly focused images of self-interest justified by a "dog eat dog" philosophy. Unlike differential association theory, control theory does not view a criminal belief system as motivating criminal behavior. Rather, criminals act according to their urges and then justify or rationalize their behavior with a set of instrumental statements such as "suckers deserve what they get," "everybody does it—why not me?" and "do unto others as they would do unto you—only do it first." These are the statements of alienated individuals reflecting and rationalizing the lifestyle of the unattached. For control theorists, behavior gives birth to the belief, rather than vice versa. It is important to understand that the lack of attachment, commitment, and involvement to and with conventional others does not constitute a motive for crime. The lack of these controls or bonds represents social deficiencies that result in a reduction of the potential costs of engaging in crime. Criminal belief systems are merely after-the-fact justifications for antisocial behavior.

GOTTFREDSON AND HIRSCHI'S LOW SELF-CONTROL THEORY

Hirschi has moved away from explaining crime and delinquency in terms of the four social controls toward explaining it in terms of a single form of control called self-control. With Michael Gottfredson, Hirschi has developed a "general theory" of crime and claims that "it explains all crime, at all times, and, for that matter many forms of behavior that are not sanctioned by the state" (1990:117). They appear to be asserting that low self-control (or what others have called impulsivity, inability to defer gratification, or low constraint) is a necessary and sufficient cause of criminal behavior, although they later acknowledge that opportunity must also exist if low self-control is to result in criminal behavior. The theory has captured the imaginations of many criminologists, and low self-control is a useful explanatory concept when shorn of the lofty claims Gottfredson and Hirschi make for it.

Self-control is defined as the "extent to which [different people] are vulnerable to the temptations of the moment" (Gottfredson & Hirschi, 1990:87). Gottfredson and Hirschi accept the classical idea that crimes are the result of the natural human impulse to enhance pleasure and avoid pain, and define them as "acts of force or fraud undertaken in pursuit of self-interest" (1990:15). Low self-control is not a motivator of antisocial behavior; it is a lack of internal constraint that permits it. There is "little variability among people in their ability to see the pleasures of crime," Gottfredson and Hirschi (1990:95) assert, but (due to variability in self-control) "there will be considerable variability to calculate pains." Most crimes, they contend, are spontaneous acts in response to a tempting opportunity. Further, they require little skill and most often earn the criminal only minimal reward or satisfaction. Such criminal opportunities do not tempt people with self-control, but people with low self-control are always strongly tempted to make some quick gain for themselves whenever opportunities present themselves.

According to the theory, people with low self-control possess the following cognitive and temperamental traits that make offending more probable for them than for others (1990:89-90). Parenthetical remarks have been added, linking those traits with previous discussions of analogous concepts in previous chapters.

- They are oriented to the present rather than to the future, and crime affords them immediate rather than delayed gratification. (They are impulsive).

- They are risk-taking and physical as opposed to cautious and cognitive, and crime provides them with exciting and risky adventures. (They have low arousal levels, are sensation seekers, and lack cognitive skills).

- They lack patience, persistence, and diligence, and crime provides them with quick and easy ways to obtain money, sex, revenge, and so forth. (They lack conscientiousness).

- They are self-centered and insensitive, so they can commit crimes without experiencing pangs of guilt for causing the suffering of others. (They lack empathy and conscience).

The theory asserts that low self-control is established early in childhood and tends to persist throughout life. The origin of low self-control according to this theory is inept parenting, which may include abuse and neglect, poor discipline practices, poor supervision, and poor attachment. One component of the theory that is important to understand is that children do not learn the characteristics associated with low self-control. Rather, such characteristics are the "default" outcomes that occur in the absence of adequate socialization. Brannigan (1997:425) puts this concept in evolutionary terms: "In the absence of interaction designed to promote empathy, identification, delayed gratification, a long time horizon, and prosocial values, the infant appears to exhibit older evolutionary scripts of adaptation which favour immediate gratification and egoism."

Thus, low self-control is not learned, but self-control is. If children are to be taught self-control, their behavior must be strictly and consistently monitored, parents and/or caregivers must recognize deviant behavior when it occurs, and the behavior must be punished. Active parental concern for the well-being of their children is central to the rearing of self-controlled children. Warmth, nurturance, vigilance, and the willingness to practice "tough love" are the necessary links between parental self-control and offspring self-control. Other family-related factors that lead to low self-control include parental criminality (criminals are not very successful in socializing their children not to be criminals), family size (the larger the family, the more difficult it is to monitor behavior), being a single-parent family (the efforts of two parents are generally better than one), and working mothers (which negatively affects the development of self-control if no substitute monitor is provided) (Gottfredson & Hirschi, 1990:100-105).

Gottfredson and Hirschi argue that children learn or fail to learn self-control in the first decade of life, after which the attained level of control remains stable across the life course. Subsequent experiences, situations, and circumstances have little independent effect on the probability of offending, because these unfolding events are heavily influenced by the level of self-control learned in childhood. Low self-control is thus considered a stable component of a criminal personality, which is why most criminals typically fail in anything that requires long-term commitment and compromise, such as school, employment, and marriage, because such commitments and compromises get in the way of immediate satisfaction of their desires.

Opportunity

According to the theory, low self-control is a necessary but not sufficient determinant of offending. Because self-control is stable across the life course once it has become dominant in the personality, variation in criminal behavior cannot be explained by variation in self-control. What does explain variation in such behavior, according to this theory, is variation in the *opportunity* to commit it. As in rational choice theory, criminal offending is the result of people with low self-control (a motivated offender) meeting a criminal opportunity. A criminal opportunity is a situation that presents itself to the offender by which he or she can immediately satisfy needs with minimal mental or physical effort (1990:12-13). Individuals with the sort of traits indicative of low self-control will sometimes manufacture their own opportunities as well as simply taking advantage of those that just happen to come along. Gottfredson and Hirschi illustrate what they mean by a low self-control individual meeting a criminal opportunity by describing typical homicide, rape, robbery, burglary, auto theft, and embezzlement incidents. These descriptions suggest that most criminal events are not the culmination of foresight, planning, and effort; rather, they are environmental events (an open door, an unlocked car with keys in the ignition, a vulnerable person walking down a dark alley) witnessed by someone ready to take advantage of them.

The impulsive nature of the typical crime incident is supported by a study in which 83 percent of offenders claimed that the crimes for which they were first arrested were unplanned and "just happened." Eleven percent of the offenders said they planned the crime on the day it was committed, and only 6 percent said they planned their crimes one or more days in advance. The impulsive tendency is, as Gottfredson and Hirschi claim, remarkably stable. When asked about their most recent crime, 83 percent of those who had not planned their first crime also had not planned their last, while 60 percent of those who had planned their first crime had not planned their last (Wolfgang, Thornberry & Figlio, 1987:126-127).

Given the assumptions of the versions of control theory examined here, it is interesting to contrast the accompanying policy recommendations with those of other criminological theories. Because low self-control is the result of the absence of inhibiting forces typically experienced in early childhood, Gottfredson and Hirschi are pessimistic about the ability of less powerful inhibiting forces (such as the threat of punishment) present in later life to deter crime. They also see little use in seeking to reduce crime by satisfying the wants and needs alleged by other theories to cause crime (reducing poverty, improving neighborhoods, more job opportunities, etc.), because crime's appeal is its provision of immediate gains and minimal cost. People who are attached and who possess self-control will do fine in the job market as it is. In short, "society" is neither the cause nor the solution to the crime problem. The only way to reduce crime, according to this theory, is to strengthen families and improve parenting skills, especially skills involved in teaching self-control to children.

The Family: Nursery of Human Nature

Despite the popularity of both versions of control theory among contemporary American criminologists, neither has escaped criticism. All versions of control theory agree that the family is central to the control and developmental mechanisms that affect criminal behavior. Given this focus, the major criticism is that the social, economic, and political factors that impede stable and nurturing families should be addressed (Lilly, Cullen & Ball, 1995). While I agree with that sentiment completely, control theory concerns itself with the alleged individual-level effects of problematic families, not with the alleged macrolevel causes of the problems faced by modern families. Control theorists stress that the most important aspect of the environment for the healthy prosocial development of human beings is love and nurturance. Because the love and nurturance of children is *typically* best accomplished (in the context of industrial and postindustrial societies) in a two-parent family, it behooves policymakers to do everything they can to strengthen the family. What those things may be, however, is not within the purview of the task control theorists have set for themselves, which is to explain the *consequences* of weak and disrupted families, not why they are disrupted.

The reasons why the family is so important to the healthy behavioral development of children are not fully developed in any variant of control theory. The family is literally the "nursery" of human nature and thus deserves a more fundamental examination. The infant arrives in this world with all the biological equipment it needs to be human, but it is the family that takes hold of the protohuman and helps to mold it into a social being. Despite the importance placed on the family and on the socialization process by sociologists, criminologists outside of the control tradition have typically placed more emphasis on factors such as bad neighborhoods, poverty, subcultural values, peer pressure, gangs, and capitalism as causes of crime. This may be so because, as a number of sociologists on both sides of the ideological fence have pointed out, to support the nuclear family and the traditional values it embodies is a dangerous thing for anyone wanting to be thought of as a "good liberal" (Hirschi, 1995; Popenoe, 1993). Judith Stacey is one of those who wants to bury what she calls the ideology of "the family" as control theorists know it. She states that nontraditional arrangements (single-parent, serial monogamy, and same-sex groupings) are preferable because they are "more egalitarian" (1993:547). Stacey goes on to imply that anyone who supports the nuclear family is classist, racist, sexist, and homophobic. Because control theory was developed in twentieth-century United States, when control theorists write about "the family" and support its strengthening, it is the traditional nuclear family that they have in mind.

In taking this position, Stacey betrays an ignorance of the evolutionary origins of the family. This ignorance is of concern to biologically oriented sociologists such as Alice Rossi. Rossi argues that the kind of "egalitarianism underlying current research on, and advocacy of, 'variant' marriage and family forms is inadequate and misleading because it neglects some fundamental human characteristics rooted in our biological inheritance" (1977:2). Sociologists Brigitte Berger and Peter Berger (1984:188-189) are also cognizant of the evolutionary history of the family:

> We do know enough about the biological constitution of *Homo sapiens* to be able to say that in many areas of behavior it acts as a tendency, rather than a compelling determi-

nant—and there seems little doubt about a tendency toward the centrality of the father-mother-child triad. In other words, the triad may be biologically "natural" even though it is not institutionalized in the child-rearing practices of the Mumbumbu tribe, say in New Guinea, and of some lesbian communes in New Hampshire.

THE EVOLUTION OF THE FAMILY

Berger and Berger's implicit assumption that the nuclear family is the only natural family form is not supported by the anthropological evidence. It is probably true that male parental investment was crucial for human evolution, but evolutionary psychologists do not assume that male investment occurs only in the context of the nuclear family. They recognize that there is a variety of reproductive and childrearing strategies cataloged in the anthropological literature and that family forms respond to ecological, economic, and cultural contingencies. Natural selection has provided us with "a set of dispositions regarding mating and kin behavior, and these interact with differing social environments to produce a variety of family systems" (M. Smith, 1987:232). In evolutionary terms, the "best" family form is that which optimally nurtures and protects its progeny to reproductive age. That depends on prevailing conditions, which may favor different family forms under different ecological conditions. Nevertheless, the optimal family rearing environment is always one in which children are surrounded by many consanguineous individuals, which was probably the case for most of our species' history as hunters and gatherers. Unfortunately, such an arrangement does not fit the economic and social requirements of modern postindustrial societies. Such societies are thus left with the nuclear family (a relatively isolated group composed of mother, father, and child[ren]) as that which "works best . . . to produce offspring who grow up to be both autonomous and socially responsible, while also meeting the adult needs for intimacy and personal adjustment" (Popenoe, 1994:94).

Given that the nuclear family as we know it is a fairly recent cultural invention, it cannot be an adaptation. The term *nuclear*, however, is aptly chosen because the triad of man, women, and children is the core, or nucleus, around which the web of kinship manifested in its various family forms revolves. This nucleus has been characterized as "the prototypical human social organization" (MacDonald, 1992:754) that can satisfy human needs for comfort, security, protection, and love. The man/woman/child triad is thus the minimal core of the "expected environment" of rearing for the human species (Scarr, 1993) and thus is an adaptation even if the nuclear family per se is not.

Again, this does not imply that the bonded man/woman/child triad is the only natural family form. Nor does it imply that the human species' natural reproductive strategy is monogamy. We cannot have evolved to be pure monogamists any more than we could have evolved to be pure cooperators, because such a population would have been highly vulnerable to invasion by promiscuous cheats. Reproductive strategies involve parenting strategies as well as mating strategies, and as already emphasized, these depend (individual differences aside) on environmental conditions. *Homo sapiens* evolved largely during the Pleistocene epoch in small hunter-gatherer kin groups in conditions characterized by low fertility, low mortality, and monogamous mating, coupled with high biparental investment and prolonged, intimate, and intense contact between parents and child (Draper & Harpending, 1988). We evolved the deep mental structures that we operate with today under these conditions (Chisholm, 1996; MacDonald, 1992, 1995; Panksepp, 1992; Rossi, 1997). Human infants are the most altricial of all infants, which means that they require care for much time before they become mature; therefore, a male would have been considered an important source of parental investment by women in our ancestral environments.

Biparental care is rarely found in nature, however. When it is, it is typically found in species in which offspring remain highly dependent for a long time, where food procurement is somewhat problematic, and in which rates of predation are neither too high nor too low (Clutton-Brock, 1991; Lancaster & Lancaster, 1987; Low, 1998). Pair bonding will be selected for, then, when the help of a male positively influences the probability of offspring survival by procuring food for lactating mothers and defending mother and child against predation. In precocial (quickly maturing) species with ready access to food, and with predation rates so high or so low that male parental investment is unlikely to have any positive effect on offspring survival, pair bonding is not necessary, and therefore no evolutionary pressures were exerted for its selection (Low, 1998).

THE EVOLUTION OF PROXIMATE MECHANISMS OF ATTACHMENT

The importance of attachment in terms of brain development was reviewed in Chapter 4. It is briefly reviewed here in terms of how human male/female pair bonding probably facilitated the development of mother/infant attachment in ancestral environments. The scenario outlined by theorists of family evolution is long and meandering. The presentation here is limited to the barest possible outline. Readers should refer to Chapter 4 for a broader explanation of some of the less familiar concepts.

The evolution of *Homo sapiens* from a simple social species into a *cultural* species required ever-increasing levels of parental investment, because humans were being selected for intelligence and, hence, for larger brains and head size. This conflicted with selection for bipedalism, a conflict that manifested itself in the cephalo-pelvic disproportion problem because the selection for bipedalism set morphological limits on the female pelvis. As we have seen, the partial solution to this problem was selection for exterogestation, which meant an extremely long period of dependency for human infants. This dependency, as well as human neoteny, allows for the behavioral flexibility of human beings and for the development of culture.

The long period of dependency required selection for strong bonds (attachment) between mother and infant, and this extra demand on females produced selective pressure for male/female bonding. Males and females who bonded to provide joint parental investment increased the probability of their offspring surviving to reproductive age, and thus improved their own reproductive success. We can therefore view the family unromantically as a reciprocal arrangement in which two people agree to cooperate in the propagation of each other's genes. Our species' propensity to form child-rearing units is thus an evolutionary adaptation in the fullest sense of the word (Fisher, 1992).

Evolutionary scenarios relating to the selection for female/infant and male/female attachment extend over millions of years, during which many mechanisms for the intensification of mothering and for male/female emotional involvement were tried, added to, or discarded. These mechanisms need not have been explicitly designed by natural selection to serve the particular function of maternal intensification or for the mechanisms underlying male/female bonding. Nature is parsimonious in that it frequently makes one mechanism serve a variety of tasks. For intensification of the nurturant or attachment emotions, any physiological system associated with feelings of joy or satisfaction, in whatever sense, could have been pressed into service.

The two kinds of affective bonds are mother/infant and male/female, which are both similar and different. Both involve an active concern for the well-being of another, but they also involve different motivational systems and goals. Mother/infant bonds had to exist in prehominid times, albeit in less intensive forms, but prehominid mating was probably bereft of emotional involvement. Unlike male/female love, mother/infant love must be unconditional, for the infant is incapable of meeting any conditions. Male/female love is very much conditional and need not *necessarily* be maintained after offspring survival is unproblematic.

Attachment is similar to MacDonald's concept of *warmth*, which he defines as "a [biological] reward system which evolved to facilitate cohesive family relationships and parental investment in children"

(1992:753). Panksepp (1992:559) also views all kinds of human affective experience as emerging "from ancient neurosymbolic systems of the mammalian brain that unconditionally promote survival." As we saw in Chapter 4, much of our knowledge about the importance of attachment for normal primate development has come from maternal-deprivation studies. These studies point to the consequences of nonattachment, but say little about what the specific neurohormonal mechanisms are that demand the formation of affectual bonds.

Whatever the proximate mechanisms of mother/infant may be, they will most likely be dependent on the permutation of several factors, probably organized by the birthing process itself, and consolidated by mother/infant contact and interaction during the immediate postpartum period (Rossi, 1984). A major candidate for such a mechanism is the neuropeptide oxytocin. Oxytocin is synthesized in the hypothalamus and is stimulated by environmental events. The most important of these events are the birthing process, infant distress, breastfeeding, and sexual behavior (Insel, 1992; Svensson, 1992). A number of studies involving a variety of mammalian species have shown that administering exogenous oxytocin increases maternal behavior, and that administering oxytocin antagonists reduces it (Insel, 1992). Breastfeeding, for instance, combines the panoply of sight, sound, smell, and touch, as well as the tangible evidence in a mother's arms that stimulates the release of oxytocin, which intensifies the feeling component of the behavior that released it. The oxytocin secreted by breastfeeding is related to reduced sensitivity to environmental stressors, which allows for greater sensitivity to the infant. Lactating mothers show significantly fewer stress responses to infant stimuli, as determined by skin conductance and cardiac-response measures, than nonlactating mothers. They also show significantly greater desire to pick up their infants in response to all infant-presented stimuli (Weisenfeld et al., 1985).

It should be noted that the distribution of oxytocin receptors in the brain is highly related to the ecology of the species being studied. For instance, prairie voles (small rodents) follow a monogamous mating system in which males and females share a nest and show high levels of parental care, while montane voles, a closely related species, follow a polygynous mating system with no nest sharing and very little maternal investment. Maternal behavior in the montane vole appears only in the postpartum period, when there is a temporary increase in oxytocin receptors. Prairie vole mothers, who are parental throughout their lives, maintain high concentrations of oxytocin receptors at all times (Insel, 1992; Shapiro & Insel, 1990).

Oxytocin may even have the effect of decreasing care-inhibiting testosterone in new fathers in monogamous rodent species. Testosterone is responsible for significant sexual dimorphism in the medial preoptic area (MPOA), an area of the hypothalamus important in the control of maternal behavior. New fathers in one biparental rodent species (*Peromyscus californicus*) undergo changes in the MPOA that render it more anatomically similar to the female MPOA than to the same area in nonpaternal males (Gubernick, Sengelaub & Kurtz, 1993). These findings do not mean that an analogous process occurs among human fathers, or even among other biparental species. What they do mean is that natural selection works on mechanisms important to parenting in males to the degree that their participation in parenting is required to raise offspring to reproductive maturity.

We may safely conclude that attachment is as normal and natural a need as is the need for food and drink. Natural selection has provided us with neurohormonal mechanisms that lead us (infants, children, and adults) to want, and expect to be, attached to others because of the vital survival role attachment has played over our evolutionary history. If we are able to look at it this way, there would be less controversy about the importance of the family.

Disruption of the Pair Bond

Cultural rules regarding anything related to survival and reproduction tend to reflect evolutionary logic. Perhaps one of the first cultural rules ever laid out by our species were rules about who has sexual access to whom, and one of the first cultural ceremonies may have been the marriage ceremony. Marriage may have originated with the recognition of the importance of the family in rearing healthy offspring to reproductive age: "Marital alliance and biparental care are part of the human adaptation" (Daly & Wilson, 1988a:187). The family is thus as much a biological as a cultural phenomenon; that is, a product of gene/culture coevolution. As such, we should expect significant social problems to arise when it is disrupted.

We only have to delve a little into recent history to see what becomes of the young when the family is in disarray. One of the goals of Marxism was to destroy the "bourgeois" nuclear family because it was considered a property-based notion that exploited women. After the Russian Revolution, the Communist Party of the Soviet Union passed legislation that legitimized unmarried cohabitation and the offspring of such, made divorce available on demand, and encouraged "free love" as the "essence of communist living" (Hazard, Butler & Maggs, 1977:470). The cost of the "reforms" in human terms was staggering. The practice of free love is incompatible with pair-bonding and biparental care throughout the animal kingdom (Clutton-Brock, 1991). The encouragement of divorce, and the legitimization of out-of-wedlock births, resulted in thousands of fatherless children roaming the streets who "formed into gangs, and who would rob and attack people in the street, or even invade and ransack apartment blocks" (Hosking, 1985:213). After assessing the damage, the Soviet government quickly responded with new laws extolling the family, the sanctity of marriage, the evils of divorce, and the joys of parenthood. They also made divorce more difficult to obtain and restored the legal concepts of legitimacy and illegitimacy (Hosking, 1985).

A similar attack on the nuclear family occurred in China after its revolution, followed by the same rapid about-face when confronted with the consequences (Fletcher, 1991:143). Perhaps more than all of the social science studies of family disruption put together, these two "natural experiments" should tell us something about the importance of the family for the development of healthy prosocial human beings. As Alfred Blumstein (1995:12), the "guru of demographics," put it, "teenage mothers, single-parent households, divorced households, unwed mothers" all constitute high risk for criminality "and certainly don't bode well for the future of the nation."

What is the evidence that family disruption translates into an elevated risk of criminality in modern Western societies? A review of 116 studies (Ellis, 1988) found that 97 (84%) reported a significant positive relationship between divorce/separation and crime and delinquency (the remaining findings were null). Another review by Loeber and Stouthamer-Loeber (1986) identified four different kinds of family influences on delinquency: *neglect, conflict, parental deviancy*, and *disruption,* all of which support both versions of control theory discussed here.

Neglect

Parental neglect contributes to the emergence of antisocial behavior due to insufficient interest and concern displayed by parents regarding their offspring's behavior. Neglectful parents are not involved with their children, are "permissive" about their activities, and in neglectful families there is little intimacy of communication or affectual identification between parents and children. Neglect (as measured by parental involvement with and/or supervision of children) emerged among the most powerful predictors in the studies reviewed, with 85 percent of the 80 studies showing a significant relationship between parental neglect and behavior problems.

Conflict

Conflict refers to escalating patterns of negative interactions between parents and children, which may be initiated by a child's chronic disobedience or by overly strict or inconsistent punishment.

Conflict may be the result of neglect because, having learned that parents are not particularly concerned about their behavior most of the time, children are confused and angered when parents do express some form of disapproval. Alternatively, neglect may follow conflict when parents, despite their best efforts, cannot effectively control temperamentally difficult, moody, and aggressive children. In families characterized by excessive conflict, parents and children will have a low opinion of each other and may reject each other, which may fuel further conflicts. Parents' rejection of the child or the child's rejection of parents had the strongest influence on delinquency, with 91 percent of the studies showing a significant effect.

Parental Deviance

Deviant influence refers to parental modeling of criminal and deviant behavior, either directly via their behavior, or by the transmission of antisocial values and attitudes. Deviant families facilitate antisocial behavior both by failing to inhibit it via adequate supervision and by providing offspring with attitudes and values favorable to it. Ninety-three percent of the studies examined by Loeber and Stouthamer-Loeber (1986) found a significant relationship between parental criminal behavior and deviant attitudes and offspring offending. Perhaps more interesting from the point of view of parental transmission of criminal behavior are the findings of a longitudinal study of 400 lower-SES British families (Farrington, 1996). This study found that just 16 (0.4%) of the families (characterized as "large-sized, multiproblem" families) accounted for 50 percent of the recorded convictions for all 400 families.

A troubling pointer to the possibility of intergenerational transmission of criminal behavior (and low SES) is assortative mating for antisocial behavior by parents of deviant children. This implies genetic transmission of traits associated with antisocial behavior, something that Gottfredson and Hirschi do not acknowledge. For example, Rowe and Farrington (cited in Rutter, 1996:19) found a correlation of 0.50 between husbands' and wives' criminal convictions in Britain, and an American study found substantial correlations (average $r = .54$) between husbands and wives for a variety of antisocial traits (Krueger et al., 1998). Krueger and his colleagues interpret this as creating "criminal families" via the effects of active and passive G/E correlation. The assortative mating process is active G/E correlation ("niche picking") in the parental generation and passive G/E correlation in the offspring generation. (See Chapter 3.) Assortative mating increases the probability of offspring receiving both paternal and maternal genes for traits that make them vulnerable to antisocial behavior, as well as a criminogenic home environment. In addition to the additive effects of the "double dose" of genetic and environmental factors, they may have effects greater than the sum of their parts (gene X environment interaction). Thus, nature and nurture "become a tightly tied bundle" (Krueger et al., 1998:183). The intergenerational transmission of antisocial behavior must therefore be considered at least partially attributable to genetics.

Disruption

Disruption refers to serious changes in normal family structure or processes that generate stress. Examples include chronic spousal stress, loss of employment, and the breakup of the family unit by divorce, desertion, or death. Disruption can lead to conflict, or conflict can lead to disruption, but either way, family disruption is related to antisocial behavior. Negative spousal relationship (marital discord) was significantly related to offspring offending in 77 percent of the analyses, and parental absence (broken home) in 82 percent.

No single factor examined in Loeber and Stouthamer-Loeber's review operates in isolation from other factors. "At risk" families suffer multiple handicaps that are cumulative and interactive, with each being a possible cause and a possible effect of the other. For instance, poor supervision can lead to antisocial conduct, which can lead to parent-child conflict, then to spousal conflict, which ultimately may lead to divorce. In fact, we may start with any of the factors mentioned and trace a long and complicated series of possible consequences leading to or from offspring offending.

"Broken Homes"

"Broken homes" have long been implicated in antisocial behavior, more strongly in studies looking at serious offenses than in self-report studies of minor misbehavior. A 1991 survey of 669,578 state prison inmates found that only 43.1 percent lived with both parents for most of the time while growing up, compared with 68.5 percent of the general population (U.S. Department of Justice, 1993). "Broken home" is often a convenient label for a number of problems preceding it, but the family fracture itself can be a precipitating factor in explaining antisocial behavior via a number of routes, such as offspring resentment, decreased supervision, or increased parent/child conflict. When traits of children from broken homes are measured or compared with those of children from intact homes, the children from broken homes tend to exhibit more traits favorable to offending and fewer favorable to conformity than do the latter. The overall conclusion from a meta-analysis of 92 studies comparing children from broken and intact homes was that children from broken homes had significantly poorer psychological adjustment, lower self-esteem, and poorer academic achievement and social relations (Amato & Keith, 1991a). Another meta-analysis of 33 studies of adult children of divorced parents concluded that children of divorced parents had significantly more psychological maladjustment and marital instability than adults reared in intact homes (Amato & Keith, 1991b).

This is not meant to unequivocally condemn divorce. There are many cases in which divorce is more beneficial to both parents and children than is remaining in an unhealthy marriage, but we should not confuse variation with central tendency. The consequences of not being reared in a two-parent family *range* from positive to negative, but the *central tendency* is negative.

We must also be careful about attributing children's negative behaviors to the effects of divorce per se, given the fairly robust findings that the heritability of divorce is around 0.50 (Jockin, McGue & Lykken, 1996; McGue & Lykken, 1992). There is, of course, no divorce gene any more than there is a crime gene. The coefficient is the result of people with traits (insensitivity, aggressiveness, impulsiveness, etc.) that increase the likelihood of unfavorable outcomes in other areas of their lives. These traits make them difficult to live with and increase the probability of divorce. Because parents pass these traits to their children genetically, their children are susceptible to antisocial behavior because of their inherited traits, not because of their parents' divorce. This does not mean that all, or even most, divorced people possess these negative traits. Marriage is a mix of two people that produces a situation-specific "third personality," which is not necessarily predictable from the personalities each bring to it.

A home broken by divorce suggests a fair amount of marital discord prior to the breakup, but less so than one broken by desertion; a home broken by death tells us nothing about family dynamics. How and when a home is broken are thus important considerations. Studies tend to show that boys from homes broken by divorce and desertion are more likely than boys from intact homes to become delinquent, but boys from homes broken by death are not (West & Farrington, 1977). A study comparing violence levels among officially defined delinquents found that boys from families broken by desertion were significantly more violent than boys from intact homes or homes broken by death or divorce, and that boys from homes broken by death were less violent than boys from any other type of family structure (Heck & Walsh, 2000).

Children experiencing a home broken at an early age may be more affected than children experiencing it at a later age (Behar & Stewart, 1982). Early family disruption implies a longer period of lax supervision during a crucial period of socialization, while later disruption may occur after the child's basic disposition vis-à-vis offending (e.g., low self-control) has already been formed (Goldstein, 1984). A reconstituted household, however, may have more negative effects than if the care-taking parent (usually the mother) had remained unmarried. Children from divorced homes whose mothers remarried tend to be more delinquent than children from broken homes whose mothers remained unmarried, probably because of parent/child conflict due to resentment of stepparents (Zingraff et al., 1993).

A broken home typically implies father absence, but perhaps the negative effects of father absence are primarily the result of its non-normativeness in Western societies. However, similar effects of father absence are found in prestate polygynous cultures, where children *typically* grow up in mother-child households separate from their fathers. As Ember and Ember (1998:14) put it, "Societies in which children are reared in mother-child households or the father spends little time in child care tend to have more physical violence by males than do societies in which fathers are mostly around." They go on to speculate that a father-absence upbringing breeds a "supermasculine" male identity. Draper and Harpending (1988) note that the same hypermasculinity (or "protest masculinity," as they call it) is observed in modern Western societies where father absence is non-normative (although it has become typical in some subcultures). Father absence also negatively affects females, bringing with it a heightened risk for premature and promiscuous sexuality and for unwed motherhood. According to conditional adaptation theory (discussed in Chapter 3), a female strategy emphasizing sexuality rather than fidelity is calibrated by early environmental experiences conveying the message that interpersonal relationships are ephemeral and untrustworthy (Draper & Harpending, 1982, 1988, Rossi, 1997; Walsh, 1995b, 1999).

THE EVOLUTIONARY CONTEXT OF CHILD ABUSE AND NEGLECT

An evolutionary explanation for child abuse and neglect is almost a contradiction in terms; after all, evolution by natural selection is all about preserving genetic material. Nevertheless, taking advantage of the theoretical insights provided by evolutionary theory may enhance our understanding of these behaviors by pointing to the conditions under which they occur in other species.

The probability of abuse, neglect, and infanticide among nonhuman animals increases when the food supply is low, when the litter size is large, when an infant has low reproductive viability, and, in biparental species, when the female lacks the assistance of a mate (Allman, 1994;

Ellis & Walsh, 1997). These are the same conditions under which most human incidences of abuse, neglect, and infanticide occur; that is, under conditions of poverty, within large and single-parent families, and against children who are physically or mentally handicapped (Daly & Wilson, 1988a; Ellis & Walsh, 1997; Gelles, 1991).

Killing offspring under such conditions may have enhanced the killers' inclusive fitness in ancestral environments in several ways. When human ancestral mothers had too many mouths to feed with available resources, lacked a mate, or had children who were unlikely to contribute to the family well-being because of illness or deformity, a "triage" strategy may have been the best one available. A triage strategy would have increased the probability of the survival of the most reproductively viable of the offspring, while a strategy of trying to nurture each offspring equally may have resulted in the survival of none. Legalities, morality, and politics aside, these conditions are often the very same conditions that lead women to decide to seek an abortion (Lamanna, 1985), which from an evolutionary point of view may be considered the functional equivalent of infanticide.

A good proportion of infanticidal behavior is either performed or instigated by males who are genetically unrelated to the victim. In many primate species, a new male claiming a female commences to kill any offspring sired by her previous mate (reviewed in Van Hooff, 1990). Killing infants puts an end to breastfeeding and prompts the female's return to estrus, thus providing the new male an opportunity to produce his own offspring (Hrdy, 1980). Human males acquiring wives with dependent children may also kill any children from a previous relationship in a number of prestate cultures (Daly & Wilson, 1988b). Although this increases the genetic fitness of the killers at the expense of the fitness of the fathers of the victims, males in these societies are no more aware of this fact than are nonhuman animals. Infanticide may have had some positive fitness consequences in ancestral environments, but as Symons points out, infanticide per se is not an adaptation, but "rather the general mechanisms of emotion [parental solicitude] and cognition [cost/benefit calculations within a stressful context] that are the adaptations, regardless of infanticide's effect on reproductive success" (1987:140). The mental mechanism behind much male-initiated infanticide is probably: "Don't waste precious resources on children for whom I have no warm feelings."

Children in modern state societies are also at greater risk for maltreatment when not raised by both biological parents. Although the vast majority of stepparents do not maltreat or kill their stepchildren, the risk of such treatment is greatly elevated in stepfamilies. In a Canadian study, Daly and Wilson (1985) found that stepchildren were between nine and 25 times more likely (depending on age, with the risk being greater the younger the child) to be abused than children residing with both biological parents. Although the killing of children by step-parents is extremely rare, a child living with a stepparent (typically a stepfather or live-in boyfriend) is approximately 65 times more likely to be fatally abused than a child living with both biological parents (Daly & Wilson, 1996).

Perhaps the dominant social science model of intrafamily homicide is the intimate contact hypothesis, whereby homicide is explained by the fact that family members are frequently in "striking distance" of one another. Ketalar and Ellis (2000) examine and reject this notion, stating that if intrafamilial homicide simply followed the "striking distance" rule, then genetic and nongenetic family members would be equally at risk for homicide. This is never the case, and the fact that it is not provides excellent evidence for the usefulness of Darwinian thinking applied to social science data. In Darwinian terms, stepparenting is a fitness reducer and a chore reluctantly undertaken as a condition for gaining access to the child's mother's reproductive potential or the father's resources.

Stepparenting also significantly increases the risk of sexual abuse of stepchildren, with stepfathers being at least five times more likely to sexually abuse their daughters than biological fathers (Finkelhor, 1984; Glaser & Frosh, 1993). Stepfathers or live-in boyfriends of mothers may find their stepdaughters as sexually desirable as any other nongenetically related female. Close physical proximity early in life appears to be the evolved mechanism that triggers the incest avoidance mechanism that dulls sexual attraction between individuals, genetically related or not (Thornhill & Thornhill, 1987; van den Berghe, 1987). The later a stepfather enters the lives of genetically unrelated females, then, the greater the likelihood that he will be sexually attracted to them.

The stepparent/stepchild relationship is more tenuous than the biological parent/child relationship because it does not rest on the firm basis of early bonding and therefore not on the mutual trust, nurturance, and solicitude that such a relationship engenders. In decrying the ever-decreasing number of children who live with both biological parents, Robert Wright (1994:104) remarks: "[W]henever marital institutions . . . are allowed to dissolve, so that divorce and unwed motherhood are rampant, and many children no longer live with both natural parents, there will ensue a massive waste of the most precious evolutionary resource: love."

THE BIOLOGY OF LOW SELF-CONTROL

A major criticism of self-control theory is that it wrongly attributes variation in self-control solely to variation in parental behavior. The theory ignores child effects on parental behavior as outlined in the concept of reactive G/E correlation (Shaw & Bell, 1993).

The theory also ignores the biology of self-control. Gottfredson and Hirschi present a negative view of biological explanations in criminology, stating that "biology connotes fixation, immutability, or even destiny" (1990:135). Yet, in the penultimate sentence in their book, they state, "The study of crime is too important to be diverted by arguments about theory ownership or discipline boundaries" (1990:275). Their first assertion is patently untrue, and their second assertion—unless they want to make an exception in the case of biology—indicates that they would, at least in spirit, welcome assistance from outside sociology in their quest for a general theory of crime. For example, a frequently voiced criticism of self-control theory is that it is tautological in that it does not provide measures of low self-control that are independent of the tendency to commit crime, which is what low self-control is supposed to explain: "low self-control causes low self-control" (Akers, 1994:123). Incorporating biological measures of self-control into the theory would be one way of rescuing it from this alleged weakness.

Calling Gottfredson and Hirschi's assertion that crime proneness can be explained by a single tendency "simplistic psychologically," Caspi and his colleagues (1994:187) contend that crime proneness is defined (at a minimum) by both low self-control (which they call low constraint) and negative emotionality. Constraint is negatively associated with negative emotionality, the tendency to experience many situations as aversive, and to react to them with irritation and anger more readily than with positive affective states (McGue, Bacon & Lykken, 1993). Negative emotionality has been found to be strongly related to self-reported and officially recorded criminality "across countries, genders, races, and methods" (Caspi et al., 1994). Individuals high on negative emotionality but also high on self-control are able to hold their anger and irritability at abeyance, but if a person high on negative affect is also low on self-control, the risk for violent behavior is high.

Impulsiveness, a synonym for (or at least a central component of) Hirschi and Gottfredson's concept of low self-control, has been found to be moderately to strongly heritable (Caspi et al., 1994; Lykken, 1995). It has also been strongly associated with low levels of the serotonin metabolite CSF 5-HIAA in human and nonhuman animals (Bernhardt, 1997; Spoont, 1992). As previously noted, various studies have estimated the heritability of serotonin levels to be between .55 and .66 (Goldman, Lappalainen & Ozaki, 1996; Hur & Bouchard, 1997). In the discussion of reward dominance theory found in Chapter 2, it was shown that serotonin is a modulator of behavior. Low serotonin turnover (a weak BIS) is like having a brain with defective brakes, resulting in a runaway emotional train (a strong BAS) that all too frequently fails to think before acting. Low serotonin, therefore, "may be a heritable diathesis for a personality style involving high levels of negative affect and low levels of constraint, which generates in turn a vulnerability to criminal behavior" (Caspi et al., 1994:188).

Although some individuals may be at greater genetic risk for higher negative emotionality and lower self-control than others, both traits are influenced by environmental factors. Neurologically, both traits appear to be a function of low serotonin, but as noted earlier, serotonin turnover rates reflect, as well as affect, environmental events (Raleigh et al., 1991). Caspi and his colleagues (1994) maintain that both negative affect and low constraint in children are affected by family dynamics that include emotional and physical abuse and neglect. The effects of abuse and neglect on the behavioral activating and inhibiting systems and on the prefrontal cortex were discussed in Chapter 4. At a minimum, then, Gottfredson and Hirschi's self-control theory would benefit from incorporating negative affect into their theory, by acknowledging that both it and low self-control are heritable and that serotonin turnover underlies both traits.

AGE IN SELF-CONTROL THEORY

Gottfredson and Hirschi contend that the age effect on crime and delinquency is basically inexplicable because it is an invariant phenomenon across time and space. They are suspicious of situational explanations of the effect because they contend that, as a stable characteristic of individuals, self-control leads people to involve or not involve themselves differentially in situations leading to antisocial behavior (1990:139). Put differently, Gottfredson and Hirschi feel that the age curve is a "law of nature" and that it presents a major problem for sociological criminology theories. These theories attempt to explain the rise in antisocial behavior at adolescence by emphasizing an increase in peer involvement during this period, and the decline thereafter by the decreasing influence of peers and the acquisition of girlfriends, wives, children, and jobs. The problem, say Gottfredson and Hirschi (1990:141), is that "the offender tends to convert these institutions into sources of satisfaction consistent with his previous criminal behavior . . . there is no drastic reshuffling of the criminal and noncriminal populations based on unpredictable, situational events."

Gottfredson and Hirschi believe that most criminological theories are unable to explain the age effect adequately because they conflate the concepts of crime (the prevalence of which changes with age) and criminality (which is stable across ages). Because the age effect is invariant (a constant) across time and place, they believe that criminologists should simply accept it as a fact and go on about other business. Thus, they seem to be saying that only criminality (which they equate with low self-control) needs explaining. In asserting this, they appear to concur with Terrie Moffitt (1993) that there are two types of delinquents: the age-dependent (Moffitt's AL offender) and the stable (Moffitt's LCP offender), but they are apparently only interested in the latter. Recall that Moffitt also stresses the stability of traits conducive to antisocial conduct across ages and situations, but she does not ignore age effects.

To maintain that the age effect cannot be explained just because sociological criminology cannot explain it is to ignore a vital component of the crime problem. As shown in the previous chapter, endocrinology and neuroscience provide excellent explanations for the changes in the probability of antisocial behavior for youths who start offending at adolescence and then desist. The only reasons for ignoring age effects are ignorance of the relevant literature in those disciplines (which is rectifiable), or ideology (which may not be).

A biosocial analysis of control theory leads to the same conclusion regarding persistent criminality as do analyses of the DASL tradition: Persistent offenders are "biologically different from the adolescent offender who stops at age 18-21" (Jeffery, 1993:494). Whether we concentrate on overall temperament or on specifics such as low self-control, negative emotionality, or cognitive deficits, we arrive at an image of a small set of offenders who are difficult to socialize. They suffer the double liability of being born to parents who tend to have temperaments unsuitable for the task of providing adequate socialization of them and who have provided them with a set of genes biasing their development in negative directions. If anything deducible from Gottfredson and Hirschi's theory is to be done to divert at-risk children from the trajectory they are on, it is to implement nurturant strategies within families and to do everything we can to strengthen those families.

Chapter 8

Human Ecology / Social
Disorganization and Race

The human ecology/social disorganization tradition is the most sociological of criminological theories because it was explicitly formulated to exclude "kinds of people" explanations of crime. As such, it is the theory most compatible with evolutionary psychology. Although human ecology and evolutionary psychology differ in their assumptions about human nature, human ecology also drew its theoretical sustenance from the writings of Charles Darwin (Voss & Petersen, 1976). The intent of the early human, or social, ecologists was to "achieve a thorough-going natural science treatment of human behavior" (Hawley, 1944:400), an ambition that was sidetracked by cultural determinists bent on thwarting such an intention. According to Amos Hawley (1950:6), the core of human ecology's conceptual debt to Darwinism lay in three main points:

> Scientific [human] ecology, then, is indebted to Darwin for the main outlines of its theory, the essential conceptions being: (1) the web of life in which organisms are adjusted or are seeking adjustment to one another, (2) the adjustment process as a struggle for existence, and (3) the environment comprising a highly complex set of conditions of adjustment.

Ecology is a term used in biology to describe the interrelations of living organisms and their environment; that is, how they affect and are affected by one another. Sociological ecologists use the term *human ecology* to describe the interrelations of human beings and the physical and cultural environments in which they live. Early human ecologists viewed the city as a kind of superorganism, with "natural areas" differentially adaptive for different ethnic groups, hence the formation of "little Italys," "Chinatowns," and so forth. These theorists saw successive waves of different ethnic groups in certain city neighborhoods displace the former inhabitants and noted the criminogenic consequences. They likened this process to the biological processes of invasion, dominance, and succession, which describe the course of occupation of ecological niches by species of plant and animal life previously alien to them.

The ecological school of criminology was developed at the University of Chicago in the 1920s and 1930s, primarily through the works of Clifford Shaw and Henry McKay (1972). Although Shaw and McKay focused primarily on Chicago, the so-called "Chicago school" applied their theories and methods to a variety of American cities. In their analysis of Cook County Juvenile Court records spanning the years from 1900 to 1933, they noted that the majority of delinquents came from the same neighborhoods regardless of the ethnic composition of those neighborhoods. This suggested the existence of "natural areas" that may be facilitative of crime and delinquency independent of other (especially individual-level) factors. Otherwise stated, there may be certain areas possessing characteristics that persist over the decades that infect individuals exposed to them in ways that increase the likelihood of antisocial behavior regardless of their race or ethnicity. Shaw and McKay did not assert that place of residence was a necessary and sufficient cause of antisocial behavior. Rather, they strove to explain why crime and delinquency were so heavily concentrated in certain neighborhoods without having to address "kinds of people" issues (Stark, 1996:139). In common with evolutionary psychology, then, human ecology concerns itself with central tendency rather than variation.

Human ecology and evolutionary psychology are in broad agreement that crime and delinquency are normal behaviors arising out of abnormal circumstances. They also agree that humans are social beings who know that they can realize their self-interests most readily by cooperating (reciprocal altruism) than by not cooperating. When "aliens" invade "natural areas," opportunities are increased for non-cooperators (cheats) to exploit cooperators. Examining how niches for antisocial behavior come to be is what ecological theory is all about. Thus, both theories examine how antisocial behavior is amplified or constrained by the physical and social setting in which it is found.

The Chicago school of social ecology readily acknowledged that its theory was about explaining rates of crime and delinquency and not individual involvement in such behaviors, and viewed antisocial conduct as a by-product of urban growth and decay. Previous work in social ecology characterized the spatial patterns of American cities as radiating outward from central business and industrial areas in a series of concentric circles or *ecological zones* (Park, Burgess & McKenzie, 1925). The Loop area of Chicago (downtown) was surrounded by the factory zone. As business and industry grew, the factory zone invaded the surrounding areas, making them less desirable as residential sites. Housing in these areas rapidly deteriorated, and those who could afford to move to better locations did. Old inner-city neighborhoods in the process of invasion and succession were labeled *transition zones* or *interstitial areas*. These areas became home to the poorest and most recently arrived of the city's families, which were typically foreign immigrants and African-American migrants from the South. This process had a rippling effect, like a stone dropped in a river. Successive waves of newcomers to the poorest neighborhoods precipitated constant movement from zone to zone as more established groups sought to escape the intrusion of the alien newcomers.

Of greatest interest to the Chicago ecologists was the fact that delinquency and crime rates varied predictably and substantially by zone. For instance, for the years 1927 through 1933, Shaw and McKay (1972) reported delinquency rates per 100 males ages 10 to 16 as 9.8 in the poorest zone, decreasing linearly to 1.8 in Zone 5 (the affluent suburbs), revealing an extraordinarily strong Pearson correlation coefficient of $-.978$ between zone and delinquency rate. Thus, different "natural areas," with their distinctive forms of social and physical organization, produced widely varying rates of delinquency. The next task for the human ecologists was to identify possible mechanisms that might explain why life in certain zones is more likely to produce delinquents and criminals than life in other zones. The answer they came up with is *social disorganization*.

SOCIAL DISORGANIZATION

Social disorganization is the key concept of ecological theory. Social disorganization is created by the continuous redistribution of the population in and out of neighborhoods, especially into the transition zones. In ecological terms, this invasion of alien species disrupted the symbiosis that had been established in natural areas. The mix of transient peoples with limited resources, bringing a wide variety of competing cultural traditions to the "melting pot," is not conducive to developing and/or maintaining a sense of community. A system of shared values and rules of conduct transmitted from generation to generation creates the kinds of "warm" social bonds that sociologists have in mind when they speak of a sense of community or a sense of belonging. The conflict of values, interests, practices, and many other issues that arise when culturally heterogeneous groups are thrown together generates social disorganization, which essentially means the breakdown, or serious dilution, of the power of social norms to regulate conduct. Social disorganization is thus a sort of Durkheimian anomie operating at the neighborhood level. Crime and delinquency arise out of social disorganization, which is both a cause and a consequence of the loss of community.

Social disorganization has an impact on crime and delinquency in two ways. The first involves the lack of social control, meaning that social disorganization facilitates crime by failing to inhibit it. Shaw and McKay conceptualized social control as a macro process involving many social institutions affecting people as groups rather than a function of the family and its effect on individuals, as it is in Hirschi's social control theory (Bursik, 1988). Ecologists viewed the control traditionally exercised by communities as a function of their ability to bring members together to organize strategies to combat community problems. Because communities in transition zones were culturally fractured due to in-and-out migration, conventional institutions of control such as the family, church, school, as well as informal neighborhood clubs and voluntary organizations, were unable to exert the proper supervision and control over restless youths living there. Without the kinds of social controls operative in more established and stable communities, slum youths were freed to follow their impulses and inclinations, which, as numerous theorists have long emphasized, do not run in prosocial directions.

The second way that social disorganization contributes to crime and delinquency is the provision of positive incentives to engage in such activities. In the absence of prosocial values, a set of values supporting antisocial behavior is likely to develop to fill the vacuum. Slum youths thus have both negative and positive inducements to crime and delinquency, represented by the absence of social controls and the presence of delinquent values, respectively. These conditions are transmitted across generations until they become, as it were, intrinsic properties of the neighborhood. This brings us to the most important finding from social ecology research: Chicago's transitional neighborhoods always had the highest rates of crime *regardless of the race or ethnicity of the dominant group* (Shaw & McKay, 1972: ch. 6). The same conclusion was reached by Shaw and McKay (1972, Part 3) in six other large American cities.

Findings such as these increased sociological faith in the environmental origins of crime. Individualistic explanations of a neighborhood's high crime rate imply that intrinsic properties of ethnic/racial groups or of individuals are responsible for crime, an idea that sociologists had long resisted. The essential argument against individualistic explanations offered by the ecologists was that if they were true, they should observe changes in relative crime rates (either up or down) across different neighborhoods as different ethnic groups move in and out, but they did not see this. It was reasoned by Shaw and McKay (1972) that if members of ethnic group X living in Zone 1 have consistently higher delinquency rates than members of the same ethnic group living in Zone 5, then it is the area itself, not characteristics of individuals or of their ethnicity, that generates antisocial behavior. Because neighborhoods tend to retain their characteristics regardless of their ethnic composition, according to ecological theorists, there must be something about neighborhoods per se that either promotes or resists crime (Stark, 1996).

The argument is valid as it relates to racial/ethnic group differences, because all members must share any general characteristics used to define those groups. Few would argue that there are *essential* differences between and among racial or ethnic groups that mark some groups as intrinsically antisocial, delinquent, or criminal, and others as intrinsically prosocial and conformist. Group differences in behavior are probably almost entirely structural and cultural in origin, as most evolutionary psychologists and behavior geneticists readily acknowledge. On the other hand, it is hardly valid when applied to individuals. After all, the majority of the inhabitants of even the worst neighborhoods did not acquire criminal records (Shaw & McKay, 1972). Thus, there must be something about individuals also that either promotes or resists crime. Individuals within racial and ethnic groups vary widely on the traits and characteristics that place them differentially at risk for antisocial behavior. Persons from ethnic group X in Zone 5 may be quite different from their counterparts in Zone 1 in terms of intelligence, conscientiousness, arousal levels, or any other trait associated with an increased probability of antisocial behavior. Group X individuals living in Zone 1 doubtless resemble their neighbors with respect to these traits, regardless of their neighbors' ethnicity, far more than they resemble their co-ethnics in Zone 5.

Related to this is an early criticism that the theory assumed a one-way causal relationship between social disorganization and crime. Could the reverse be possible; that is, could crime lead to social disorganization? High crime rates in an area lead to fear, which leads to a drop in community activities, followed by psychological, and finally physical, withdrawal from deteriorating neighborhoods (Bursik, 1988). Consider the following "broken windows" scenario of how a stable neighborhood can change in a very short time into a fearful jungle, beginning with something as minor as an abandoned piece of property:

> A piece of property is abandoned, weeds grow up, windows are smashed. Adults stop scolding rowdy children: the children, emboldened, become more rowdy. Families move out, unattached adults move in. Teenagers gather in front of the corner store. . . . Fights occur. Litter accumulates. People start drinking in front of the grocery . . . [Because of rising perceptions of disorder and crime, people] will use the streets less often. . . . cars will be stripped, drunks will be robbed . . . Muggings will occur (Wilson & Kelling, 1982:32).

Thus, law-abiding people will withdraw from the areas experiencing high levels of antisocial behavior and property values will plummet, which attracts less desirable residents to the neighborhood. This change in the composition of the neighborhood generates even more disorder and crime and delinquency, which leads to further flight from the area, another influx of undesirables, and still more crime. There thus appears to be a reciprocal rather than a unidirectional relationship between social disorganization and crime and other forms of antisocial behavior, with each feeding on the other (Skogan, 1991; Stark, 1996).

MODERN ECOLOGICAL THEORY: PEOPLE OR PLACES?

It is safe to say that all studies in the United States and other nations have supported the most fundamental of ecological theory's propositions; that is, socially disorganized slum neighborhoods have higher rates of crime and delinquency than more affluent and stable neighborhoods. To many, this is merely stating the obvious—and only the first of a number of steps in the epidemiological process. The assertion that the same high rates of crime are found in high-crime neighborhoods regardless of their ethnic or racial composition is more contentious. This brings us to the major issue in modern ecological theory: Are people or places most responsible for crime? Wilson and Kelling's (1982) "broken windows" theory, while acknowledging that certain physical environments invite crime, makes no bones about asserting that people are responsible for the state of those environments.

After a period of prominence lasting into the 1960s, the popularity of ecological theory declined rapidly (Bursik, 1988; Byrne & Sampson, 1986). One of the criticisms that helped to hasten its demise was W. S. Robinson's (1950) concept of *ecological fallacy*, which asserts in part that we cannot validly make inferences about individuals and groups on the basis of information derived from a larger population of which they are a part. Even in the heyday of ecological theory, research indicated that Asian-Americans living in high-crime areas had very low crime rates (Hayner, 1933), a finding supported by many studies, including those of Shaw and McKay themselves (1972). Low Asian crime rates in high-crime neighborhoods suggested to many that the rejection of group and individual differences as explanations for crime and delinquency may have been premature (Vold & Bernard, 1986). Although Shaw and McKay found that the same neighborhoods always had the highest delinquency and crime rates, they ignored differences in rates in these same neighborhoods when different ethnic groups inhabited them. That is, while neighborhood X always had the highest crime rates regardless of its ethnic makeup, perhaps when ethnic group Z was its most populous inhabitant the crime and delinquency rates were significantly higher than when ethnic group Y was its most populous inhabitant. Shaw and McKay (1972) did report differences by ethnic group, but failed to incorporate the data into their theory. To have done so would not necessarily have been an embarrassment to their theory, because it was designed only to explain why antisocial behavior is concentrated in certain areas.

The "people versus places" issue became a key research issue in human ecology in the 1980s, with the disentanglement of individual effects from ecological effects being a major focus (Byrne & Sampson, 1986). Much of this research may have been promoted by Ruth Kornhauser's (1978:104) trenchant question: "How do we know that area differences in delinquency rates result from the aggregated characteristics of communities rather than the characteristics of individuals selectively aggregated into communities." This pointed question implies that some people remain in slum areas, while others leave as soon as they are able, and that the decision to stay or leave may depend as much on individual factors, such as ability and ambition, as on situational factors such as poverty, unemployment, or ill health. The point is that macro-level data are not necessarily generated by macro-level processes, and that causal explanations do not necessarily have to be decided by the unit of analysis. Compositional theorists argue that ecological factors have no independent effect on crime once the human composition of areas (what kinds of people live there) is taken into consideration. Others argue the opposite, while still others argue that people and places are equally important in explaining crime and delinquency (Laub, 1983).

We now call the poorest areas of the United States cities the "inner city." These areas are almost exclusively inhabited by African-Americans. This unfortunate fact has placed something of a damper on the "people versus places" debate (Stark, 1996). As sociologist William Julius Wilson has pointed out, social scientists have tended either to ignore issues attending "the tangle of pathology in the inner city" or to address them in "circumspect ways" (1987:22). Many shy away from dealing forthrightly with matters of race because they are aware of the tendency to label those who do as racists, which has led to "an unproductive mix of controversy and silence" (Sampson & Wilson, 2000:149). The racist label has been applied to such a range of acts (including that of reporting research containing any hint of possibility that it could be construed as unfavorable to minorities) that all meaning has been washed out of the accusation. Lacking in real meaning or not, once applied, it sticks like hot tar and may severely burn a career. Other scientists ignore the subject of race and crime less out of fear than out of a genuine concern that an already disadvantaged group will be further stigmatized. Whatever the reason for avoiding the race/crime issue, it is both ethically and scientifically the wrong thing to do. LaFree and Russell (1993:279) argue that the race/crime connection should be studied honestly and courageously because "no group has suffered more than African-Americans by our failure to understand and control street crime." The corollary of this is that no other group can benefit more from a candid examination of race and crime.

African-Americans constituted 13 percent of the United States population in 1999 (U.S. Bureau of the Census, 2000). If race were not a factor in predicting the probability of criminal behavior, we would observe that arrest rates for African-Americans appear to fluctuate randomly around that percentage. This is not what we see, however. The percentages of blacks arrested for each index crime in 1999 were: murder (53.4%), rape (37.5%), robbery (55.3%), aggravated assault (36.3%), burglary (29.5%), larceny/theft (31.8%), motor vehicle theft (39.2%), and arson (24.2%) (FBI, 2000). Blacks are also overrepresented by a factor of about 2.3:1 in relation to whites in white-collar crimes such as forgery, fraud, and embezzlement (FBI, 2000), and by a factor of about 1.4:1 in hate crimes (FBI, 2000). Black overrepresentation in arrests for all sorts of crimes has been consistently observed as long as crime statistics have been collected (Flowers, 1988:83). Given such figures, it is evident that the race/crime issue cannot be ignored, regardless of its political "sensitivity." As LaFree and Russell (1993:273) put it, "All roads in American criminology eventually lead to issues of race."

Figures such as those cited above could be the result of a racist criminal justice system, and thus reflect systemic biases rather than the actuality of large differences in criminality between the races. Although this has been a stock explanation for some time, studies comparing official arrest data from the Uniform Crime Reports with National Crime Victimization Survey (NCVS) data find that they accord extremely well (Flowers, 1988; Wilson, 1987). For example, about 60 percent of robbery victims describe their assailants as black, and about 60 percent of the suspects arrested for robbery are black (Wilbanks, 1987). Additionally, ever since at least the 1930s, black females have had a higher homicide rate than white males. These women typically kill spouses and partners in self-defense situations, which makes it extremely difficult to blame police bias for their arrest. The consensus among criminologists who have researched the issue is that the black/white arrest ratio is primarily (perhaps entirely) due to racial differences in crime participation (Blumstein & Cohen, 1987).

If crime statistics accurately reflect actual differences in racial patterns of criminal behavior, the question then becomes *why*? Racism, as reflected in fewer educational and economic opportunities for blacks, has often been cited as the prime mover behind black crime rates. No one would deny that blacks have historically had to bear heavier crosses than other races and ethnic groups. Yet, an analysis of crime, education, and labor statistics in the United States from 1957 through 1988 found that black crime rates rose even as black income and educational attainment rose (LaFree, Drass & O'Day, 1992). According to this study, similar increases in white income and educational attainment led to a decrease in white crime rates. Curiously, opportunity structure variables appear to have had opposite effects on blacks and on whites. The increase of crime rates among blacks during the 30-year period of black political, legal, economic, and educational gain renders it difficult to maintain the simplistic notion that white racism is the cause of black crime. Effects should be proportionate to their causes, and it is arguable that the undeniable disabilities suffered by previous generations of blacks are adequate to account for the current high level of black crime. As one sociologist put it:

> Although it would be naive to suggest that slavery, racism, deprivation, and related factors American blacks have uniquely endured have not had at least some negative effect on behavior within this group, the fault of the theory is that it cannot adequately explain why blacks would be affected more by their victimization and injustice than other ethnic minorities, such as American Indians and Chinese-Americans, whose history in this country has also been one of considerable hardship (Flowers, 1988:92).

LaFree and his colleagues (1992:178) suggest that increased education among blacks may have led to stronger *perceptions* of blocked opportunities and racial discrimination than actually exists, giving rise to a sense of injustice. Thomas Bernard (1990) has theorized that members of "subcultures of poverty" have a greater tendency to attribute blameworthiness for their frequent anger to outside factors. A number of studies that have reported that the black community is fertile ground for conspiracy theories relating to white genocidal intentions support this view (reviewed in Gordon, 1997). It does not matter if these perceptions are groundless or not, for as the Thomas theorem reminds us, a person's perception of reality *is* that person's reality. These perceptions, and the sense of injustice they generate, may lead to increases in illegal activities and in "angry aggression" (Bernard, 1990a).

African-American crime rates are particularly high compared with those for Asian-Americans. Asians (including Pacific Islanders) constituted 4.1 percent of the American population in 1999 (U.S. Bureau of the Census, 2000) but were arrested for only 1.2 percent of all violent crimes and 1.7 percent of all property crimes in 1999 (Federal Bureau of Investigation, 2000). British data reveal a similar pattern; that is, blacks commit more crimes than whites, and whites commit more crimes than Asians (Rutter & Giller, 1984). Violent crimes account for most of the black crime surplus in Britain, as they do in the United States. This same black-over-white-over-Asian pattern of criminal activity was found in 88 different countries (Rushton, 1990). From the available between- and within-nation data, it would seem that the black-over-white-over-Asian pattern of criminal offending is invariant: "No societies were found for which this pattern has not been reported" (Eysenck & Gudjonsson, 1989:139).

RACE AND CRIME: EXPLANATIONS

The role of science is to go beyond simple description to attempt explanations. Explanations, of course, can be value-laden. We may choose to emphasize the effects of social aggregates on individual behavior, or we may choose to emphasize the characteristics of individuals who selectively aggregate. The best studies pit alternative explanations against one another and allow the data to speak for themselves.

The rural/urban residence is one of the most important macro-level correlates of crime explored by criminologists. It is almost invariably found worldwide that rural areas have lower crime rates than urban areas (Ellis & Walsh, 2000). As villages grow into towns and towns into cities, interpersonal ties become less intimate, friendships become transitory, and secondary groups take the place of primary groups. As a consequence, normative consensus breaks down to various degrees, and the anonymity of it all allows its inhabitants to indulge in any deviant activities for which they may have an urge. At the extremes of this process, which occurs in the poorest areas of the city, informal social control mechanisms tend to break down to intolerable degrees, and delinquent gangs replace the family, school, and church as role models and sources of fulfillment of the needs for affiliation and approval among the young.

Few criminologists seriously doubt that the impersonality and anonymity of the city are conducive to crime and that city slums contain everything to excess that is negative and criminogenic about urbanism. But do the slum conditions at the city core "cause" crime, or is the correlation explained away by a variable that "causes" both, namely the characteristics of individuals living there? Although it borders on anathema in social science to suggest that people may be more responsible for the kind of environment they live in than the environment is responsible for the kind of people it produces, some researchers have suggested that the relationship between urbanism and crime is confounded by race (Byrne, 1986; Kleck & Patterson, 1993; Laub, 1983; Rosenfeld, 1986; Sampson, 1985). These studies used a variety of methods to test the relative strength of a range of demographic characteristics in accounting for crime rates when pitted against the race variable.

John Laub (1983) examined the "place versus race" issue by looking at National Crime Survey data from rural and urban areas for blacks and for whites. Laub's research question was essentially "does the black/white difference in crime rates exist because cities provide more criminal opportunities than rural areas, and blacks just happen to disproportionately live in cities (thus making place more important than race), or does it exist because blacks tend to commit more crimes than whites, and a greater proportion of blacks live in large cities than in rural areas (thus making race more important than place)"? Focusing on"serious personal" crime rates, Laub found that both races had higher rates of offending in urban areas than in rural areas, with urban rates being 2.06 and 1.81 times higher than rural rates for blacks and for whites, respectively. Standardizing by race thus left a fairly large independent rural/urban effect. The race effect was much larger, however. In urban areas, the black rate was 4.23 times greater than the white rate, and in rural areas it was 3.71 times greater. Laub concluded that "race appears to be a key variable in accounting for variation in urban and rural crime rates as well as crime rates across various place size categories" (1983:193).

An alternative example arguing that place matters more than race is presented by Stark (1996). He found that the ratios between black/white arrest and incarceration rates are greater in the northern Midwestern states such as Minnesota, which had a 22:1 black/white incarceration ratio, than in the South (e.g., South Carolina at 3.2:1). Stark dismissed racism as a causal factor because it would not be credible to claim that the police and courts in Minnesota were more racist than their counterparts in South Carolina. His explanation was that relatively few blacks in the South (9% in South Carolina) live in the central core of large cities, but 80 percent of blacks in Minnesota do. Southern blacks thus live in more "ecologically normal" areas, and northern blacks live in areas facilitative of crime. Stark's data, like Laub's, show an independent effect of place, but also show that race matters as well in that blacks were more involved in the criminal justice system in both ecologically "normal" and "abnormal" settings.

Moving from rural/urban differences to comparisons between cities, Byrne's (1986) sample of 910 United States cities found that the best predictor of robbery rates was percentage of black residents (β = .46); the independent effect of city size was much weaker at .16. These standardized betas were obtained controlling for a host of city characteristics, such as density and housing type, and population compositional variables, such as average income and education levels. Sampson's (1985) study of homicide rates in the 55 largest United States cities found that "percentage black" (β = .55) had more than twice the explanatory power of other variables in the regression such as population size, poverty, racial income inequality, and unemployment. Finally, Chilton's (1986) study of the 125 largest SMSAs controlled for a wide variety of variables in a number of different regression models. In all cases, percentage of black residents emerged as the best predictor of murder (β = .55) and assault (β = .22) rates, although population size was a better predictor of rape (.17) and robbery (.62).

Inner-City Neighborhoods and the Tipping Point

As instructive as the above studies are, they are not directly relevant to the concerns of the early ecologists, who concerned themselves with differences between neighborhoods in the same cities, not between rural and urban areas or crime rates in cities as a whole. Just because blacks and whites live in the same cities does not mean that they share the same neighborhoods as well. Neighborhoods define the pulse of an individual's life far more strongly than do the more distant residential concepts of "rural/urban" or "city."

The seemingly intractable problems of inner-city neighborhoods can be fruitfully examined using the epidemiological concept of the *tipping point*. A tipping point is the point at which growth in some phenomenon reaches a critical threshold and ceases to increase linearly and becomes exponential. Malcolm Gladwell (1996) provides an example of the tipping point phenomenon. Suppose that 1,000 tourists from Canada carrying a 24-hour flu virus arrive in New York City in early winter. Suppose that with an infection rate of 2 percent, one out of every 50 people who come into close contact with the virus carrier becomes infected, and that 50 is the average number of people a carrier comes into close contact with every day. With these suppositions, and a recovery time of 24 hours, 1,000 people will infect 1,000 other persons each day until the flu season is over. The steady rate of infection and recovery indicates that a disease is equilibrium.

Now suppose that with the onset of the Christmas season, subways, buses, stores, and restaurants become more crowded, and that each virus carrier now comes into close contact with 55 rather than 50 other people a day. This will result in 1,100 new cases the first day. These 1,100 will infect 1,210 people, and that group will infect 1,331, and by the end of the week, the number of infected people will be 2,000, double the equilibrium rate of the previous week. The disease lost its equilibrium and became an epidemic because of a small initial increase in the average number of people with which each carrier came into contact. A small change that tips beyond a threshold is more important than a large one that does not; it is "the straw that breaks the camel's back."

The tipping point model has been used to examine "white flight" from neighborhoods being "invaded" by blacks (Schelling, 1971), dropping out of school and teenage pregnancy as "high-status" families move out of a neighborhood (Crane, 1991), and the effect of the concentration of bars on police calls (Saville, 1996). All these studies demonstrated an exponential rather than linear increase in the phenomenon of interest once they reached their tipping point.

No extensive literature review is needed to convince anyone that black inner-city neighborhoods are the most dangerous places in America. When we hear of "epidemics" of gang violence, teenage pregnancy, crack smoking, and so forth, we know that the reference is to ghetto neighborhoods. The problem is not simply one of black poverty, for even when compared to whites similarly situated economically, blacks still commit more crimes (Sampson, 1995). But being poor and black does not equate with being poor and white: "[E]ven given the same objective socioeconomic status, blacks and whites face vastly different environments in which to live, work, and raise their children" (Sampson & Wilson, 2000:152). White poverty is considerably more dispersed across different neighborhoods than is black poverty, where it is highly concentrated in single neighborhoods (Sampson, 1995).

A recent study of serious juvenile offending comparing the effects of individual-level risk factors with neighborhood context supports this contention (Wikstrom & Loeber, 2000). Wikstrom and Loeber found that among the 90 neighborhoods in Pittsburgh, the percentage of families living in poverty ranged from zero in the most advantaged neighborhood to 86 in the most disadvantaged neighborhood. Seventy-two percent of families in the most disadvantaged neighborhoods were on public assistance and 54 percent were on unemployment, compared with zero percent in both cases in the most advantaged neighborhoods. The most advantaged neighborhoods had zero percent black residents, while the most disadvantaged had 99 percent.

On the basis of these and other similar demographic measures, the neighborhoods were categorized into *advantaged, middle-range, disadvantaged-nonpublic,* and *disadvantaged-public.* The percentage of youths reporting serious offending in each of these neighborhoods was 30.9, 43.4, 50.5, and 63.7, respectively. Do these quite large percentage differences reflect neighborhood effects? They could, but unlike earlier ecological studies that ignored individual differences, Wikstom and Loeber measured individual risk and protective characteristics (e.g., impulsiveness, guilt, parental supervision) of the 1,530 boys in the sample. On the basis of these measures, boys were placed into *high-risk, balanced,* and *high-protective* categories. The percentage of boys scoring high on the protective index in each of the four neighborhood categories were 24.1, 18.0, 6.4, and 5.4, respectively, and the percentage of boys scoring high on the risk index were 13.3, 19.9, 28.8, and 34.9, respectively. These figures suggest that neighborhood influences might disappear once individual risk factors are considered.

The most interesting aspect of this study is that boys at high risk for antisocial behavior committed antisocial acts at about the same level (all in the 70% range) across all four neighborhood types. The percentage of boys in the advantaged neighborhood category reporting serious delinquency actually exceeded the percentage of boys reporting such behavior in the most disadvantaged neighborhood (77.8% versus 70%). This finding suggests that there is no independent neighborhood effect for high-risk boys. On the other hand, for boys in the *high-protective* category, the percentages reporting committing serious offenses ranged from 11.1 percent in the most advantaged neighborhood category, to 37.5 percent in the most disadvantaged neighborhood category. For boys in the *balanced* category, the percentages were 27.3, 40.1, 48.5, and 60.7 across neighborhood categories. These findings do imply neighborhood influences on boys at low to medium risk for antisocial behavior based on individual-level measures. The conclusion derived from these data is that advantaged neighborhoods do not appear to protect boys who are otherwise at risk, but that disadvantaged neighborhoods appear to corrupt a fair percentage of boys who are otherwise protected.

It should be noted that neighborhood effects applied only to boys whose offending was late-onset (postpuberty), suggesting that these boys might be adolescent-limited offenders, a possibility that Wilkstrom and Loeber's data did not allow them to pursue.

The Wikstrom and Loeber study may help us to understand why "good" boys find it difficult to stay that way in the worst of our neighborhoods. According to sociologist Elijah Anderson (1999:107), the concentration of disadvantages in many black neighborhoods has spawned a hostile and violent oppositional subculture that spurns most things valued by mainstream America, as in "the rap music that encourages its young listeners to kill cops, to rape, and the like." The concentration of numerous angry and alienated individuals lacking adequate institutional and personal coping skills to counteract daily stress creates a constant feedback loop of angry aggression (Bernard, 1990a). The ghetto has always been a violent place, but at some point in history, the violence and the attitudes that support it reached its tipping point and became epidemic. Anderson points out that although there are still many "decent" families in such neighborhoods, the cultural ambience is set by "street" families. "Decent" individuals often have to adopt the oppositional attitudes and behavior of "street" individuals to survive. Valuing education and striving for upward mobility is viewed as "dissing" the neighborhood, and street people often "mount a policing effort to keep their decent counterparts from 'selling out' or 'acting white'" (Anderson, 1999:65).

The black ghetto is thus at the confluence of multiple disabilities, ranging from the deindustrialization of the inner cities and the resulting loss of well-paying jobs for the semieducated, to the presence of crack, to the spawning of an explicitly hostile oppositional culture. A culturally isolated community can absorb only so many problems before reaching epidemic proportions. Anderson's ethnography of inner-city life points time and again to the great influence exerted by scores of unsupervised youths in developing and maintaining the present cultural ambience of the inner city. But why do we see so many unsupervised young people in the inner cities of the United States?

ENVIRONMENTALLY CONTINGENT STRATEGIES: THE SEX RATIO AND ILLEGITIMACY

The ecological studies previously cited speculated that the black/white crime rate difference may be due to a combination of motivational and control factors (Laub, 1983) or a "subculture of violence" (Byrne, 1986). These macro-level variables require explanations themselves. A common macro-level factor underlying all these alleged causes might be the differential rate of out-of-wedlock births in black communities and white communities. That is, poverty, lack of social bonds, and a violent subculture may themselves be in large part a function of illegitimacy: "If there is a single statistic that underlies the crime, poverty, and failure that beset blacks in America today, it is an illegitimacy rate of 66 percent" (Taylor, 1992:305). David Lykken agrees, and states that much of the difference in black/white crime rates might disappear if the illegitimacy gap between the races disappeared (1995).

Illegitimacy has been called "the new American dilemma" by a variety of scholars and political figures from across the political and ideological spectra (Hamburg, 1993; Hirschi, 1995; Wilson, 1983). Many criminologists have considered the problem of illegitimacy to be taboo ever since Senator Daniel P. Moynihan issued the "infamous" Moynihan report (1965), which placed the black illegitimacy rate (then 25 percent) at the heart of the problem of the deterioration of the black community. Although Moynihan received support from none other than Martin Luther King Jr., who expressed "alarm" at such statistics (Norton, 1987:53), his report was attacked by many as racist (Ryan, 1972).

A number of studies have shown illegitimacy to be a relatively strong predictor of antisocial behavior. At the macro level, there is evidence that violent crime in the United States (Lykken, 1995) and Britain (Himmelfarb, 1994) rose almost directly proportional to illegitimacy rates over the past 30 years in those countries. Another study comparing the out-of-wedlock birth rates and crime rates in each of the 50 states found a very strong partial correlation of .82 after controlling for unemployment rates (Mackey, 1997). A British longitudinal study comparing delinquency among legitimate and illegitimate boys concluded that "the boys born illegitimate were singularly delinquent prone" (West & Farrington, 1977:197), and another British study concluded that there were "relatively high levels of behavioral and adaptive problems in the illegitimate group" (Maughan & Pickles, 1990:55). An American study comparing delinquents born in and out of wedlock found that the illegitimate boys were almost twice as violent and that they were significantly more deprived on all indices of emotional, economic, and social well-being (Walsh, 1991).

Single-parent families increase a child's risk of future offending for a variety of reasons. For instance, it "decreases community networks of informal control," and it increases "the prevalence of unsupervised teenage peer groups" (Messner & Sampson, 1991:697). Unwed mothers tend to be younger than women who bear their first child in wedlock, and tend to come from educationally and economically deprived families (Vedder & Gallaway, 1993; Zuravin, 1988). They also tend to lack the same level of social support enjoyed by married mothers, which socially isolates them and increases the probability of child abuse and neglect (McLeod, Kruttschnitt & Dornfield, 1994; Walsh, 1991).

The personality traits of the typical unmarried mother raise the issue of the genetic transmission of antisocial traits. Unmarried mothers (in general) have a tendency to follow an impulsive and risky lifestyle and to have a number of antisocial personality traits, be more sexually promiscuous, and to have a below-average IQ (reviewed in Cleveland et al., 2000). Add to this the heritable traits of the men who father these children and it would seem that many children born out of wedlock have the cards stacked against them from the beginning. The many problems associated with high illegitimacy rates led Gottfredson and Hirschi (1997:33) to focus on the issue as leading to *the* policy recommendation deducible from self-control theory: "Delaying pregnancy among unmarried girls would probably do more to affect the long-term crime rates than all the criminal justice programs combined." This is not a statement of moral condemnation. It is a statement that implicitly recognizes the evolutionary importance of the reproductive team to the healthy development of offspring.

Messner and Sampson (1991) attempt to account for the high rate of single-parent families in the black community with reference to the sex ratio. Messner and Sampson reasoned that because gender is the major predictor of antisocial behavior, we should expect that populations with more males than females should have higher rates of crime than populations with more females than males. Populations with a greater number of males than females (a high sex ratio), however, are associated with family stability and lower rates of illegitimacy. Populations with more females than males (low sex ratio) means that there are fewer males available to commit crimes, but a low sex ratio also signals a licentious environment in which males are reluctant to commit to one women (Geary, 2000). This situation leads to high rates of illegitimacy and divorce, in short, to family disruption, which affects crime rates in many ways.

Messner and Sampson tested their hypothesis separately for blacks and for whites based on data from 153 cities in the United States with populations greater than 100,000. They first examined the effect of the sex ratio on the percentage of female-headed households in multiple-regression models. In the black model, the sex ratio was by far the most powerful of the eight predictors included in the model ($\beta = -.60$), and in the white model (a population with a less skewed sex ratio), it was the third most powerful predictor ($\beta = -.29$), behind per capita income and welfare availability. These results indicate that cities with low sex ratios are characterized by high rates of female-headed households, and cities characterized by high sex ratios are characterized by low rates of female-headed households.

What accounts for fluctuating rates of illegitimacy? Messner and Sampson indicate that the low sex ratio is a factor, and hint that it operates by decreasing male commitment to women and to family life. The complex links between illegitimacy and antisocial behavior, illegitimacy and race, and illegitimacy and the sex ratio are in need of explanation. Evolutionary theory should be particularly useful in exploring them and providing explanations.

The sex ratio is the most important environmental factor affecting sexual behavior within a variety of animal species. Monogamy is rare or nonexistent whenever there are significantly more females than males, but when there are more males than females, monogamy is more likely (Krebs & Davies, 1993; Trivers, 1972). Humans are no exception. The laws of supply and demand determine mating strategies. When there is a significantly greater number of one sex of marriageable age than of the other, the less numerous sex is a scarce resource and thus holds the power in dating and mating relationships and can dictate the conditions of the relationship (Pedersen, 1991). Because the mating strategies of men and women are very different, when sex ratios are significantly skewed, mating environments are considerably altered.

Guttentag and Secord (1983) surveyed the historical and sociological literature on cultures ranging from ancient Greece to the modern United States and found in all cases that when males or females are freer to choose their mating behavior (because the sex ratio favors them), they will behave in ways compatible with their innate inclinations. Members of the more numerous sex must compromise their natural mating strategies and conform to the strategy of the sex favored by the sex ratio or risk being mateless. That is, under low-sex-ratio conditions, the typical mating strategy is characterized by behavioral ecologists as the r-strategy; under high-sex-ratio conditions, mating tends to follow the K-strategy (see Chapter 3 for a discussion of these strategies). Changes in the social and moral climate can be anticipated when the sex ratio is skewed in either direction. A low sex ratio (a surplus of marriageable-age women) leads to weaker commitments of men toward women, more illegitimate births, increased sexual promiscuity, increased sexually transmitted diseases, greater misogyny, greater female depression, and an increase in women's liberationist sentiment as women become more conscious of the negative aspects of a low sex ratio (Guttentag & Secord, 1983; for similar analyses, see Gilder, 1976; Heer & Grossband-Shechtman, 1981; and Pedersen, 1991).

Guttentag and Secord show that the sex ratio in the United States was consistently high until 1970. According to this line of thinking, the female-favoring ratio helped to shape American mores as they relate to dating, mating, and marriage. With the high sex ratio, men had to compromise with the female strategy, because if they did not, there were many others who would. Women were prized and respected, marriage was considered an attractive and permanent prospect, sexual intimacy was an expression of love, and adultery was morally unacceptable and legally punishable. It was difficult for males to adopt a promiscuous strategy under these conditions: "[T]he adaptive payoff of a given trait for each sex decreases as the members of that sex become more numerous" (Buss, 1990:11).

In the 1960 census, there were still 111 men of marriageable age for every 100 women. However, the 1970 census showed that the sex ratio had become male-favoring, with only 78 white men of that age for every 100 white women, and 73 black men for every 100 black women. Now females had to compromise with the male strategy, and predictably, a licentious and misogynistic environment ensued. Women tended to respond to this male-favoring environment by requiring lower levels of commitment before agreeing to have sex with males, although many found this to be distasteful (Doudna & McBride, 1981; Wilson, 1983).

Illegitimate birth rates are the most palpable indicator of the rate of nonmarital sexual activity. Estimates of illegitimacy in the black community range from 60 to 70 percent of all live births (Lykken, 1995). Interestingly, both low sex ratios and levels of gonadotropins (a class of hormones that regulate the functions of the gonads) in females (Lynn, 1990; Sieff, 1990) appear to follow the black-over-white-over-Asian gradient. Gonadotropin levels appear to be partially responsible for skewing the sex ratio in the direction of excess female births (James, 1986, 1987). On this basis alone (the hormonal tendency to bias births in the direction of a greater number of females), we might expect to see more illegitimacy in African-American communities than in European- and Asian-American communities.

Guttentag and Secord (1983:219) correlated sex ratios for whites and for blacks and illegitimacy rates state by state. They found a highly significant correlation of –.87 for blacks and a –.27 correlation for whites. This does not imply that blacks have some innate characteristic that makes them more promiscuous than whites; there was simply more variation in black sex ratios across the states. For instance, the sex ratio in the state of New York was low in 1980, with 86 black males for every 100 black females, and 50 percent of black families were headed by a single female. In North Dakota that same year, where the sex ratio favored females, with 160 black males for every 100 black females, only 2.9 percent of black families were headed by a woman. This 2.9 percent figure was less than one-fifth of the national white average of 17 percent in 1980 (Guttentag & Secord, 1983:221). Similar findings from 117 countries provide further support for the sex ratio/illegitimacy hypothesis (South & Trent, 1988).

Guttentag and Secord and South and Trent focused on social exchange theory to explain their data. Social exchange theory works well as a proximate explanation of dyadic power relationships, but it assumes that all parties in an exchange relationship desire the same things and employ the same strategies to achieve them. Darwinian sexual selection theory is superior to exchange theory in this instance because it informs us that although reproductive success is the fundamental goal of both sexes in all sexually reproducing species, males and females employ quite different strategies.

Sexual selection theory avers that the primary constraint on maximizing reproductive success for males is access to females; for females, it is acquiring resources for herself and her offspring (Geary, 2000; Krebs & Davies, 1993). Thus, males can be expected to employ a strategy aimed at maximizing their access to as many females as possible, and females will be attracted to males who can demonstrate their ability to provide resources. For Pedersen (1991:276), the primary criterion for favoring sexual selection theory over social exchange theory to explore the correlates of skewed sex ratios is that "sexual selection theory specifies more directly the criteria for male and female choice on the basis of asymmetries in reproductive constraints." A low sex ratio removes much of the constraint for males, and a high sex ratio removes much of it for females. Pedersen goes on to state that sexual selection theory subsumes everything in social exchange theory and adds substantially to it by making sense of the psychological processes Guttentag and Seccord highlight, by identifying sex-specific reasons (beyond dyadic power differentials) why the mating environment is radically different depending on whether sex ratios are high or low, and by pointing to similar processes in other species.

Conditional adaptation theory (discussed in Chapter 3) augments sexual selection theory at the individual level (Cashdan, 1993; Walsh,

1999). Recall that this theory is also ecologically based and that it proposes that people adopt different sexual strategies based on direct and indirect childhood perceptions of the nature of interpersonal relationships (Belsky & Draper, 1991). The theory is a developmentally contingent one positing that the person's mind and physiology are calibrated by early life experiences. Individuals will tend to adopt an unrestricted (promiscuous) sexual strategy if they learned during their childhood that interpersonal relationships are ephemeral and unreliable, and individuals who learned the opposite will tend to adopt a more restricted strategy. Neither of these strategies is consciously chosen; rather, the "chosen" strategy is considered to be a developmental "programmed" strategy arising from taken-for-granted expectations about the reliability of male/female relationships.

THE ECOLOGY OF THE INNER CITY

Because of the severe shortage of black males in the inner city, and the inability of many of them to obtain decent employment and provide resources, inner-city females tend not to view them as possible permanent partners (Anderson, 1999; Wilson, 1987). Under such circumstances, both sexual selection theory and conditional adaptation theory predict that inner-city girls and women will emphasize their sexuality rather than their fidelity. The empirical data support this prediction. Rushton and Bogaert (1987) surveyed a voluminous literature showing a lower average age of menarche and first sexual experience for African-American females than for European- or Asian-American females, and that blacks of both sexes have more sexual partners within and outside of bonded relationships.

Social scientists find it highly contentious to intermingle issues of race, crime, and sexuality, as Fredrick Goodwin, former director of the National Institute of Mental Health (NIMH) found out. Goodwin made the following remarks in a 1992 meeting of NIMH's advisory council (cited in Breggin & Breggin, 1995:27)

> If you look, for example, at male monkeys especially in the wild, roughly half of them survive to adulthood; the other half die by violence. That is the natural way of it for males, to knock each other off. And, in fact, there are some interesting evolutionary implications of that, because the same hyper-aggressive monkeys who kill each other are also hypersexual, so they copulate more and therefore they reproduce more to offset the fact that half of them are dying.
>
> Now, one could say that if some of the loss of social structure in this society, and particularly within the high-

impact inner areas, has removed some of the civilizing evolutionary things we have built up, and that maybe it isn't a
careless use of the word when people call certain areas of the
cities jungles, that we may have gone back to what might be
more natural, without all of the social controls that we have
imposed upon ourselves as a civilization over thousands of
years in our own evolution.

Goodwin's statement was interpreted by many as "right-wing" and
"reactionary," a claim that inner-city youths behave like violent and
hypersexed monkeys in the jungle, and he was forced out of his job
because of it. Had he used the "Forty-niner" gold fields, the old Western cowtowns, or even the English schoolboys stranded in the jungle
in *Lord of the Flies* as his setting rather than the inner cities of modern America, it is doubtful whether his remarks would have elicited anything more than a yawn.

Although they may have used more politically correct imagery, Shaw
and McKay reached the same conclusion. Goodwin was saying that the
behavior of human beings is shaped by their ecology; that is, their choices are environmentally structured. He was also saying that the loss of
social structure releases antisocial impulses, and that violence and
other forms of antisocial behavior are greatest in areas in which social
disorganization is greatest. One would be hard-pressed to find a sociologist who would disagree with this, or that social disorganization is
greatest in the inner city. Goodwin was also implicitly agreeing with
the human ecologists by maintaining that under the circumstances ("the
loss of social structure"), such behavior is normal, not pathological.
Far from being a right-wing or reactionary position, it is decidedly left-
wing in its claim that inner-city males are simply responding to environmental contingencies.

Human ecologists Bursik and Grasmick (1993:266) state that
criminal activity in disorganized areas is "an alternative means of
gaining economic and social sustenance from the environment." There
is nothing in that statement with which an evolutionary psychologist
would take issue (although "right-wingers" and "reactionaries" certainly would), for it is a central tenet of evolutionary theory that the
human brain evolved in the context of overwhelming concerns for
acquiring such sustenance. When the acquisition of economic and
social sustenance is unproblematic, pursuing it deceitfully and/or violently is unwise because of the risk of loss of freedom, serious injury,
or death, but when for whatever reason they become difficult to
obtain legitimately, acquiring them any way one can is often worth the
risk. The evolutionary importance of this observation is that the most
successful of our ancestral males in acquiring resources gained status
and thereby access to a disproportionate number of females. Because

status brought more copulation opportunities, genes inclining males to pursue it (which sometimes meant in ways we consider immoral and illegal today) enjoyed greater representation in subsequent generations. From the evolutionary point of view, "gaining economic and social sustenance" is something humans are designed by nature to do. Whether they go about acquiring these things by means fair or foul depends, all other things being equal, on environmental conditions. Let us not, however, fall into the naturalistic trap of excusing such behavior on the grounds of its assumed evolutionary origins. We must be careful not to conflate an *explanation* of the facts with a *moral evaluation* of them.

Perhaps it was Goodwin's comparison with monkeys that offended most people. His choice of monkeys to illustrate his point simply points to the fact that humans are primates too, and like nonhuman primates, the "removal of dominant individuals [in the human case read "the removal of civilizing influences"] sharply increases aggression in the lower ranks" (Lopreato & Crippen, 1999:223). Wrangham and Peterson, an anthropologist and primatologist, respectively, provide many Goodwin-like examples of the similarity in violent and sexual behaviors between various primate species and human males in their book *Demonic Males* (1996). Although they emphasize that the gulf between nonhuman primates and humans is enormous, their work also underlines nature's conservation of ancestral strategies and mechanisms closely associated with reproductive success across closely linked species, and perhaps even across all vertebrate species (Oliveira, 1998). The de facto refusal to view humans as animals (albeit animals with an evolved sense of morality that enables us to defy our biology), and to vilify any perspective that does, precludes social science from accepting and benefiting from comparative animal data.

It is undeniable that adolescent human males share with the adolescents of many primate species the tendency to roam around in gangs and engage in interpersonal violence and gang "warfare." Compare the following two descriptions, the first involving chimpanzees and the other involving black inner-city youths, and note the striking commonness of purpose:

> According to [Jane] Goodall, the violence appeared to be rooted in the ability of chimpanzees to distinguish members of the in-group from those of the out-group and to behave in ways that reflected "ethnocentric" urges. Chimpanzees do not merely defend a territory. They "actually expend considerable energy in *creating* opportunities to encounter intruders at close range." Moreover, they "not only attack trespassers, but may. . . . make aggressive *raids* into the very heart of the core areas of neighboring groups" (Lopreato & Crippen, 1999:263, emphasis in original).

It is easy to spot the human analogs of gang colors, symbols, and signs, and the thrill of gang-banging in this description. Now consider the words of Sanyka Shakur, a former leader of the South Central Los Angeles Crips:

> Our war, like most gang wars, was not fought for territory or any specific goal other than the destruction of individuals, of human beings. The idea was to drop enough bodies, cause enough terror and suffering so that they'd come to their senses and realize that we were the wrong set to fuck with. Their goal, I'm sure, was the same (cited in Wrangham & Peterson, 1996:193).

Elijah Anderson's ethnographic study of a black neighborhood in Philadelphia in *Code of the Streets* makes many Goodwin-like points without the instructive but offending metaphors, although he does write that the "law of the jungle" characterizes much of street life (1999:84). Anderson calls the violent posturing among inner-city males a "campaign for respect" (1999:68), the search for which consumes these males because it is "the core of the person's self-esteem" (1999:66). Like Goodall's chimpanzees, Anderson points out that in the inner city, "there are always people looking around for a fight in order to increase their share of respect—or 'juice'" (1999:73). Anderson could have been describing males of any race or ethnicity unconstrained by formal and informal laws from seeking status in its most primordial form. Even "highly civilized" males from the aristocracies of Europe and the old American South sought "honor" through violence when laws and custom allowed it (Daly & Wilson, 1988a). The ethnographic and historical literature support the view that we are "naked apes" when our moral and social garments are stripped away.

What of Goodwin's "hypersexual" comment? Sampson and Wilson make much the same point when they write of "[g]hetto-specific practices such as an overt emphasis on sexuality and macho values" (2000:156). Far from being an insult, to call an inner-city male (or almost any male for that matter) hypersexual is to pay him a valued compliment. According to Anderson (1999:150), because sexual activity is "taken quite seriously as a measure of the boy's worth" in the inner city, a young male's "primary goal is to find as many willing females as possible. The more 'pussy' he gets, the more esteem accrues to him." Finding willing females is all the easier when one has accumulated lots of "juice" in the streets and when females constrained by a low sex ratio prove receptive. As in the animal world, the accumulation of status that brings with it the prospect of greater access to females is based on credible threats of violence. It is in this way that violence and sexuality are intimately related to reproductive success in almost all animal species, including humans. The two are more closely linked when status hierarchies are in flux, or in the case of humans, when social and cultural constraints are severely compromised.

It is instructive to compare the inner-city subculture of violence and sexual promiscuity with the Mundurucu culture discussed in Chapter 3 in terms of the link between ecology, violence, and mating effort. A further example from a prestate society is that of the Ache, a group of South American Indians. Intertribal warfare and intratribal status-driven club fights among the Ache result in high male mortality and thus great shortages of available mates for females. A fatherless Ache child has about a 50 percent chance of surviving childhood, compared with about 86 percent for children with fathers. Under conditions of severe male shortage, it is adaptive for females unlikely to secure a permanent mate to copulate with a number of males, thereby gaining some resources of each male, or even convincing one of them that the child is his. Such behavior increases the probability that her child will survive to adolescence, and by doing so she increases the probability that her genes will be represented in subsequent generations (Hill & Hurtado, 1996).

TESTOSTERONE, DOMINANCE, AND HONOR SUBCULTURES

It has been proposed that testosterone might be the primary biochemical mechanism underlying racial differences in both sexual and criminal activity, because testosterone levels appear to follow the black-over-white-over-Asian gradient (Lynn, 1990). A study assessing testosterone levels among 100 college males found that blacks had 19 percent more than whites (Rose et al., 1986), and a larger study of more than 4,000 males found blacks to have 3.3 percent more testosterone than whites (Ellis & Nyborg, 1992). No reputable researcher in this area, of course, claims that high levels of testosterone *cause* aggressive or sexual behaviors, only that they *facilitate* such behavior. Whatever our evolutionary history of these behaviors, and whatever mechanisms were designed to facilitate them, any inclination to act one way or another is necessarily channeled by the brain, a system designed by natural selection to generate behavior appropriate to the situations in which we find ourselves. It is meaningless to discuss our behavioral biology apart from its environmental context.

Testosterone is the primary androgen responsible for developing and maintaining masculine morphological and behavioral features, and the stuff that energizes male competition, particularly in adolescence. Individuals differ in their basal levels of plasma testosterone, with a heritability of about 0.60 (Harris, Vernon & Boomsma, 1998). Testosterone has been found to be significantly related to violent crime, prison rule violations, and a number of other problem behaviors, such as spousal abuse, marital disruption, trouble on the job, substance abuse, and general rebelliousness (reviewed in Mazur & Booth, 1998). These effects, however, appear to be modest and most noticeable at extreme levels of the hormone. For instance, Dabbs and Morris's (1990) study of 4,462 male military veterans compared the upper 10 percent (based on testosterone level) with the remaining 90 percent and found the high-testosterone group to be at greater risk for a number of antisocial acts. The risk ratios ranged from 1.3:1 for number of sex partners to 2.1:1 for hard drug use. Splitting the sample at the median on SES, the risk ratios increased among low-SES men and decreased among high-SES men, indicating that the effects of testosterone are mediated by sociocultural variables and/or the individual-level characteristics associated with low SES.

Environmental variables not only mediate the effects of testosterone, they also cause testosterone levels to fluctuate in response to them. That is, testosterone and environmental context have reciprocal effects on one another. The literature is replete with studies evaluating pre- and postgame testosterone levels of winners and losers at various sporting events, and even of spectators of these events due to their vicarious participation (reviewed by Kemper, 1990). Compared with baseline measures, winners and the fans of winners show a rise in testosterone levels and losers and fans of losers show a decline, although these fluctuations are very short-lived (Tsai & Sapolsky, 1996).

These studies prompt the thought that perhaps higher testosterone levels among black males relative to their white peers may reflect the greater status challenges black males face in their "honor subcultures" rather than true racial differences in testosterone base levels (Mazur & Booth, 1998; Walsh, 1991). Significantly, no racial differences in testosterone levels tend to be found among prepubescent males, older males, males who have attended college, and males raised outside honor subcultures (Mazur & Booth, 1998). In other words, significant black/white differences in testosterone are not found when black males not participating in honor subcultures are compared with their white peers. The available evidence thus supports the contention that natural selection has provided us with the necessary neurohormonal mechanisms that allow us to respond to challenges to our reproductive efforts (either directly or indirectly) in ways dictated by the environments in which we find ourselves. For males in violent subcultures, these mechanisms will be activated more frequently than for males in other subcultures.

How might elevated testosterone be adaptive in socially disorganized areas? It has been suggested by a number of researchers that testosterone is more directly linked to dominance behavior than to aggressiveness per se (Bernhardt, 1997; Booth & Osgood, 1993;

Mazur & Booth, 1998). As has been repeatedly stressed, dominance and status seeking is an almost universal cross-species male feature because of its role in promoting reproductive success in environments of evolutionary adaptation. Aggressiveness of some sort is almost required in order to achieve dominance, although it is seldom expressed violently in modern state societies in which it is constrained by formal and informal rules. According to Jerome Barkow (1989:186-192), displays of self-esteem and self-assurance that signal the ability (if not necessarily the willingness) to invest in offspring have replaced dominance based on aggressive fighting ability. This is also true in many primate species in which alliance-building and subtle displays of fighting ability rather than brute force sustain dominance rankings. Violent attempts to gain status tend to be expressed most readily among non-human primates when alliances and coalitions break down and alpha males can no longer get away with mere bluster.

It has been proposed that elevated testosterone is most likely to result in violent aggressiveness when it is present in conjunction with low serotonin (Bernhardt, 1997). Experimental evidence with rats shows an inverse relationship between testosterone and serotonin (Bonson et al., 1994). Injecting nondominant rats with testosterone increases dominance behavior, and administering a serotonin booster reverses the process and returns the rats to nondominant status. Bernhardt's model of aggressive behavior is based on rodent experiments such as these, and thus may not be wholly applicable to humans. He postulates that individuals with high base rates of testosterone are more inclined than those with lower base levels to engage in dominance-seeking behaviors. The more dominance-seeking behavior a person engages in, the greater the likelihood of that person experiencing a frustrating event as he interacts with others seeking the same thing. If such a person has a low level of serotonin, he will likely interpret frustration more aversively (recall from the previous chapter that negative emotionality is associated with low serotonin) and more impulsively, which increases the likelihood of responding to frustration aggressively. All of this points to the futility of attempting to explain criminal behavior exclusively in either biological or environmental terms, and for the importance of an evolutionary frame of reference.

Chapter 9

Critical and Feminist Theories and Conflict

The theories discussed in this chapter represent a sharp discontinuity from the theories contained in the previous chapters in that they emphasize conflict rather than consensus. Although most mainstream sociological theories of criminal behavior necessarily contain elements of underlying social conflict, they are best described as consensus theories. They are broadly construed as consensus theories because they tend to judge alternative normative systems from the point of view of what they consider to be mainstream values, and because any policy recommendations flowing from them do not require a major restructuring of the social system. Although consensus theorists may criticize certain aspects of society (e.g., racism, poverty, capitalism) as criminogenic, they do not attack society in its totality nor seek radical changes in it. Many critical theorists, on the other hand, do just that. They view the law, criminal behavior, and differential sanctions for those who break it as all originating in class and/or gender conflict with its origins in an inequitable social system.

The term *critical* is used here as a generic name for a variety of left-wing criminologies united by the assumption that the nature of society is best characterized by conflict and power relations. These criminologies are known under labels such as *conflict, radical, critical, neo-Marxist,* or *left realists,* and it is fair to say there is far more agreement among them about what they are against than what they support. Probably the major differences within these various schools is the degree to which they integrate the ideas of Karl Marx versus Max Weber on the nature of conflict and of society into their thinking, and whether they are reformist or revolutionary in their recommendations. (Bohm, 1982:566). The more radical theorists favor Marx and revolution, and the less radical theorists favor Weber and reform. Given the large variety of critical theories and the goals of this book, this discussion will be limited to general Marxist and feminist theories only.

ARE CRITICAL THEORIES INCOMPATIBLE WITH BIOLOGY?

Criminologists who favor the theories in this chapter tend to be the most biophobic of all criminologists. Wright and Miller's (1998) analysis of textbooks discussed in Chapter 1 found that writers embracing critical/radical perspectives were by far the most likely to espouse the view that biological explanations of crime and delinquency are racist, sexist, and classist. Perhaps this is so because they are the most committed to changing the status quo, to the infinite malleability of human nature, and to the dream of perfectibility. Apparently, if something is acknowledged as "biological," critical theorists believe it to be immutable and predestined, thus it dare not be acknowledged as such. This position is derived, as we have seen, from a poor understanding of the role of biology in human behavior. Biology is, however, certainly incompatible with the proposition that humans are infinitely malleable, or that humans and/or their societies can be perfected. We have seen the nightmares produced when attempts to put these abstractions into practice are made.

There is nothing in critical or feminist theories that is *intrinsically* incompatible with biology. Degler (1991) reminds us that the French political left enthusiastically embraced sociobiology as a sort of neo-Rouseauism even as the American political left just as enthusiastically rejected it. Leading figures in modern evolutionary theory, such as J. B. S. Haldane, John Maynard Smith, and Robert Trivers, have all been active supporters of radical left-wing causes (Singer, 2000), and prominent social scientists such as Melvin Konner and Alan Mazur are well known for both their liberal politics and their commitment to biosocial science (Degler, 1991). Many feminists such as Anne Campbell, Sara Hrdy, Alice Rossi, Meredith Small, and Barbara Smuts are also favorably disposed to biosocial explanations. Karl Marx himself appeared to be in favor of the integration of the social and biological sciences and claimed that: "Darwin's book [*The Origin of Species*] is very important and serves me as a natural-scientific basis for the class struggle in history" (quoted in Singer, 2000:20).

Many concepts central to Marxist-based theories, such as conflict, self-interest, dominance, false consciousness (self-deception), and exploitation, are also central to evolutionary psychology, suggesting that the two theories may be proximate- and ultimate-level explanations of essentially the same set of phenomena. The major difference between Marxism and evolutionary psychology is the presumed origins of these things. For the Marxist, they are the bitter fruits of the mode of production (the dominant method of making a living of a given society such as hunting and gathering, feudalism, capitalism, socialism) of a particular historical period. The mode of production with which Marx was concerned was capitalism because it alienated individuals from themselves and from others. Capitalism produced these morally repugnant things, and socialism can eliminate them. By way of contrast, evolutionary psychology views these characteristics as having evolved to promote individual survival and reproductive success, morally repugnant though they may be. They are universal species characteristics that cannot be eliminated, although they are certainly expressed facultatively rather than stereotypically and can thus be controlled and minimized.

MARX'S CONCEPT OF HUMAN NATURE

With all this similarity of conceptual interest, and with Marx's own enthusiasm for Darwin, why is the mainstream radical left so anti-Darwinian, at least when Darwinism is applied to human behavior? The short answer is that early Darwinism was captured by the radical right, and thus the friend of an enemy became an enemy. The radical right transmuted Darwinism into the notorious aberration called "social Darwinism." This philosophy, with which Darwin had no part, justified—and even sometimes exalted—exploitation, the class system, selfishness, "dog-eat-dog" competition, poverty, and the entire status quo as "natural" and therefore good (the naturalistic fallacy again). Many felt that the insidious philosophy of social Darwinism had to be opposed, and the leaders of the opposition were predominantly left-leaning humanitarians. However, rather than striving to show how Darwinism was being misunderstood and misused, they apparently determined that the point of least resistance was to deny the role of evolution in human affairs and the concept of a universal human nature altogether.

This is not to suggest that the left's denial of a universal human nature was simply forced on them in reaction to the radical right. Left-wing social ideology was already hostile to the idea of a universal human nature, and the evils of social Darwinism helped to cement that position. The general position held by the left vis-à-vis human nature may be seen as issuing from Marx's statement of his materialistic theory of history: "The mode of production of material life conditions the social, political and intellectual life processes in general. *It is not the consciousness of men that determines their being, but, on the contrary, their social being that determines their consciousness*" (1977:389, emphasis added). If by consciousness Marx is referring to what others call human nature, he is denying the existence of an unchanging human nature, for it changes every time the mode of production changes. The optimism in the perfectibility of humanity and the ushering in of a utopia demands such a view of human nature, because to change it all one has to do is change the mode of production.

Marx's work is so voluminous that a hermeneutic tradition has been erected around it. No one can claim definitive knowledge of exactly what Marx's position was on human nature because he seems to have vacillated so much that, as has been said of the Bible, even the devil can quote it to suit his own ends. On several occasions throughout his writings, Marx rather strongly implies the existence of a general human nature (he frequently used the term "species being") independent of the elaborations attached to it by a particular mode of production. For instance, I can imagine an evolutionary psychologist writing the following passage, although it was Karl Marx (not the romantic "young" Marx, but the "mature" Marx of *Capital*) who did so: "To know what is useful for a dog, one must study dog nature . . . Applying this to man, he that would criticize all human acts, movements, relations, etc., by [Jeremy Bentham's] principle of utility, must first deal with human nature in general, and then with human nature as modified in each historic epoch" (quoted in Schaff, 1970:85). In this passage Marx appears to be saying:

1. There is a discoverable universal human nature.

2. The explication of human action must be predicated on an adequate understanding of that nature.

3. Aspects of human nature are developed or constrained contingently; for example, the ethos of the capitalist mode of production facilitated rationality, creativity, and acquisitiveness.

In another place, Marx anticipates Durkheim's contention that human wants are insatiable in that each satisfied need "leads to new needs and this production of new needs is the first historical act" (cited in Coser, 1971:43). This perpetual dissatisfaction leads humans to "antagonistic cooperation" with one another, a strategy evolutionary psychologists call "tit-for-tat" cooperation or "reciprocal altruism." Social classes emerge when the division of labor emerges, and antagonism then becomes group antagonism (conflict between alliances, in evolutionary terms). However, the view that collective interests drive class structure and class conflict is only true insofar as collective interests subsume individual interests. That is, like group selectionism in biology, class conflict is only *apparently* driven by group interests. Analyzing group processes is interesting and valuable in its own right, but it has led to the reification of class and away from the understanding that "the undercurrent of alliances is the quest for individual power" (Lopreato & Crippen, 1999:211). This may be more the fault of Marx's followers than of Marx himself, for he warned us "to avoid postulating 'society' once more as an abstraction confronting the individual" (in Coser, 1971:46). In a sentiment entirely consistent with evolutionary psychology, Marx also stated: "The separate individuals form a class only insofar as they have to carry on a common battle against another class; otherwise they are on hostile terms with each other as competitors" (in Coser, 1971:48).

Marx and Engels on Crime

The core of Marxist philosophy relevant to understanding the critical view of crime causation is the concept of the *class struggle*. This struggle takes place between the wealthy owners of the means of production (the *bourgeoisie*) and the working class (the *proletariat*), with the former striving to keep the cost of labor at a minimum, and the latter striving to sell their labor at the highest possible price (Bohm, 1982). These opposing goals are the major source of conflict in a capitalist society. The bourgeoisie enjoy the upper hand because capitalist societies typically have large armies of unemployed workers anxious to secure work at any price, thus driving down the cost of labor. Herein lies one of the most important inherent contradictions of capitalism identified by Marx. On the one hand, the unemployed and unemployable form the core of the "criminal classes" that threatened the capitalist system, but on the other, they were functional for capitalism. Worker exploitation led to a period of abject misery in the industrial cities of Europe and the United States in the nineteenth century. According to Marx, these economic and social arrangements—the material conditions of people's lives—determine what they will know, believe, and value, and how they will behave. It follows from this that if people act and think in antisocial and criminal ways, they do so because their economic and social positions are not conducive to acting and thinking prosocially.

The ruling class develops ideologies (including an ideology of law) to justify and legitimize their exploitation, which the subordinate classes usually accept as valid. Marx called the workers' acceptance of ideologies counter to their best interests *false consciousness*. The ruling classes are able to generate false consciousness because they control key institutions such as the church and the law and control the flow of information from educational institutions and the media. False consciousness functions to deflect anger and criticism away from the ruling class.

Marx believed that capitalist competition would drive the less able capitalists into the ranks of the proletariat, as indeed it often did. These men would provide the intellectual leadership that would overthrow capitalism, and would help the workers to understand their false consciousness. In time, false consciousness would be replaced by *class consciousness*; that is, the recognition of a common class condition and the development of a common unity in opposition to capitalist exploitation. This would set the stage for revolution and the "dictatorship of the proletariat," marking the end of exploitation and social conflict. Because exploitation and conflict are considered the causes of crime, the revolution would end most forms of crime also.

Marx wrote about crime only to illustrate the bitter fruits of capitalism and did not develop any systematic criminological theory. As Alvin Gouldner (1973:xii) has pointed out, "Viewing criminals and deviants as a Lumpenproletariat that would play no decisive role in the class struggle, and indeed, as susceptible to use by reactionary forces, Marxists were not usually motivated to develop a systematic theory of crime and deviance." Unlike thinkers such as Durkheim, who viewed crime as a natural part of social life and even functional in some ways, Marx and his collaborator, Freidrich Engels, saw it as a palpable indicator of social sickness that had to be cut out. Although some Marxist criminologists tend to defend and romanticize criminals as victims rather than victimizers (Inciardi, 1980:14), Marx and Engels made plain their profound disdain for them. In the *Communist Manifesto*, Marx and Engels referred to them as: "The dangerous class, the social scum (lumpenproletariat), that rotting mass thrown off by the lowest layers of the old society" (1948:11). Although they viewed crime and criminals as the products of an unjust, alienating, and demoralizing social structure that denied productive labor to masses of unemployed—the struggle of the isolated individual against the prevailing conditions—these conditions were not construed as a justification of criminal behavior. After all, these "scum" were victimizing the honest laboring class, or "providing demoralizing services such as prostitution and gambling" (Bernard, 1981:365).

Marx and Engels were also concerned with the origin and use of law ("bourgeois legalism"), noting that the rich and powerful in every age make rules to favor themselves and subordinate the classes below them. Capitalist societies pass laws that criminalize any action that jeopardizes private property, and tend to overlook many socially injurious activities that may be viewed as economically beneficial for the ruling class. It is for this reason that critical criminologists tend to explore such topics as lawmaking, white-collar and corporate crime, and differential criminal sanctioning in order to emphasize the alleged evils of capitalism and the unjustness of the criminal justice system (Toby, 1980).

The First Marxist Criminologist

Dutch criminologist Willem Bonger has been credited with the first work completely devoted to a Marxist analysis of crime. His book *Criminality and Economic Conditions* (1916/1969) is widely recognized as a classic. Like any good Marxist, Bonger saw the roots of crime in the exploitive and alienating conditions of capitalism. Unlike many modern Marxists, Bonger incorporated individual differences into his work. He believed that some individuals are at greater risk for criminality than others due to biological differences, and that people varied in their "moral qualities . . . according to the intensity of their innate social sentiments" (1969:88). The social sentiments that concerned him were *altruism*—an active concern for the well-being of others—and its opposite, *egoism*—a concern only for one's own selfish interests. As noted in Chapter 3, various studies have placed the heritability of altruism—and hence also of egoism, its polar opposite—at around 0.5, which corroborates Bonger's view that individuals differ in their "innate social sentiments." He was adamant, however, that these individual factors are secondary to environmental ones, for it is only by the transformation of society from capitalism to socialism, from oppression to equality, that it is possible to enhance the altruistic sentiment and thus reduce crime.

Regardless of the individual's innate propensity for altruism or egoism, then, whether one or the other is the dominant sentiment in society depends on the way society is organized, or more specifically, how it produces its material life (its mode of production). Altruism, Bonger (1969:33) wrote, is the predominant sentiment among "primitive" peoples among whom the ideas of surplus, profit, and social classes did not exist (Marx's "primitive communism"). In short, the uniformity of existence, and thus of interests, is conducive to a general culture-wide altruistic sentiment, or a Durkheimian mechanical solidarity, if you will, regardless of any innate individual variability in this sentiment. Capitalism, on the other hand, by its very nature (an alienating forced division of labor) generates egoism and blunts altruism. The intense competition for wealth, profits, status, jobs, and so forth, leaves many of the less fortunate in its wake. Such a moral climate generates alienation, greed, and crime. All individuals in capitalist societies are infected by egoism because they are alienated from authentic social relationships with their fellow human beings, and all are thus prone to crime—the poor out of economic necessity, the rich from pure greed.

Bonger (1969:108) provides an example of how greed and envy are generated by capitalism. His words have a very Mertonian "American dream" ring to them:

> Modern industry manufactures enormous quantities of goods without the outlet for them being known. The desire to buy, then, must be excited in the public. Beautiful displays, dazzling illuminations, and many other means are used to attain the desired end. [In the modern department store] the public is drawn as a moth to a flame. The result of these tactics is that the cupidity of the crowd is highly excited.

Although Bonger never wavered from the position that the "root cause" of crime is the capitalist mode of production, he was careful to delineate the mechanisms by which he believed capitalist-generated egoism translated into criminal behavior. For instance, he traces the effects of poverty on family structure (broken homes, illegitimacy) and on parental inability to properly supervise their children. He also writes about "the lack of civilization and education among the poorer classes" (1969:195). This emphasis on family structure and the moral deficits of the poor show an affinity for the concepts of control theory, an affinity for which he has been criticized by other Marxists as being nonMarxist (Taylor, Walton & Young, 1973).

Modern Marxist Criminology

Because Marx wrote so little about crime, it is better to characterize modern Marxist criminologists as left-wing radicals for whom Marxism serves as a philosophical underpinning. Early Marxist criminologists typically explained crime and criminality in terms of Marx and Engels's *primitive rebellion* thesis; that is, the struggle of alienated and isolated individuals against the prevailing social order. Additionally, unlike Bonger or Marx, many Marxist criminologists are prone to view the class struggle as the *only* source of *all* crime (Bohm, 1982). These criminologists, especially those writing in the 1970s, the heyday of Marxist criminology, tended to defend and excuse the acts of ordinary street criminals (Marx's "social scum") as rational responses to the brutality of their existence (or even as revolutionary heroes) and to view "real" crime as consisting of such things as racism, sexism, imperialism, and capitalism itself (Platt, 1975).

According to many of Marxism's critics, this view is little more than maudlin sentimentality for criminals (Toby, 1980). Some Marxists are themselves critical of this romanticized view of common street crime, because crime prevents the formation of proletarian class consciousness, and thus diverts attention away from true revolutionary activity (Lynch & Groves, 1986). Still others find the primitive rebellion thesis simplistic. They strive to formulate a specific Marxist criminology relating crime rates to the political economy of a given society. These are the so-called Marxist *structural* theorists (Greenberg, 1980). Their theories differ very little from nonMarxist theories except they attempt to link the concepts of these theories (e.g., strain, social control) to the broader context of the political economy of the particular society they are examining (Vold, Bernard & Snipes, 1998).

Another important way in which Marxist and nonMarxist theories of crime differ is the links between social class, values, and crime. There can be little argument that social class is an important concept in criminology; it plays some role in all sociological theories of crime and delinquency. However, there is a fundamental difference between the way theorists such as Merton and Sutherland and Marxist theorists view the class/crime nexus. For subcultural theorists, crime and delinquency are motivated by conformity to lower-class values and beliefs, meaning that people commit crimes because they have learned that it is something almost demanded by their class heritage. It is crucial for Marxists to counter this view, for if crime is really a valued social activity in some settings, it would mean that it is not an indicator of alienated social relationships, a concept central to their explanation of crime (Groves & Sampson, 1987).

Marxists accuse cultural and subcultural theorists of never identifying the origins of the values and beliefs thought to generate crime, and are skeptical of values and beliefs as behavioral motivators, especially if one neglects to point out their origins. For Marxists, all behavior, as well as the values and beliefs said to motivate it, is generated by the concrete *material conditions of social life* (Groves & Sampson, 1987). People have the values they do because they occupy a particular place in the socioeconomic structure; they do not occupy that place because of the values they have. In other words, values are simply a reflection of self-interest; therefore, we cannot stop crime by changing values. It is the *material* source of criminal values that must change, and this will only occur (as leftists used to be fond of saying) with the collapse of capitalism and the birth of socialist society (Quinney, 1975).

This, however, is not likely to occur. It is in the capitalist societies of the modern world where human rights are most respected and human wants and needs are most readily accessible. One does not have to be a Marxist (or even a liberal) to acknowledge the many faults of capitalism, such as obscene levels of inequality and the subordination of almost everything to the "god" of the "bottom line," and that they can and should be rectified. If changes are to be made, the left will need a more realistic view of what changes are possible and desirable and thus a more realistic view of human nature. Peter Singer (2000:60-62) offers a number of propositions that a "Darwinian left" would and would not accept. To the extent that a Darwinian left accepts these propositions, they will enhance both their reputations as scientists and their chances of having their policy recommendations taken seriously. According to Singer, a Darwinian left *would not*:

1. Deny the existence of human nature, nor insist that it is inherently good and infinitely malleable.

2. Expect to end all conflicts between humans by revolution, social change, or better education.

3. Assume that all inequalities are due to such things as prejudice and discrimination, although some inequalities are, many others are not.

On the other hand, a Darwinian left *would:*

1. Accept the reality of human nature and seek to understand it so that leftist policies can be grounded in the best available evidence of what people are like.

2. Reject any inference from what is "natural" to what is "right."

3. Expect that under any social, political, or social conditions, many people will act competitively to enhance their own status and power and those of their kin.

4. Expect that under any social, political, or social system, most people will respond positively to opportunities for beneficial cooperation.

5. Promote structures that foster cooperation and attempt to channel competition in prosocial directions.

6. Stand by the traditional values of the left by supporting the weak, poor, and oppressed, but think carefully about whether proposed changes will really benefit them.

In summary, Marxism and Darwinism are not natural enemies; they are simply estranged. Learning more about biosocial approaches can have only a beneficial effect on the theory and practice of the left. Marxists may well be more interested in changing the world than in interpreting it, as Marx asserted, but surely change can be more easily accomplished and be more acceptable to all if predicated on a strong biosocial knowledge of human nature. Marxists have nothing to fear from such a human nature. As Robert Wright (1995) has pointed out, it is surprising how far to the left a modern Darwinian view of the human mind can take us. Darwinism has far more sustenance to offer the radical left than it ever had to offer the radical right.

FEMINIST CRIMINOLOGY

Broadly defined, feminism is a set of theories and strategies for social change that take gender as their central focus in attempting to understand social institutions, processes, and relationships. Feminists hold that women suffer oppression and discrimination in a society run for men by men who have passed laws and created customs to perpetuate their privileged position (Daly & Chesney-Lind, 1988). Feminist criminologists take these core elements and apply them to criminology.

There are many varieties of feminist criminology just as there are of "male" critical criminology, and they are just as hard to capture with a single stroke of the pen. These varieties—liberal, radical, socialist, Marxist, and various positions in between—have at least one thing in common with each other and with the various critical criminologies: they are largely opposed to mainstream culture. The extent of the opposition varies according to the faction. Feminist criminology is therefore conflict-oriented, but it shifts emphasis to issues of gender and power rather than class and power. Feminists see women as being doubly oppressed by gender inequality (their social position in a sexist culture) and by class inequality (their economic position in a capitalist society). Class-based conflict in the context of capitalism gives way to gender-based conflict within the context of a patriarchal society, and the bourgeoisie and powerful interest groups of male critical theorists become gendered, and defined as "rich white *men*" (Sokoloff & Price, 1995:14, emphasis in original). For many feminists, the only answer to their oppression is the overthrow of the two-headed monster—capitalism and patriarchy.

Gender Differences in Criminal Behavior

Feminist criminology evolved out of an awareness that female crime has been virtually ignored by mainstream criminology or has been interpreted in sexist ways. Feminists want to put women on the criminological agenda. They especially want to be able to interpret female crime from a feminist perspective. Thus, feminist criminology has two major concerns: (1) Do the traditional male-centered theories of crime apply to women? and (2) What explains the universal fact that women are far less likely than men to involve themselves in criminal activity? (Price & Sokoloff, 1995). The first concern is not relevant for the purposes of this book; the second is.

Whenever and wherever records have been kept, it has been found that males commit the overwhelming proportion of criminal offenses, and the more serious and violent the offense, the more males dominate in its commission (Campbell, 1999). This fact is not in dispute, although explanations of it are. The traditional sociological view of gender differences in crime and other forms of deviant behavior is that they are products of differential socialization. This "blank slate" view is favored by liberal, socialist, and Marxist feminists, who assert that men are socialized to be aggressive, ambitious, and dominant, and women are socialized to be nurturing and passive. Male traits are conducive to antisocial behavior in some environments, but female traits are always conducive to conformity. The logical conclusion of this view suggests that if females were socialized in the same way as males (and vice versa), their rates of offending would be roughly the same. Radical feminists differ dramatically from this view; they assert that gender differences are biologically determined: males and females have the gender-linked traits they have because that is the way nature made them (Lanier & Henry, 1998).

The first serious attempt at a feminist criminology adopted the blank-slate assumption of gender differences. In her book *Sisters in Crime* (1975), Freda Adler advanced the *masculinization hypothesis*, which attributed the rise in female crime rates in the 1960s and 1970s to an increasing number of females adopting "male" roles. Asserting that the female's adoption of male roles leads to masculinized attitudes, and eventually to greater female crime, Adler argued that "determined women are forcing their way into the world of crime," adding that "increasing numbers of women are using guns, knives, and wits *to establish themselves as full human beings,* as capable of violent aggression as any man" (1975:15, emphasis added).

Adler's masculinization thesis was not well received by many feminists who did not share her opinion of how women might establish their humanity and who also perceived it as providing ammunition for those who oppose women's liberation ("We're asking for more crime by putting women in the work force"). Nor has the thesis been supported by research. Female crime in the United States has increased over the past 30 years, but as a proportion of total arrests, the female arrest rate has not varied by more than five percentage points, and the male/female gap—which is the real issue—has remained essentially unchanged (Campbell, 1999; Daly & Chesney-Lind, 1988).

Rita Simon offered a different view in her book *Women and Crime* (1975). Simon concentrated on the increased opportunities afforded women to commit job-related crime by virtue of their increased presence in the work force (the *emancipation hypothesis*) rather than the masculinization of attitudes. Although it is obvious that to commit job-related crimes one must first be employed in positions making them possible, some feminists dismissed Simon's theory as a theory of white middle-class female crime that ignores the crimes of African-American and lower-class white women. After all, female crime reflects male crime in that black and lower-class white females commit more offenses than white and middle-class females (Morris, 1987). Moreover, the majority of studies actually support the *opposite* of the emancipation hypothesis; that is, as the trend toward gender equality has increased, females have tended to commit fewer rather than more crimes relative to males (Ellis & Walsh, 2000:388).

A more recent effort to account for gender differences concluded that the genders differ in exposure to delinquent peers and that males are more likely than females to be affected by delinquent peers (Mears,

Ploeger & Warr, 1998). Substantively, this is nothing more than a roundabout way of saying "boys will be boys" and "girls will be girls." Mears and his colleagues also contend that a greater sense of morality among females has a strong inhibitory effect. These "explanations" are, of course, couched in terms of sex role socialization: females commit fewer crimes because they are more strictly supervised and are socialized more strongly to conformity. These factors certainly impact decisions to misbehave for both genders, but controlling for supervision level results in the same large gap in male/female offending; that is, comparably supervised boys have higher rates of delinquency than girls (Gottfredson & Hirschi, 1990). Further adding to the misery of this position is a meta-analysis of 172 studies that found a nonsignificant tendency for boys to be *more* strictly supervised than girls (Lytton & Romney, 1991). Subsequent studies have shown that large sex differences in antisocial behavior exist regardless of level of supervision and whether or not the family is patriarchal (implying strict control of females) or egalitarian (implying more equal treatment of boys and girls) (Chesney-Lind & Shelden, 1992; Morash & Chesney-Lind, 1991). As Diana Fishbein (1992:100) summed up the issue, "[C]ross cultural studies do not support the prominent role of structural and cultural influences of gender-specific crime rates as the type and extent of male versus female crime remains consistent across cultures."

Biosocial Explanations

Biological explanations for gender differences do not sit well with many sociologists. Steffensmeier and Allan (1996:464) provide us with a statement that is embarrassing to anyone having a professional connection with sociology when they write: "If the gender gap had a biological basis, it would not vary, as it does, across time and space." In other words, if biology played any role at all, the gender gap would be precisely of the same magnitude at all times and all places. This may be a logical conclusion for anyone who thinks that biology is destiny. Proponents of that idea do not grasp the logic that it is precisely the fact that the magnitude of the gender gap varies across time and space and yet still remains constantly wide at all times and in all places that biological factors *must* play a part.

The gender gap, especially for violent crime, is so universally pervasive that the most logical explanation must lie in fundamental innate differences between the sexes (Ellis, 1989; Fishbein, 1992; Walsh, 1995c). The notion that sex differences are solely "socially constructed" grates against so much natural science data (as well as simple common sense) that advocates of such a position are simply not taken seriously outside of their own circle, probably not even by the majority of nonfeminist social scientists. If sex role socialization, supervision levels, and so on, are important in accounting for gender differences, there should be a set of cultural conditions under which crime rates would be equal for both sexes, or even under which female rates would be higher. As Fishbein (1992) noted, no such conditions have ever been discovered.

Biosocial explanations of gender differences in many different spheres of human life rest on a foundation of differential neurological organization reflecting the influence of prenatal hormones, which in turn reflect sex-specific evolutionary pressures. Sex role socialization is not incompatible with biosocial arguments insofar as it reflects these mechanisms, but biosocial explanations are just as unwelcome among mainstream feminists as biosocial explanations for the origins of social class are among Marxists. However, robust gender differences are noted in all human cultures from the earliest days of life. These differences are dramatically underscored during the teen years and are observed in all primate and most mammalian species (Archer, 1996; Geary, 1998).

A large number of studies comparing the family backgrounds of male and female delinquents and criminals have found that female delinquents and criminals tend to come from more dysfunctional families (broken home, alcoholism, parental sexual promiscuity, mental illness, abuse, and neglect) than boys (reviewed in Walsh, 1991). From these studies it is apparent that it requires a greater degree of environmental disability to push females over the line from conforming to nonconforming behavior. This suggests to a number of scholars that there is a stronger genetic component to female crime than to male crime (Baker et al., 1989; Mealey, 1995; Raine, 1993; Widom & Ames, 1988). In other words, because females are more resistant to crime-generating environmental forces (whatever they may be) than males, there probably is a stronger genetic "push" toward crime for women who engage in it than for men who engage in it.

The greater male susceptibility to environmental forces also suggests that maleness per se is a potent genetic risk for antisocial behavior. All traits discussed in this book that are known to be heritable and associated with criminality (such as ADHD, CD, aggressiveness, pain tolerance, dominance seeking, impulsiveness, and serotonin, MAO, and testosterone levels) are also related to gender—with males being much more vulnerable. At the proximate level, male vulnerability is largely a function of the differential exposure of male and female brains to androgens in utero (Fishbein, 1992; Kimura, 1992; Lopreato & Crippen, 1999).

The Proximate Origins

In all mammalian species, maleness is induced from an intrinsically female form: it is not the presence of two X chromosomes that makes a female, it is the absence of the Y-chromosome. It is not the Y chromosome per se, but rather a single-copy gene called the SRY ("sex-determining region of the Y") that determines sex. All XY individuals would develop as females without the SRY gene, and XX individuals have all the material needed to make a male except this one gene. The SRY gene induces the development of the testes, which produce androgens that will masculinize (or defeminize) various brain structures, as well as the Mullerian inhibiting substance (MIS), which causes the atrophy of internal female sex organs.

Perhaps the best way to study neurohormonal effects of gender differences in behavior is to study what happens when the process of "sexing" the brain goes somewhat awry. Sometimes infants are born with ambiguous genitalia, prompting physicians to ponder what sex these infants "really" are. Indifferent to the warring factions of social science, physicians use a classification scheme based on the appearance of the external genitalia to determine sex of rearing (Luks et al., 1988). Their only motive is a concern with the practical issue of raising children in a manner consistent with the degree of their brain virilization, and the degree of virilization of the genitalia provides an indication of the extent of this. That is, the more masculinized the genitalia, the more likely the brain has been organized along male lines, and the more feminine the genitalia, the less brain masculinization (or defeminization) has taken place.

Intersex anomalies (pseudohermaphrodites) are "deviations from the norm." As such, they may provide us with important clues to the biological substrates of sex-typical behavior, just as mutants serve biologists to clarify the species norm and brain-damaged patients provide valuable information about the organization of the normal brain (Ellis & Ames, 1987; Shallis, 1991). Brain masculinization is not an all-or-nothing process; it is a continuum that may contain significant male/female overlap. The female fetus is protected from the diverting effects of androgen, but not completely. However, once prenatal androgens have sensitized receptors in the male brain to their effects, they activate the brain to engage in male-typical behavior, particularly at puberty, when the brain receives its second great surge of androgens.

Walsh (1995c) explored the pseudohermaphrodite literature to explore the behavioral consequences of the various levels of virilization (as indexed by basal testosterone levels) each type represents. These types are briefly described below.

Turner's syndrome females (TS). TS females either lack a second sex chromosome or have a structurally abnormal second X. Lacking normal, functioning ovaries, they are deficient in sex hormones and evidence many of the deficits in right-hemisphere brain functioning that one would expect from prenatally androgen-absent or -deficient individuals, such as an extreme VIQ > PIQ discrepancy. They also possess many exaggeratedly feminine traits, especially those associated with prosocial behavior such as passivity and high levels of nurturance and empathy.

Androgen-insensitivity syndrome (AIS) is a syndrome in which the receptor sites of XY males that normally bind androgens are partially or fully inoperative. If the receptors are completely inoperative, the male genotype develops a female phenotype. Although AIS individuals have androgen-producing testes (undescended), their androgen receptors are insensitive to its effects and the internal male sex structures do not develop. Because the testes secrete normal male amounts of MIS, AIS individuals have neither male nor female internal sex organs, although the external genitalia are unambiguously female. Unresponsive to the masculinizing effects of androgens on the brain, AIS individuals conform to typical behavioral patterns of normal females—and, as with TS females, exaggeratedly so.

Congenital adrenal hyperplasia (CAH) is an autosomal recessive trait that prevents the synthesizing of cortisol from androgen by the adrenal cortices. Instead of cortisol, androstenedione (a precursor of testosterone) is secreted, resulting in precocious sexual development in males and variable degrees of masculinization of the genitalia and brains of females. CAH females engage in more male-typical behavior, possess more male-typical traits (e.g., "tomboyism," slightly better visual/spatial than verbal skills, lower maternal interests, less interest in marriage, a greater interest in careers), and have a greater probability of homosexuality than normal females. Although there are no studies directly assessing the criminal behavior of CAH women, because they are higher than hormonally normal women on characteristics positively associated with crime (a liking for rough-and-tumble play, a tendency toward PIQ > VIQ, and experimental sexual behavior) and lower on characteristics negatively associated with crime (maternal interest, commitments to relationships), they are likely to be present in criminal populations in numbers relatively greater than their number in the general population.

Klinefelter's syndrome (KS) males have two or more X chromosomes and one or more Y chromosomes. They tend to be taller than normal males, to have smaller than normal genitalia, to develop relatively well-formed breasts at puberty, to have about one-half of the male postpubertal amount of testosterone, to exhibit a low level of sexual activity, and to have difficulty forming pair-bonds. Understandably, KS males often have sexual identity problems and are significantly more likely than XY males to be homosexual, bisexual, and inmates in prisons and mental hospitals. KS individuals tend to be unaggressive and passive, and their crimes are almost always nonviolent or of a sexual nature.

The *XYY syndrome* is the anomaly that has generated more interest than any other. The XYY male is not a "supermale" or a homicidal maniac, but he is significantly more likely than XY males to evidence pathological exaggeration of male-typical behavioral traits. XYY males are significantly more likely than XY males to be impulsive, enuretic, short-tempered, to have a PIQ > VIQ intellectual profile, and to show atypical brain-wave patterns. Plasma testosterone concentrations of XYY men are usually found to be significantly higher than in matched samples of normal XY men. Although most XYY males lead fairly normal lives, they are imprisoned or in psychiatric hospitals at rates exceeding their incidence in the general population by 7.0 and 2.6 times, respectively.

Thus, antisocial behavior (or at least the traits associated with it) is predictable from masculinity/androgen levels across the gender continuum. TS and AIS individuals are the least masculine in terms of androgen levels and are the most socially conforming of all individuals on the continuum. Normal XX females have higher androgen levels and higher levels of deviance than TS or AIS individuals, but as a group they are still very much at the lower end on both. CAH females have both higher androgen levels and higher deviance levels than normal females, although they have lower levels than normal males on both. KS males have significantly less testosterone than normal males but significantly more than normal females, and have a higher level of deviance than both normal females and normal males. If sexual deviance were omitted, KS males fall below the normal male average level of deviant behavior. Finally, XYY males have higher androgen levels and higher levels of behavioral deviance than normal males.

Although the facilitative influence of testosterone does not appear strong enough to account for much variance in antisocial behavior when assayed solely within the normal male range, the normal male range is a severely restricted one in a much larger distribution across the full range of human gender possibilities. Intersex anomalies reflect extreme variance in androgen levels, ranging from either complete absence or insensitivity to it (TS, AIS), to the upper level of the normal male range, where most XYY males are located. Although the rarity of pseudo-hermaphrodism renders the evidence sparse, it is both consistent and convincing: Antisocial behavior and nonconformity of all kinds increase as we move from extreme femininity to extreme masculinity, as defined by androgen levels. While some feminists may insist that male/female differences in socially disapproved behavior are explicable in terms of sex role socialization, it would require extraordinary sophistry to explain the pattern revealed here similarly. Social science has no theory capable of making sense of this pattern, but an understanding of the behavioral organizing effects of gonadal steriods circulating in the developing fetal brain renders it intelligible.

The Ultimate Origins

Neurohormonal differences between the sexes provide a proximate-level explanation of gender differences in the propensity to commit antisocial acts, but they do not explain why these differences should exist in the first place. Although most feminists dismiss biosocial explanations as "sexist," in contrast to the images of helpless females as the pawns of powerful males presented in many feminist writings, evolutionary theory focuses on female choice (sexual selection) as the major mechanism that drove the evolution of sex differences. The evolutionary perspective may thus be viewed as offering a more affirmative view of women than the feminist perspective.

Anne Campbell (1999) surveyed a multitude of studies from anthropology, sociology, psychology, and primatology to provide the best contemporary evolutionary explanation for sex differences in criminal behavior in her *staying alive* hypothesis. Campbell's argument has to do with evolved sex differences in basic biology relevant to parental investment and status striving. Because a female's obligatory parental investment is greater than a male's, and because of the greater dependence of the infant on the mother, a mother's presence is more critical to offspring survival (and hence to the mother's reproductive success) than is a father. Given that a female's survival ("staying alive") is more critical to her reproductive success (in terms of maximizing the probability that her offspring will survive) than is a male's survival to his, Campbell argues that females have evolved a propensity to avoid engaging in behaviors that pose survival risks. The practice of keeping nursing children in close proximity in ancestral environments posed an elevated risk of not only the mother's personal injury but also that of the child if the mother placed herself in risky situations (Beckerman, 1999). The evolved proximate mechanism Campbell proposes is a greater propensity for females to experience many different situations as fearful. She surveys evidence showing that there are no sex differences in fearfulness across a number of contexts *unless* a situation contains a significant risk of physical injury. Fear of injury accounts for the greater tendency of females to avoid or remove themselves from potentially violent situations, and to employ indirect and low-risk strategies in competition and dispute resolution, relative to those used by males.

The greater female concern for personal survival also has implications for sex differences in status-seeking. Recall that males exhibit greater variance in reproductive success than females but less parental certainty, and thus have more to gain and less to lose than females by engaging in intrasexual competition for mating opportunities. Striving for status and dominance was a risky business in evolutionary environments and still is in some environments today. Because dominance and status is less reproductively consequential for females than for males, there has been less evolutionary pressure for the selection of mechanisms useful in that endeavor for females than for males (Barash & Lipton, 2001). Campbell points out that although females do engage in intrasexual competition for mates, it is rarely in the form of violence and aggression in any primate species. Most of it is decidedly low-key, low-risk, and chronic as opposed to male competition, which is high-key, high-risk, and acute. The female assets most pertinent to reproductive success are youth and beauty, which one either does or does not have. Male assets are the resources females desire for their reproductive success; unlike youth and beauty, they can be achieved in competition with other males. Males are willing to incur high risks to achieve the status and dominance that bring them resources and thus access to more females.

Campbell shows that when females engage in crime, they almost always do so for instrumental reasons and the crimes themselves rarely involve risk of physical injury. Both robbery and larceny theft involve expropriating resources from others, but females constitute about 43 percent of arrests for larceny/theft and only about 7 percent of arrests for robbery, a crime carrying a relatively high risk for personal injury. There is no mention in the literature that female robbers crave the additional payoffs of dominance that male robbers do or that they seek reputations as "hard-asses" (Katz, 1988). High-status, dominant, and aggressive females tend not to be particularly desirable as mates, and a woman with a reputation as a "hard-ass" is generally considered to be most unattractive. Campbell (1999:210) notes that while women do aggress and do steal, "they rarely do both at the same time because the equation of resources and status reflects a particularly masculine logic."

It is important to realize that sex differences in aggression, dominance-seeking, and sexual promiscuity are related to parental investment rather than biological sex per se. It is the level of parental investment and its accompanying process, sexual selection, that exert pressure for the selection of the neurohormonal mechanisms that underlie these behaviors. There are species in which females do not carry the primary burden of parental investment. In a number of bird and fish species, males contribute greater parental investment (e.g., incubating the eggs and feeding the young); in these species, it is the female who takes the risks, who is promiscuous and the aggressor in courtship, and who engages in intrasexual competition for mates (Barash & Lipton, 2001; Betzig, 1999). Males and females in these species thus assume characteristics that are opposite those of males and females in species in which the females assume all or most of the burden of parenting. This sex-role reversal provides support for Campbell's thesis and underlines the usefulness of cross-species comparisons.

EVOLUTIONARY CONTRIBUTIONS TO UNDERSTANDING RAPE AND DOMESTIC VIOLENCE

This section addresses two issues at the forefront of feminist criminology: rape and domestic violence. Women are overwhelmingly the victims of these crimes, and thus would benefit most from a better understanding of their origins. Naturalistic explanations for crimes such as these tend to evoke strong emotions in those who believe that such explanations seek to excuse them. They do no such thing. As we shall see, although evolutionary theory differs from feminist theory in terms of explaining these crimes, in many respects, they are surprisingly consistent.

Rape

The fundamental assumption of the feminist theory of rape is that it is motivated by power, not sexual desire. It is viewed as a crime of violence and degradation designed to intimidate and keep women "in their place" (Gilmartin, 1994). Most feminist theorists believe that to understand rape we have to understand that there are large social, legal, and economic power differentials between men and women and that these differentials affect all social interactions between men and women. Because men enjoy the power advantage, they are able to use any and all means to control women, including rape.

According to feminist theory, males are socialized to rape via the many gender-role messages society sends them asserting their authority and dominance over women (Gilmartin, 1994). Rape is the major weapon males have used to establish and maintain culture-wide patriarchy and the dominance of individual men over individual women, because the threat of rape forces a woman to seek the protection of a man from the predations of other men, thus forcing her into permanent subjugation. The most extreme statement of this position was made by Susan Brownmiller, who asserted that rape "is nothing more or less than a conscious process of intimidation by which *all* men keep *all* women in a state of fear" (1975:5, emphasis added) Many feminists, then, view rape as a violent *political* act, not as a sexual act.

Given this politicized view, many feminists tend not to interpret rape as an act committed by a few psychologically unhealthy men. As the master symbol of women's oppression, it is considered an act that all men may commit and one that is indicative of the general hatred of women that characterizes the behavior of "normal" adult men (Herman, 1990:178). Supporters of this view provide evidence for this by pointing to "rape proclivity" studies indicating that between 35 and 69 percent of surveyed males admit that they would commit rape given assurances of never being exposed and punished (Skinner et al., 1995), as well as the widespread use of rape in war.

The major problem with feminist theories of rape is the insistence that it is a nonsexual act. While it is obvious that rape is a violent act, it is just as obvious that it is a sexual act also. Most clinicians engaged in the treatment of rapists insist that rape is primarily sexually motivated (Barbaree & Marshall, 1991), and very few men (about 6%) or women (about 18%) believe that it is motivated by anything other than sex (Hall, 1987). Even some feminists have acknowledged that the "not sex" argument is ideologically motivated and that they now recognize the sexual, as well as the violent, nature of rape (Gilmartin, 1994; Herman, 1990).

Evolutionary explanations of rape posit that males in some primate species, including humans, are predisposed toward forced copulation. Evolutionists argue among themselves as to whether the disposition is an adaptation per se or a by-product or "side effect" of other adaptations (e.g., aggression, dominance-striving) that may promote sexual assault in the absence of internal or external constraints (see Thornhill & Thornhill, and commentaries, 1992). In fact, the coauthors of a recent book on rape that is written from the evolutionary perspective admit that they differ on this point (Thornhill & Palmer, 2000). The adaptationist argument avers that ancestral males who were most inclined to pursue multiple sexual opportunities, forcefully or otherwise, would have enjoyed greater reproductive success than males who did not, thus leaving modern males with a genetic legacy inclining them to do the same. Men are thus monomorphic for genes inclining them to rape, meaning that rapists are "normal" rather than pathological men, which is exactly what many feminists have long argued (Brownmiller, 1975).

The by-product argument essentially contends that rape would not have occurred frequently enough or successfully enough (in terms of resulting in pregnancy) to induce an evolutionary trajectory that resulted in a mental mechanism dedicated to rape in the male brain. It is difficult to view rape as an adaptation per se because the vast majority of copulations in any mammalian species are voluntary.

When force is used to secure compliance, it tends to be a tactic of last resort pursued only after other tactics have failed (Ellis, 1991; Wrangham & Peterson, 1996). In other words, rape is probably not common enough to qualify as an adaptation, but it is common enough to be considered an unfortunate part of our evolutionary baggage. Both positions view rape as a high-risk behavior most likely to be committed by males lacking the status or power to acquire consenting partners, that is, by low-status young males living in environments in which high rates of other forms of violence are common (Ellis & Walsh, 1997; Figueredo & McCloskey, 1993).

The huge disparity in parental investment between males and females is the key to understanding the alleged evolutionary origins of rape. The energy expended in copulation is the only necessary male investment in genetic reproduction. Male reproductive success in the ancestral environment rested on the ability to obtain access to as many partners as possible. Males who were most inclined to pursue multiple sex partners, which occasionally may have included forced copulation, probably enjoyed greater fitness than those who did not, thus passing on these inclinations to their male offspring (Smuts, 1992; Thornhill & Thornhill, 1992).

Because of greater obligatory investment, female fitness rested on the ability to secure paternal investment in exchange for exclusive sexual access. Female promiscuity is only evolutionarily viable in species requiring no paternal investment and very little maternal investment after weaning (Diamond, 1992), or in species in which the parental burden rests almost entirely on males. Promiscuous mating leads to paternal uncertainty and thus would have been maladaptive for human females because paternal uncertainty is not likely to result in male investment (Buss, 1994; Wright, 1994). Females have thus evolved a tendency to resist casual copulation with multiple partners (Buss & Schmitt, 1993). The reckless and indiscriminate male strategy and the careful and discriminating female strategy are conflicting strategies, and according to this view, rape is sometimes the result of this conflict.

Many of us find this line of reasoning distasteful because of our propensity to conflate the natural with the good (the naturalistic fallacy). However, this author is not aware of any evolutionary theorist, male or female, who excuses, condones, justifies, or considers rape any less onerous on the basis of its assumed natural origins (i.e., a product or by-product of natural selection). Rape is considered a maladaptive consequence of a mating strategy assumed to have been adaptive in the environments in which our species evolved (Thornhill & Thornhill, 1992). It is also a morally reprehensible crime that requires strong preventive legal sanctions. Calling something "natural" does not dignify it or place it beyond the power of culture to modify, as manifestly it is not.

The evolutionary theory of rape has been criticized on the grounds that it cannot explain the rape of males, children, or postmenopausal women, or sexual attacks that do not include vaginal intercourse, because such acts do not enhance reproductive success (Grauerholz & Koralewski, 1991). This criticism also reveals a misunderstanding of evolutionary logic. As discussed in Chapter 3, organisms are not adapted to seek ultimate goals directly; they are adapted to seek proximate goals that themselves generally blindly serve ultimate goals. More often than not, we consciously attempt to thwart maximizing our fitness via the use of contraception even as we continue to enjoy the mechanism that promotes it. Just as a hammer can be used for purposes other than those for which it was designed, we can use and misuse our adaptations in various ways. Nonreproductive sex is not adaptive, and neither is the nurturing of pets, but both are examples of the nonadaptive diffusion of tendencies that *are* adaptive (Lykken, 1995). Nurturing pets (nonadaptive) calls on the same kinds of tendencies that give us pleasure in nurturing our human offspring (adaptive), just as nonreproductive sexual acts (nonadaptive) call on the same tendencies that lead males to want to copulate with fertile females (adaptive). Evolution is a mindless algorithmic process; it does not instruct us to use our nurturing and sexual inclinations for one thing but not another. Human cultures have constructed moral norms to instruct us in these matters.

This author is frankly agnostic regarding the evolutionary origins of rape. There are as many reasons to doubt the adaptation argument as there are not to doubt it. Rape within small ancestral bands of hunters and gatherers would surely have resulted in intragroup conflict and punishment for the perpetrator, thus making it maladaptive. On the other hand, it is plausible that it may have been adaptive if practiced against females outside the group. As for the by-product argument, surely this is true by definition, because any behavior is the result of a conglomeration of adaptive features interacting with culture. For example, baseball prowess is a by-product of such adaptive features as eye-hand coordination, competitiveness, and speed, interacting with a culture in which this particular sport has a special place. The same design features are just as easily utilized for cricket in other cultures. By definition, any phenotypical trait necessarily involves genes interacting with environments. Yet, the myriad games played across the globe since the beginning of time are cultural inventions; rape is not. It is an insidious act practiced at all times, probably in all cultures, and in many related primate species. Biology thus contributes to its emergence more strongly than other phenotypical behaviors.

An adequate theory of rape that goes beyond species-wide or culture-wide tendencies requires that the many individual differences between males who rape and males who do not rape be examined. Lee

Ellis (1989; 1991a) integrates evolutionary, feminist, and social learning theories in his *synthesized biosocial theory* to carry out such an examination. Ellis's basic thesis is that rape *behavior* is learned via reinforcement principles (i.e., being "pushy" yields increasing levels of sexual satisfaction, thus reinforcing "pushiness"), but the *motivation* behind rape behavior is not learned. According to Ellis, the motivation behind rape behavior is the male sex drive coupled with the drive to possess and control. Because of neurohormonal factors, these evolved drives are stronger in some males than in others, and the stronger the drives, the more easily they will learn the kinds of behavior that may lead to rape. These same neurohormonal factors also result in lessened sensitivity to the painful consequences of their behavior, both for themselves and for their victims. Ellis pulls together many lines of evidence to integrate the most empirically supported concepts from each theory and finds a great deal of similarity, as well as many differences, among them.

In conclusion, the evidence offered by biosocial theories of rape makes it difficult to maintain the position that rape is nonsexual, that it is motivated by hatred of females or by attempts to maintain male social and economic privilege, or that it is a product of differential gender socialization. Rape is obviously a violent and despicable act, but from an evolutionary perspective, violence is a tactic used to obtain sex, not an end in itself. However, the feminist contention that rape is designed to control females cannot be dismissed, as certain evidence in the next section will show.

Domestic Violence

Males in several nonhuman animal species have been observed attacking females showing sexual interest in males other than those who claim proprietary rights over them (Smuts, 1993). It is significant that females among some primate species are particularly likely to be assaulted when they are ovulating and stray too far away from the male who has claim to them (Smuts, 1992). Given the strong evidence of violence, including rape, against females designed to control their sexual behavior in other mammalian species, we can assume with some confidence that similar behavior among humans has the same ultimate goal. Worldwide, domestic violence (except for minor forms of abuse) is overwhelmingly committed by males against females (Arias, Samois & O'Leary, 1988; Harrison & Esqueda, 1999).

According to evolutionary theory, assaults against spouses or lovers are primarily driven by male fitness-promoting mechanisms such as sexual proprietariness, jealousy, and suspicion of infidelity. Evidence from around the world indicates that the single most important cause of domestic violence (including homicide) is male jealousy and suspicion of infidelity (Burgess & Draper, 1989; Lepowsky, 1994). To the extent that males invest resources in females and their offspring, assaultive tendencies aimed (consciously or subconsciously) at maintaining a mate's fidelity will have been favored by natural selection (Buss, 1994; Smuts, 1993). DNA data indicate that between 1 and 30 percent (depending on the culture or subculture) of children are sired by someone other than the putative father (Birkenhead & Moller, 1992; Brock & Shrimpton, 1991). Thus, the threat of cuckoldry is real. So it would appear that males who were least tolerant of threats of cuckoldry—real or imagined—would have left the most offspring. We can be sure that males who were indifferent to the adaptive problem of paternal certainty are not our ancestors. This intolerance does not mean that males have a dedicated mechanism for domestic abuse; it means they have evolved mechanisms, such as jealousy and possessiveness, that upon perceived threats of infidelity sometimes result in the battering of women in whom they may have invested resources.

If male violence against spouses and lovers is a mechanism that evolved largely to prevent real or imagined infidelity, it should be most common in environments where the threat of infidelity (and, hence, cuckoldry) is most real. Such environments would be those in which marriages are most precarious, in which moral restrictions on premarital and extramarital sexual relationships are weakest, and where illegitimacy rates are highest (Burgess & Draper, 1989). These are precisely the same environments in which intrasex assault and homicide (often directly or indirectly over women) are most common (Centerwell, 1995). Domestic violence is not only more prevalent in such environments, it also tends to occur more frequently and to be more violent (Rasche, 1995; Mann, 1995). This is reflected in a homicide rate for African-American women that has exceeded that of white men in the United States since records have been kept (Barak, 1998). Most instances of black female homicide (as well as white female homicide) involve women killing their husbands or boyfriends in self-defense situations (Mann, 1988).

Although by no means limited to the lower classes, domestic violence is most often committed by "competitively disadvantaged (CD) males" (Burgess & Draper, 1989; Figueredo & McClosky, 1993). As many sociologists (e.g., Wilson, 1987) have pointed out, CD males have low mate value because they have less to offer in terms of resources or prospects of acquiring them, which, all other things being equal, should make their mates less desirous of maintaining the relationship with them and thus more likely to seek other partners. Lacking alternative means of controlling their partner's behavior (i.e., of assuring sexual fidelity), CD males may turn to violently coercive tactics to intimidate them (Figueredo & McCloskey, 1993).

Evolutionary psychologists consider efforts to control the sexual behavior of females in whom males have invested resources to be "normal" or "natural" under the circumstances, which evokes anger from feminists and other social scientists. However, behavior should be judged by its consequences, not by its origins, and as is the case with other violent behaviors, evolutionary psychologists soundly condemn domestic violence as onerous behavior deserving of punishment.

Nonevolutionary theories would also predict that most domestic violence would occur in the more deprived environments and be committed by CD males, but would invoke supraindividual factors such as discrimination, status-frustration, or "subculture of violence" explanations. These factors doubtless provide part of the picture, but they are descriptors that require explanation themselves. Such descriptors are generic terms for a number of functionally integrated psychobiological structures and processes we call evolved adaptations. They do not specify why men everywhere find it so important to control "their" women by behavior identical with that observed in other animal species under the same general conditions, or why CD males more readily turn to violence in attempts to accomplish this than do their higher-status counterparts (Figueredo & McCloskey, 1993).

Chapter 10

Looking Back and Looking Forward

This book has been an attempt to convince sociologically trained criminologists to at least examine the possibility that the biosocial sciences can provide valuable insight and promote further understanding of the phenomena of crime and criminality. The objective has been to demonstrate that the key to progress in other sciences has been to maintain consistency with the methods, theories, and concepts of the more fundamental sciences. History has shown that initial opposition to such integration based on supposed threats to the younger disciplines' autonomy soon dissipated when the benefits became apparent. This chapter offers a brief review of the potential benefits that integration with the biosocial sciences should provide criminology. The primary benefit, of course, is that we will recognize that there is nothing antihumanistic about injecting biology into the study of human nature. Recognizing this, we can stop senseless ideological debates that very often end up attacking individual researchers and/or throwing stifling epithets (e.g., "racist," "sexist") at his or her work. Only when such tactics are no longer tolerated can we begin a cooperative endeavor that will eventually lead to a truly scientific criminology. There will still be arguments enough, for the data rarely speak unequivocally for themselves, but hopefully the arguments will be less personal and more useful.

Biosocial criminology is *an* answer, not *the* answer, to progress in criminology. Biosocial research, dealing as it does with the quicksilver of human behavior, has certainly been bedeviled by poor research practices. We can find many examples of less than adequate conceptualizations of phenomena, poor operationalization of variables, small and nonrepresentative samples, lack of control groups, narrow focus, and sometimes unwarranted extrapolations from animal models. All these faults except the last have also bedeviled other approaches to the study of human behavior (and, I would argue, more seriously so). A truly multidisciplinary criminology would serve a "check and balance" function to minimize most of these problems.

WHAT HAVE WE LEARNED FROM BIOSOCIAL PERSPECTIVES?

Behavior Genetics

The primary lesson from our discussion of behavior genetics in Chapter 2 is that the accusation of genetic determinism leveled at biosocial science is a red herring of the ripest kind. This author has yet to hear any biosocial scientist make the kind of statements they are accused of making. Neither, probably, have any of their critics. There are no genes for any kind of nontrivial human behavior. Behavior geneticists are acutely aware that genes simply make proteins that interact with other proteins and the environment in complicated ways. The final products of these interactions do not cause behavior, they simply bias the organism's trait values in one direction or another. It cannot be emphasized enough that genes are not self-activated; rather, they are activated by environmental information, including information that originates in our own thoughts and feelings.

There is a determinism in all this, but because it implies self-determinism, it is a determinism that is more respectful of human dignity than the kinds of cultural determinism favored by so many social scientists. After all, our genes are *ours*; they are at the beck and call of our purposes whether those purposes are morally good, bad, or neutral. They manufacture the proteins that facilitate the traits that modulate our personal responses to the variety of situations we encounter or fashion for ourselves. The concept of gene/environment interaction informs us that the impact an environmental situation (i.e., living in a criminogenic neighborhood) has on us depends on who we are. Who we are, as the concept of gene/environment correlation tells us, is a product of our unique genotype and the environments in which we find ourselves, as well as the environments we have partially created for ourselves from our abilities and the reactions our behavior has evoked from others. This vision of human nature derived from behavior genetics can be viewed as liberating, invigorating, and uplifting.

Evolutionary Psychology

Evolutionary psychology focuses on why we have the traits and characteristics we do. It is more interested in their universality than in their variability. The major lesson from Chapter 3 is perhaps the notion that crime and criminality are normal responses to environmental contingencies. This does not imply simplistic statements such as "They are forced into it by racism/discrimination/poverty (take your pick, or choose an alternative)," nor is it intended to be morally exculpatory. Rather, evolutionary psychology avers that many human adaptations forged by natural selection in response to survival and reproductive pressures in ancestral environments are easily co-opted to serve morally obnoxious purposes. In common with all sexually producing species, humans are designed to be selfish—to be preeminently concerned with our own survival and reproductive success. There are bright and dark sides to selfishness: one side leads to mutual affection and support (reciprocal altruism), and the other to a crabbed selfishness, an egoism shorn of concern for others (a cheater strategy).

Lanier and Henry (1998:91) have written, "The idea that crime is 'in the blood,' that certain criminal behaviors are inherited, is the hallmark of the biological approach to criminological explanation." They go on to explore various "biological" perspectives, including the evolutionary perspective. If evolutionary psychology is deterministic, it is environmentally so, and if crime (more correctly, criminality) is "in the blood," it is in the blood of us all. All humans share the same psychological, as well as morphological, features by dint of a common evolutionary history. Criminal behavior is thus likely to be explained by evolutionary psychologists in environmental terms. They are definitely not likely to say that it is "in the blood." What they are likely to say is that criminal behavior is an alternative method of resource acquisition used by individuals (e.g., the young) who are not yet in a position to gain them legitimately. This certainly does not imply "hard-wired" determinism. It simply means that behavior that we have labeled "criminal" will emerge when evolutionarily relevant triggers signal the possibility of acquiring resources for those otherwise denied them. Thus, rather than being a right-wing brand of hard-wired determinism, evolutionary psychology can be called upon to support many of the propositions of left-wing thinkers. Certainly, evolutionary psychology reminds us of humanity's dark side, but it also reminds us of our nobler side and how both sides aided in our ancestors' reproductive success. We are alive and kicking today because of aspects of our species' characteristics that we would like to disown as well as because of those of which we are justly proud.

The Neurosciences

Study of the neurosciences best captures how wrong critics are to accuse "biological" perspectives of hard-wired determinism. The lesson to take away from the neurosciences is that the genes have surrendered control of the human organism to that wondrous organ of adaptation we call the brain. It was noted in Chapter 4 that following some elementary genetic wiring to jump-start the process, the brain literally wires itself in response to environmental input. Neurons eventually make trillions of connections with each other, with each connection reflecting the organism's experiences (experience-dependent brain development). However, this does not mean that the human mind is a blank slate at birth; there are certain built-in algorithms guiding responses to the environment that are too important to be left to the vagaries of learning (experience-expected brain development).

When the early results of the genome project were released, there was much commentary in the popular press on the finding that the human genome consists of 30,000 to 40,000 genes rather than the 100,000 previously estimated. For many, this news somehow implied greater human freedom. The logic behind this is that fewer genes equal fewer biological controls, a logic that reveals the erroneous belief that genes do indeed control us. According to this logic, a common field mouse must be even freer, because it has 300 fewer genes than a human does. However, we have seen that even 100,000 genes (or even 10 times that number) could not come close to being able to specify all the neuronal connections our brains will make. Neural Darwinists have long claimed that the brain's self-programming function can be viewed as the basis of human freedom—and they may well be right.

Knowledge about the developing brain's responsiveness to environmental input adds impetus to the fight against child abuse and neglect. The realization that protracted abuse and neglect is physically captured by the brain can only aid in securing the financing and implementation of liberal programs aimed at eliminating this scourge. Thus, along with behavior genetics and evolutionary psychology, the neurosciences contain nothing that can honestly be construed as anti-humanistic. On the contrary, all three perspectives offer an image of the human condition that is more liberating that that offered by standard social science, which still views the human mind as a blank slate hammered into form solely by external factors.

SUMMARIZING THE INTEGRATION OF BIOSOCIAL AND TRADITIONAL CRIMINOLOGICAL THEORIES

Anomie and Status Striving

Anomie/strain theory was examined in Chapter 5 with emphasis placed on the central concept of this tradition—SES and status-striving. Status-striving is central to both evolutionary psychology and anomie/strain theory. Perhaps no concept in this book generates more opposition among sociological criminologists than the idea that in an open society a person's SES is caused by individual traits and characteristics. Opposition to this idea is particularly strong when one of those traits is IQ. Yet, the correlations between IQ and income, occupation, and education are consistent and robust, much more so than between parental SES and those variables. The high heritability coefficients found for IQ do not mean that low-IQ people are destined to failure—there is more to SES than intelligence. Nor does it mean that we should give up on trying to educate low-IQ people and place all our resources at the service of high-IQ people, as some have argued. Indeed, resources should be more concentrated where they are needed the most.

Conscientiousness was also shown to be very important for achieving occupational success. Conscientiousness is an aspect of personality developed from temperament. It is a highly heritable trait, but it is also something that must be nurtured. Without conscientiousness, intelligence will not get one very far. High conscientiousness, even if paired with a somewhat less-than-average IQ, will lift a person up the status hierarchy. An intelligent and conscientious person is able to embark on long-term strategies to obtain status and resources legitimately. Those less well endowed need not be abandoned to "innovation" and "retreatism" if programs recognizing and attacking these deficiencies can be implemented.

Social Learning and Adolescence

The main theme in Chapter 6 is adolescence and the antisocial behavior it generates. It was emphasized that differential association and social learning are not enough to account for the high levels of antisocial behavior we observe among adolescents. People are drawn to others on the basis of similarity, and they become more similar because of their associations. Most adolescents are drawn to those among their peers who demonstrate disdain for authority, and in some senses, this is healthy and normal (adaptive). They are sloughing off the apron strings of childhood and seeking autonomy as adults. Delinquents who have built up a store of social capital will desist from offending when their brains fully mature and they have acquired socially responsible roles. These are the offenders that Terrie Moffitt calls "adolescent-limited offenders."

The real problem offenders are those who begin offending prior to puberty and continue well into adulthood. Moffitt calls this relatively small group of individuals "life-course-persistent offenders." These individuals suffer neuropsychological and temperamental impairments that initiate a cumulative process of negative person-environment interactions resulting in a life-course trajectory that propels them toward ever-hardening antisocial attitudes and behaviors. These impairments tend to be accompanied by (and interact with) inept parenting.

Life-course-persistent offenders form the core of gangs and ad hoc delinquent groups that are temporarily attractive to adolescent youths. If the life-course-persistent offender is to be rescued from a life of crime, early intervention emphasizing nurturant strategies is imperative.

Control Theories and the Family

Control theories, both the social- and self-control variations, emphasize the importance of the family. For these theories, antisocial behavior is the default option that occurs in the absence of adequate socialization. As is the case with the anomie/strain tradition, control theory has progressed from a theory that almost saw the offender as irrelevant to one that examines the offender's cognitive and temperamental traits. These traits are subsumed under the label of "low self-control," which is a variable that Michael Gottfredson and Travis Hirschi assert "explains all crime, at all times" (1990:117). According to the control tradition, low self-control (as well as the bonds that are the basis of social control) is solely a function of family dynamics.

Neither version of control theory has much to say about *why* the family is so important to human development in any ultimate sense. Chapter 7's discussion of the family (the reproductive team of male, female, and offspring) focused on its evolutionary origins. It claimed that the family is an adaptation in the fullest sense of the word. If this is so, then we can expect problems when the family is disrupted. It was acknowledged that family problems could have preceded family disruption, and that the nuclear family of today's industrialized societies places tremendous burdens on parents. Nevertheless, we must be aware of the many disadvantages that accrue when children are reared in evolutionarily unexpected family arrangements.

The theory of low self-control was also taken to task for ignoring both child effects on parents and the biology of self-control. The theory appears to take for granted that socialization is a one-way street running from parents to children rather than a busy intersection in which children are very much involved. The theory also ignores the facts that low serotonin underlies low self-control and that serotonin levels are heritable. Thus, given an equal level of parenting, some children will develop self-control and others will not. The theory was also taken to task for not at least taking negative emotionality into consideration and for ignoring the age effects on antisocial behavior that were so brilliantly addressed by Moffitt (1993).

Human Ecology/Social Disorganization and Race

The major concern of the human ecology/social disorganization tradition is the influence of the physical and sociocultural environment on antisocial behavior. Social disorganization is greatest in America's inner cities, which are inhabited overwhelmingly by African-Americans. Moreover, the proportion of blacks in a city has long been the best predictor of a city's crime rate. The question asked in Chapter 8 was: "Are people or places more important in terms of crime causation?"

The inner cities suffer from multiple disabilities ranging from deindustrialization, to the presence of crack cocaine, to the spawning of an explicitly hostile oppositional culture. A culturally isolated community can absorb only so many problems before reaching epidemic proportions (the tipping point). These areas are overflowing with unsupervised youths who have formed themselves into gangs and who wreak havoc in their neighborhoods. The existence of so many unsupervised youths was accounted for by the huge illegitimacy rates in black communities, which in turn is a function of a male-favoring sex ratio that inclines many men to be unwilling to commit to one woman. Various lines of evidence were introduced, showing that promiscuity is common in cultures with an excess of females.

It was also shown that the inner-city environment may alter the biology of a person in ways conducive to criminal behavior. Black males are often found to have higher levels of testosterone and lower levels of serotonin than white males, but this is not found to be true when whites are compared to blacks who are not reared in inner-city "honor subcultures." High testosterone coupled with low serotonin often leads to angry aggression in environments in which gaining status is of the utmost importance and in which dominance hierarchies are often in flux.

Critical and Feminist Theories and Conflict

The theories in Chapter 9 are all leftist, and all are vehemently opposed to applying biological thinking to criminal behavior. It was emphasized that Marxist theories are not inherently antibiological, because Marx often spoke of human nature. The opinion was expressed that a Darwinian view of human nature has more to offer the left than it does the right. The message in Peter Singer's (2000) plea for a "Darwinian left" is that leftists must make their knowledge commensurate with their compassion if they are to avoid the horrendous mistakes of the past.

A major concern of feminist criminology is to understand why everywhere and always males commit far more antisocial acts than females. Explanations in terms of environmental variables just will not wash. The proximate answer to this central concern appears to be neurohormonal. Male brains and female brains are different because male brains are diverted from their default female form by androgen surges that occur in utero. The male brain is further sensitized to the effects of androgens at puberty. Male-typical behaviors (status-striving, dominance, aggressiveness) are facilitated by androgen-activated brain areas that subserve reproductive efforts. These same behaviors also facilitate criminal behavior in certain situations.

In terms of the ultimate origins of male/female differences in the propensity to commit crime, we explored Anne Campbell's (1999) "staying alive" hypothesis. Campbell posits that the mothering role is so important to a female's reproductive success that natural selection favored women who had a fear of placing themselves in physical danger. It was noted that as the potential for physical harm becomes increasingly greater in the commission of a crime, female participation becomes increasingly less frequent. Females' greater parental investment, and thus their greater need to avoid dangerous situations, also accounts for the lower level of status-striving, an activity that can lead to criminal behavior (in some instances) among women.

BIOSOCIAL CRIMINOLOGY AND ETHICS

Whenever someone completes a work for a general audience having anything to do with the biology of human behavior, he or she is inevitably confronted with the expectation that it should be defended on ethical grounds. Biological explanations have long provided an axe to be ground by those of any political persuasion, probably because they are seen as more mysterious and powerful, and thus more threatening, than environmental explanations. Theorists who write from a purely environmental perspective are never burdened with the task of defending their theories, despite history's sad catalogue of inquisitions, gulags, pogroms, genocides, and wars fought in the name of religious and secular ideologies that are far removed from any whiff of the demon biology. Thus, although ethical issues of potential concern have been raised on several occasions in this book (particularly in Chapter 1), they will be summarized and added to here.

Little more than one century old as a respectable science, biology has become the whipping boy of the heartfelt protectors of the disadvantaged. Their concern is appreciated; findings in biology that are relevant to human nature can indeed be used against disadvantaged and disvalued people. However, bigots and hatemongers will mount any vehicle that will give their prejudices a free ride, and they did so for centuries before anyone ever heard of genes.

Nazi Germany is frequently evoked as an example of the dangers of biology. The Nazis were certainly enamoured with eugenics, but surely we do not believe that if Hitler and his cronies had never heard of eugenics, the holocaust would not have happened. The nightmares of racial purity and ethnic cleansing that have bedeviled us throughout human history did not wait for Gregor Mendel or Charles Darwin to sanctify them. Nationalism, not genetic meddling, was used to hypnotize the people of Germany. The Nazis created a myth—Aryan superiority—and a monster—Jews, Slavs, anyone not belonging to the "master race"—and set the myth to devour the monster. While the Nazis tapped into ancient biological underpinnings of tribalism and xenophobia, the mechanisms allowing them access to these ancient traits were social and psychological. Control of the media, the destruction of institutions mediating the relationship between the individual and the state, the frighteningly magnificent rallies, and the cult of the Fuehrer were among the many mechanisms employed.

As pointed out in Chapter 1, the communist terror, which (unlike the Nazi terror) was based squarely on a well-articulated theory of causation, was both longer-lived and quantitatively more heinous. The theory, of course, was purely environmental. The Marxist ideal of equality sounds admirable in theory, but it has been far less so in practice. In practice, it reduced almost everyone to a numbing equality of "propertylessness" and powerlessness. An egalitarian ideology that goes beyond the ideals of equality of justice and opportunity is biologically doomed. It is doomed because it is founded on the assumption that all people are essentially equal in their capacities, and if they are not, we will do our best to make them so.

The evils of the gulag and the firing squad do not simply reflect the corruption of the ideal by human beings, the separation of theory from practice, as some Marxist apologists are wont to claim. It was the proponents of such views who sought to remold societies and individuals in the image of their theory, who did, after all, call for the destruction of an entire class of people. It was flesh-and-blood Marxists who imposed the terror necessary to implement their vision, for only force and repression could mold human beings in ways alien to their nature. Repression and terror are inherent in *any* ideology that brooks no dissent.

Perhaps, however, we should focus less on comparisons and more on the potential for foul deeds that does exist in biological theories. Social Darwinism is dead, wounded by science when it was realized that it was a perverse misinterpretation of Darwinian concepts, and killed off by an evolving sense that in some ways we are our brothers' keepers. Could such a philosophy return? Yes, but it will receive no sustenance from a modern understanding of Darwinism.

We hear less of social Darwinism these days, but we continue to hear of eugenics. Perhaps eugenics is feared more because it is activist and interventionist, whereas social Darwinism promoted only a laissez-faire (neglectful) attitude toward the less fortunate. Early eugenic programs in the United States and Britain were endorsed as sensible and humane by individuals on both sides of the ideological divide, persons such as Sidney Webb, Beatrice (Potter) Webb, Oliver Wendell Holmes, Karl Pearson, Winston Churchill, and George Bernard Shaw. The basic principle of eugenics was that it is best to prevent suffering by sterilizing individuals who were likely to give birth to "defective" children.

A form of "back door" eugenics is practiced today by parents who elect to abort the fetus after being informed that it has some form of genetic defect. Many of us probably see no ethical issue here because the decision is made by individuals in consultation with their physicians and not by some oppressive government. It is government control that most bothers critics of "biological" approaches to crime rather than eugenics per se. They tend to view such approaches as ultimately leading to a kind of therapeutic tyranny, with parolees running around with wires sticking out of their heads, sex offenders with their testes in a jar, and former gang-bangers reduced to pliant zombies cleaning off the tables at fast food restaurants. That these hypothetical measures might reduce crime is not the issue. The issue is that treating individuals diverts attention away from the social factors that critics "know" are responsible for criminal behavior.

At one level, I agree with this assessment. I have repeatedly acknowledged that environmental interventions are the best crime-control methods because such interventions reduce the prevalence of crime. On another level, though, I strongly disagree. Flesh-and-blood people commit crimes, not disembodied "social factors," the influence of which depends on individual vulnerability to them. Proponents of the treatment approach view treatment as humane and as morally and effectively more superior to years of soul-destroying imprisonment. They also aver that advocating a therapeutic approach for individuals with a demonstrated need for it is a far cry from advocating it as a general method of social control. They would also point out the success of their methods with syndromes that were also once "known" to be caused exclusively by social factors, such as schizophrenia and depression. This author, at least, would love to see a form of long-acting implant that calms the violent, shames the psychopath, brings tears to the eyes of the heartless, makes the impulsive contemplate, and causes a man contemplating rape to have intensely graphic visions of pit bulls devouring his sexual organs. Yes, this is "treating symptoms, not causes," but medicine treats symptoms rather than elusive causes all the time. It is the symptoms that cause the patient's pain, and it is the criminal's manifest symptoms that cause his or her victim's suffering, not the supposed "root causes" of those symptoms, whatever they may be.

We may have the technology to implement such interventions one day, but if we do it will be a political decision, not a scientific one. Biology can no more be blamed for the uses we may decide to put it to than can electricity be blamed for electrocutions. Whatever biological therapies we eventually come up with, they almost certainly will not be genetic. As has been constantly emphasized, there are genes that bias traits in certain directions, but there are no genes that lead directly to any kind of nontrivial behavior. Genes act in concert with other genes, and collectively, they act in concert with the environment.

Suppose we did find a recessive allele that coded "for" sensation-seeking/risk-taking. Because we know that this trait is significantly related to antisocial behavior, should we counsel people to abort fetuses carrying such an allele? If we did, we would be depriving society of millions of vibrant people, for the same sensation-seeking/risk-taking trait that gets some people into trouble with the law is also a characteristic of explorers, police officers, firefighters, inventors, and entrepreneurs.

What if the hypothetical allele was "for" something with no apparent social usefulness, such as extreme impulsiveness, and what if we could exorcise it through genetic engineering? Our extremely impulsive people might just become prudent and restrained, but what else might they become? Because genes interact with each other and with the environment in ways far from perfectly predictable, the elimination of the "impulsive gene" might upset a whole fleet of genetic applecarts to the benefit of neither the individual or society. All genes have potential pleiotropic effects, meaning that they can have multiple effects on the organism via the proteins they produce. Thus, we would potentially eliminate positive as well as negative effects if we were able to engineer the allele out of existence. We do nothing less than play with fire when we imagine that we can eliminate a particular allele and thereby change behavior in the directions we desire.

The real ethical dilemma accompanying our increasing genetic knowledge is the use of genetic information to fire employees or refuse people medical insurance on the basis of genetic screening that reveals some genetic anomaly. Thousands of such cases occur every year, a fact that often prevents individuals from undergoing potentially life-saving genetic testing (Martindale, 2001). Is this a genetic or a social problem? It is, of course, the latter—and so must be the solution. We can benefit from the positive fruits of genetic research without fear of negative consequences simply by passing legislation forbidding access to personal genetic information to anyone but the individual and his or her physician. Neither genetics nor any other branch of biology is going to go away because there is potential for misuse.

Nothing written here will change the mind of the true believer. Such people are so ideologically driven themselves that they cannot imagine that others could conduct their research not similarly driven. For those with open minds, any remaining fear of "biology" as it pertains to explanations of criminal behavior will be assuaged by learning something about it. Misuse of knowledge should be opposed when and where is it misused, but knowledge must never be swept under the rug because some feel that it could be misused. As Bryan Vila (1994:329) has remarked, "Findings can be used for racist or eugenic ends only if we allow perpetuation of the ignorance that underlies these arguments."

References

Abitol, M. (1987). "Obstetrics and Posture in Pelvic Anatomy." *Journal of Human Evolution* 16:243-255.

Adler, F. (1975). *Sisters in Crime: The Rise of the New Female Criminal*. New York: McGraw-Hill.

Agnew, R. (1992). "Foundations for a General Strain Theory of Crime and Delinquency." *Criminology* 30:47-87.

Agnew, R. (1995). "The Contribution of Social-Psychological Strain Theory to the Explanation of Crime and Delinquency." In F. Adler & W. Laufer (eds.), *The Legacy of Anomie Theory*, pp. 113-137. New Brunswick, NJ: Transaction.

Agnew, R. (1997). "Stability and Change in Crime Over the Lifecourse: A Strain Theory Explanation." In T. Thornberry (ed.), *Developmental Theories of Crime and Delinquency*, pp. 101-132. New Brunswick, NJ: Transaction.

Akers, R. (1985). *Deviant Behavior: A Social Learning Approach*. Belmont, CA: Wadsworth.

Akers, R. (1992). "Linking Sociology and Its Specialties: The Case of Criminology." *Social Forces* 71:1-16.

Akers, R. (1994). *Criminological Theories: Introduction and Evaluation*. Los Angeles: Roxbury.

Albanese, J. & R. Pursley (1993). *Crime in America: Some Existing and Emerging Issues*. Englewood Cliffs, NJ: Prentice Hall.

Alcock, J. (1998). *Animal Behavior: An Evolutionary Approach*, 6th ed. Sunderland, MA: Sinauer Associates.

Alexander, R. (1987). *The Biology of Moral Systems*. New York: Aldine de Gruyter.

Allman, William (1994). *The Stone Age Present*. New York: Simon & Schuster.

Allen, G. (1999). "Modern Biological Determinism: the Violence Initiative, the Human Genome Project, and the New Eugenics." In R. Sussman (ed.), *The Biological Basis of Human Behavior: A Critical Review*, pp. 294-304. Upper Saddle River, NJ: Prentice Hall.

Amato, P. & B. Keith (1991a). "Parental Divorce and Well-Being of Children: A Meta-Analysis." *Psychological Bulletin* 110:26-46.

Amato, P. & B. Keith (1991b). "Parental Divorce and Adult Well-Being: A Meta-Analysis." *Journal of Marriage and the Family* 53:43-58.

Anderson, E. (1999). *Code of the Street: Decency, Violence, and the Moral Life of the Inner City*. New York: W.W. Norton.

Archer, J. (1996). "Sex Differences in Social Behavior: Are the Social Role and Evolutionary Explanations Compatible?" *American Psychologist* 51:909-917.

Arias, I., M. Samois & K. O'Leary (1988). "Prevalence and Correlates of Physical Aggression During Courtship." *Journal of Interpersonal Violence* 2:82-90.

Armstrong, E. (1991). "The Limbic System and Culture: An Allometric Analysis of the Neocortex and Limbic Nuclei." *Human Nature* 2:117-136.

Axelrod, R. (1984). *The Evolution of Cooperation*. New York: Basic Books.

Badcock, C. (2000). *Evolutionary Psychology: A Critical Introduction*. Cambridge, England: Polity Press.

Bagozzi, R. & P. Warshaw (1992). "An Examination of the Etiology of the Attitude-Behavior Relation for Goal-Directed Behavior." *Multivariate Behavioral Research* 27:601-634.

Bailey, M. (1997). "Are Genetically Based Individual Differences Compatible with Species-Wide Adaptations?" In N. Segal, G. Weisfeld & C. Weisfeld (eds.), *Uniting Psychology and Biology*, pp. 81-100. Washington, DC: American Psychological Association.

Bailey, M. (1998). "Can Behavior Genetics Contribute to Evolutionary Behavioral Science?" In C. Crawford & D. Krebs (eds.), *Handbook of Evolutionary Psychology: Ideas, Issues, and Applications,* pp. 211-233. Mahwah, NJ: Lawrence Erlbaum.

Baird, A. (1999). Personal communication.

Baird, A., S. Gruber, D. Fein, L. Maas, R. Steingard, P. Renshaw, B. Cohen & D. Yurgelun-Todd (1998). "Functional Magnetic Resonanace Imaging of Facial Affect Recognition in Children and Adolescents." *Journal of the Acadamy of Child and Adolescent Psychiatry* 38:195-199.

Baker, L. & D. Daniels (1990). "Nonshared Environmental Influences and Personality Differences in Adult Twins." *Journal of Personality and Social Psychology* 58:103-110.

Baker, L., W. Mack, T. Moffitt & S. Mednick (1989). "Sex Differences in Property Crime in a Danish Adoption Cohort." *Behavior Genetics* 16:127-142.

Baldwin, J. (1990). "The Role of Sensory Stimulation in Criminal Behavior, with Special Attention to the Age Peak in Crime." In L. Ellis & H. Hoffman (eds.), *Crime in Biological, Social, and Moral Contexts*, pp. 204-217. New York: Praeger.

Barak, G. (1998). *Integrating Criminologies*. Boston: Allyn & Bacon.

Barash, D. & J. Lipton (2001). "Making Sense of Sex." In D. Barash (ed.), *Understanding Violence*, pp. 20-30. Boston: Allyn & Bacon.

Barbaree, H. & W. Marshall (1991). "The Role of Male Sexual Arousal in Rape: Six Models." *Journal of Consulting and Clinical Psychology* 59:621-630.

Barkow, J. (1989). *Darwin, Sex and Status: Biological Approaches to Mind and Culture*. Toronto: University of Toronto Press.

Barkow, J. (1992). "Beneath New Culture is an Old Psychology: Gossip and Social Stratification." In J. Barkow, L. Cosmides & J. Tooby (eds.), *The Adapted Mind: Evolutionary Psychology and the Generation of Culture,* pp. 627-637. New York: Oxford University Press.

Barkow, J. (1997). "Happiness in Evolutionary Perspective." In N. Segal, G. Weisfeld & C. Weisfeld (eds.), *Uniting Psychology and Biology*, pp. 397-418. Washington, DC: American Psychological Association.

Barnett, R., L. Zimmer & J. McCormack (1989). "P>V Sign and Personality Profiles." *Journal of Correctional and Social Psychiatry* 35:18-20.

Baumrind, D. (1993). "The Average Expected Environment is Not Good Enough: A Response to Scarr." *Child Development* 64:1299-1317.

Beckerman, S. (1999). "Violence, Sex, and the Good Mother." *Behavioral and Brain Sciences* 22:215-216.

Beckstrom, J. (1993). *Darwinism Applied: Evolutionary Paths to Social Goals*. Westport, CT: Praeger.

Behar, D. & M. Stewart (1982). "Aggressive Conduct Disorder of Children: The Clinical History and Direct Observations." *Acta Psychiatrica Scandinavia* 65:210-220.

Beirne, P. & J. Messerschmidt (2000). *Criminology*. Boulder, CO: Westview.

Belsky, J. (1997). "Attachment, Mating, and Parenting." *Human Nature* 8:361-381.

Belsky, J. & P. Draper (1991). "Childhood Experience, Interpersonal Development, and Reproductive Strategy: An Evolutionary Theory of Socialization." *Child Development* 62:647-670.

Benes, F. (1997). "Corticolimbic Circuitry and the Development of Psychopathology During Childhood and Adolescence." In N. Krasnegor, G. Lyon & P. Goldman-Rakic (eds.), *The Development of the Prefrontal Cortex: Evolution, Neurobiology, and Behavior*. Baltimore: Brooks.

Berger, B. & P. Berger (1984). *The War on the Family: Capturing the Middle Ground*. Garden City, NY: Anchor.

Bernard, T. (1981). "The Distinction between Conflict and Radical Criminology." *Journal of Criminal Law and Criminology* 72:362-379.

Bernard, T. (1987). "Testing Structural Strain Theories." *Journal of Research in Crime and Delinquency* 24:264-270.

Bernard, T. (1990a). "Angry Aggression Among the 'Truly Disadvantaged.'" *Criminology* 28:73-96.

Bernard, T. (1990b). "Twenty Years of Testing Theories: What Have We Learned and Why?" *Journal of Research in Crime and Delinquency* 27:325-347.

Bernard, T. (1998). "Foreword to the Fourth Edition." In G. Vold, T. Bernard & J. Snipes, *Theoretical Criminology*. New York: Oxford University Press.

Berndt, T. (1982). "The Features and Effects of Friendships in Early Adolescence." *Child Development* 53:1447-1460.

Bernhardt, P. (1997). "Influences of Serotonin and Testosterone in Aggression and Dominance: Convergence with Social Psychology." *Current Directions in Psychological Science* 6:44-48

Betzig, L. (1999). "When Women Win." *Behavioral and Brain Sciences* 22:217.

Birkenhead, T. & A. Moller (1992). "Faithless Females Seek Better Genes." *New Scientist* (July):34-38.

Bjorklund, D. (1997). "The Role of Immaturity in Human Development." *Psychological Bulletin* 122:153-169.

Black, J. & W. Greenough (1997). "How to Build a Brain: Multiple Memory Systems Have Evolved and Only Some of Them are Constructivist." *Behavioral and Brain Sciences* 20:558-559.

Blonder, L. (1991). "Human Neuropsychology and the Concept of Culture." *Human Nature* 2:83-116.

Blau, J. & P. Blau (1982). "The Cost of Inequality: Metropolitan Structure and Violent Crime." *American Sociological Review* 47:114-129.

Blumstein, A. (1995). "A LEN Interview with Professor Alfred Blumstein of Carnegie Mellon University." *Law Enforcement News* 21:10-13.

Blumstein, A. & J. Cohen (1987). "Characterizing Criminal Careers." *Science* 237:985-991.

Bogin, B. (1993). "Why Must I Be a Teenager at All?" *New Scientist* 137:34-38.

Bohm, R. (1982). "Radical Criminology: An Explication." *Criminology* 19:565-589.

Bonger, W. (1916/1969). *Criminality and Economic Conditions*. Bloomington: Indiana University press.

Bonson, K., R. Johnson, D. Fiorella, R. Rabin & J. Winter (1994). "Serotonergic Control of Androgen-Induced Dominance." *Pharmacology, Biochemistry, and Behavior* 49:313-322.

Booth, A. & D. Osgood (1993). "The Influence of Testosterone on Deviance in Adulthood: Assessing and Explaining the Relationship." *Criminology* 31:93-117.

Bouchard, T. & M. McGue (1981). "Familial Studies of Intelligence: A Review." *Science* 250:1055-1059.

Bouchard, T. & N. Segal (1985). "Environment and IQ." In B. Wolman (ed.), *Handbook of Intelligence: Theories, Measurements, and Applications*, pp. 391-464. New York: John Wiley.

Bouchard, T., D. Lykken, M. McGue, N. Segal & A. Tellegen (1990). "Sources of Human Psychological Differences: The Minnesota Study of Twins Reared Apart." *Science* 250:223-228.

Boyd, R. & P. Richerson (1992). "Punishment Allows the Evolution of Cooperation (or Anything Else) in Sizable Groups." *Ethology & Sociobiology* 13:171-195.

Bradley, R. & B. Caldwell (1991). "Like Images Refracted: A View from the Interactionist Perspective." *Behavioral and Brain Sciences* 14:389-390.

Brammer, G., M. Raleigh & M. McGuire (1994). "Neurotransmitters and Social Status." In L. Ellis (ed.), *Social Stratification and Socioeconomic Inequality, Vol. 2: Reproductive and Interpersonal Aspects of Dominance and Status*, pp. 75-91. Westport, CT: Praeger.

Brand, C. (1995). "How Many Dimensions of Personality? The Big 5, the Gigantic 3, or the Comprehensive 6?" *Psychologica Belgica* 34:257-275.

Brannigan, A. (1997). "Self-Control, Social Control and Evolutionary Psychology: Towards an Integrated Perspective on Crime." *Canadian Journal of Criminology* (Oct.):403-431.

Breggin, P. & G. Breggin (1995). "Genetic Theories of Crime are Racist." In P. Winters (ed.), *Crime and Criminals: Opposing Viewpoints*. San Diego: Greenhaven.

Brennan, P., A. Raine, F. Schulsinger, L. Kirkegaard-Sorenen, J. Knop, B. Hutchings, R. Rosenberg & S. Mednick (1997). "Psychophysiological Protective Factors for Male Subjects at High Risk for Criminal Behavior." *American Journal of Psychiatry* 154:853-855.

Brock, D. & A. Shrimpton (1991). "Nonpaternity and Prenatal Genetic Screening." *Lancet* 388:1151-1153.

Bromage, T. (1987). "The Biological and Chronological Maturation of Early Hominids." *Journal of Human Evolution* 16:257-272.

Bronfenbrenner, U. & S. Ceci (1994). "Heredity, Environment, and the Question 'How'—A First Approximation." In R. Plomin & G. McClearn (eds.), *Nature, Nurture, and Psychology*, pp. 313-324. Washington, DC: American Psychological Association.

Brown, D. (1991). *Human Universals*. New York: McGraw-Hill.

Brownmiller, S. (1975). *Against Our Will: Men, Women, and Rape*. New York: Simon & Schuster.

Bruinsma, G. (1992). "Differential Association Theory Reconsidered: An Extension and its Empirical Test." *Journal of Quantitative Criminology* 8:29-49.

Buchanan, C., J. Eccles & J. Becker (1993). "Are Adolescents the Victims of Raging Hormones?: Evidence for Activational Effects of Hormones on Moods and Behavior at Adolescence." *Psychological Bulletin* 111:62-107.

Buck, R. (1999). "The Biological Effects: A Typology." *Psychological Review* 106:301-336.

Buckley, P., R. Buchanan, S. Schultz & C. Tamminga (1996). "Catching Up on Schizophrenia." *Archives of General Psychiatry* 53:456-462.

Burgess, R. & R. Akers (1966). "A Differential Association-Reinforcement Theory of Criminal Behavior." *Social Problems* 14:128-147.

Burgess, R. & P. Draper (1989). "The Explanation of Family Violence: The Role of Biological, Behavioral, and Cultural Selection." In L. Ohlin & M. Tonry (eds.), *Family Violence*. Chicago: University of Chicago Press.

Bursik, R. (1988). "Social Disorganization and Theories of Crime and Delinquency: Problems and Prospects." *Criminology* 26:519-552.

Bursik, R. & H. Grasmick (1993). *Neighborhoods and Crime: The Dimensions of Effective Community*. New York: Lexington Books.

Buss, D. (1990). "Toward a Biologically-Informed Psychology of Personality." *Journal of Personality* 58:1-16.

Buss, D. (1991). "Evolutionary Personality Psychology." *Annual Review of Psychology* 42:459-491.

Buss, D. (1994). *The Evolution of Desire*. New York: Basic Books.

Buss, D. (1995). "Evolutionary Psychology: A New Paradigm for Psychological Science." *Psychological Inquiry* 6:1-30.

Buss, D. & H. Greiling (1999). "Adaptive Individual Differences." *Journal of Personality* 67:209-242.

Buss, D., R. Larsen, D. Westen & J. Semmelroth (1992). "Sex Differences in Jealousy: Evolution, Physiology, and Psychology." *Psychological Science* 3:251-255.

Buss, D. & D. Schmitt (1993). "Sexual Strategies Theory: An Evolutionary Perspective on Human Mating." *Psychological Review* 100:204-232.

Byrne, J. (1986). "Cities, Citizens, and Crime: The Ecological/Nonecological Debate Revisited." In J. Byrne & R. Sampson (eds.), *The Social Ecology of Crime*, pp. 116-130. London: Springer-Verlag.

Byrne, J. & R. Sampson (eds.) (1986). *The Social Ecology of Crime*. London: Springer-Verlag.

Cacioppo, J. & G. Brenston (1992). "Social Psychological Contributions to the Decade of the Brain." *American Psychologist* 47:1019-1028.

Cadoret, R., W. Yates, E. Troughton, G. Woodworth & M. Stewart (1995). "Genetic-Environmental Interaction in the Genesis of Aggressivity and Conduct Disorders." *Archives of General Psychiatry* 52:916-924.

Campbell, A. (1999). "Staying Alive: Evolution, Culture, and Women's Intrasexual Aggression." *Behavioral and Brain Sciences* 22:203-214.

Capron, C. & M. Duyme (1989). "Assessment of Effects of Socio-Economic Status on IQ in a Cross-Fostering Study." *Nature* 340:552-554.

Casear, P. (1993). "Old and New Facts about Perinatal Brain Development." *Journal of Child Psychology and Psychiatry* 34:101-109.

Cashdan, E. (1993). "Attracting Mates: Effects of Parental Investment on Mate Attraction Strategies." *Ethology and Sociobiology* 14:1-23.

Caspi, A. (2000). "The Child is the Father of the Man: Personality Continuities from Childhood to Adulthood." *Journal of Personality and Social Psychology* 78:158-172.

Caspi, A., D. Bem & G. Elder (1989). "Continuities and Consequences of Interaction Styles Across the Lifecourse." *Journal of Personality* 57:375-406.

Caspi, A., B. Henry, R. McGee, T. Moffitt & P. Silva (1995). "Temperamental Origins of Child and Adolescent Behavior Problems: From Age Three to Age Fifteen." *Child Development* 66:55-68.

Caspi, A., D. Lynam, T. Moffitt & P. Silva (1993). "Unraveling Girls' Delinquency: Biological, Dispositional, and Contextual Contributions to Adolescent Misbehavior." *Development Psychology* 29:19-31.

Caspi, A., T. Moffitt, P. Silva, M. Stouthamer-Loeber, R. Krueger & P. Schmutte (1994). "Are Some People Crime-Prone? Replications of the Personality-Crime Relationship Across Countries, Genders, Races, and Methods." *Criminology* 32:163-194.

Centerwell, B. (1995). "Race, Socioeconomic Status, and Domestic Homicide." *Journal of the American Medical Association* 273:1755-1758.

Chagnon, N. (1988). "Life Histories, Blood Revenge, and Warfare in a Tribal Population." *Science* 239: 985-992.

Chagnon, N. (1996). "Chronic Problems in Understanding Tribal Violence and War-fare." In G. Bock & J. Goode (eds.), *Genetics of Criminal and Antisocial Behav-ior*, pp. 202-236. Chichester, England: John Wiley.

Changeux, J. (1985). "On the Singularity of Nerve Cells and its Ontogenesis. *Progress in Brain Research* 58:465-478.

Chesney-Lind, M. (1986). "Women and Crime: The Female Offender." *Signs* 12:78-96.

Chesney-Lind, M. (1995). "Girls, Delinquency and Juvenile Justice: Toward a Fem-inist Theory of Young Women's Crime." In B. Price & N. Sokoloff (eds.), *The Crim-inal Justice System and Women: Offenders, Victims, and Workers*, pp. 71-88. New York: McGraw-Hill.

Chesney-Lind, M. & R. Shelden (1992). *Girls, Delinquency and Juvenile Justice*. Pacif-ic Grove, CA: Brooks/Cole.

Chess, S. & A. Thomas (1996). *Temperament: Theory and Practice*. New York: Brunner/Mazel.

Chilton, R. (1986). "Urban Crime Rates: Effects of Inequality, Welfare Dependency, Region, and Race." In J. Byrne & R. Sampson (eds.), *The Social Ecology of Crime*, pp. 116-130. New York: Springer-Verlag.

Chipeur, H., M. Rovine & R. Plomin (1990). "LISREL Modeling: Genetic and Envi-ronmental Influences on IQ Revisited." *Intelligence* 14:11-29.

Chisholm, J. (1996). "The Evolutionary Ecology of Attachment Organization." *Human Nature* 7:1-38.

Clark, C. & N. Gist (1938). "Intelligence as is a Factor in Occupational Choice." *Amer-ican Sociological Review* 3:683-694.

Cleveland, H., R. Wiebe, E. van den Oord & D. Rowe (2000). "Behavior Problems Among Children from Different Family Structures: The Influence of Genetic Self-Selection." *Child Development* 71:733-751.

Cloninger, C., T. Reich & S. Guze (1975). "The Multifactorial Model of Disease Trans-mission: II. Sex Differences in the Familial Transmission of Sociopathy (Antiso-cial Personality)." *British Journal of Psychiatry* 127:11-22.

Cloward, R. & L. Ohlin (1960). *Delinquency and Opportunity*. New York: Free Press.

Clutton-Brock, T. (1991). *The Evolution of Parental Care*. Princeton, NJ: Princeton University Press.

Clutton-Brock, T. & G. Parker (1995). "Punishment in Animal Societies." *Nature* 373:209-216.

Cohen, A. (1955). *Delinquent Boys: The Culture of the Gang*. Glencoe, IL: Free Press.

Cohen, L. (1987). "Throwing Down the Gauntlet: A Challenge to the Relevance of Soci-ology for the Etiology of Criminal Behavior." *Contemporary Sociology* 16:202-205.

Cohen, L. & R. Machalek (1994). "The Normalcy of Crime: From Durkheim to Evo-lutionary Ethology." *Rationality and Society* 6:286-308.

Collins, W., E. Maccoby, L. Steinberg, M. Heatherington & M. Bornstein (2000). "Contemporary Research on Parenting: The Case for Nature *and* Nurture." *American Psychologist* 55:218-232.

Cornell, D. & L. Wilson (1992). "The PIQ>VIQ Discrepancy in Violent and Nonviolent Delinquents." *Journal of Clinical Psychology* 48:256-261.

Coser, L. (1971). *Masters of Sociological Thought*. New York: Harcourt Brace Jovanovich.

Cosmides, L., J. Tooby & J. Barkow (1992). "Evolutionary Psychology and Conceptual Integration." In J. Barkow, L. Cosmides & J. Tooby (eds.), *The Adapted Mind: Evolutionary Psychology and the Generation of Culture*, pp. 3-15. New York: Oxford University Press.

Costello, B. & P. Vowell (1999). "Testing Control Theory and Differential Association: A Reanalysis of the Richmond Youth Project Data." *Criminology* 37:815-842.

Crane, J. (1991). "The Epidemic Theory of Ghettoes and Neighborhood Effects on Dropping Out and Teenage Childbearing." *American Journal of Sociology* 96:1226-1259.

Crawford, C. (1998a). "Environments and Adaptations: Then and Now." In C. Crawford & D. Krebs (eds.), *Handbook of Evolutionary Psychology: Ideas, Issues, and Applications,* pp. 275-302. Mahwah, NJ: Lawrence Erlbaum.

Crawford, C. (1998b). "The Theory of Evolution in the Study of Human Behavior: An Introduction and Overview." In C. Crawford & D. Krebs (eds.), *Handbook of Evolutionary Psychology: Ideas, Issues, and Applications*, pp. 3-42. Mahwah, NJ: Lawrence Erlbaum.

Crawford, C. & J. Anderson (1989). "Sociobiology: An Environmental Discipline?" *American Psychologist* 44:1449-1459.

Crippen, T. (1994). "Neo-Darwinian Approaches in the Social Sciences: Unwarranted Concerns and Misconceptions." *Sociological Perspectives* 37:391-401.

Crnic, K., M. Greenfield, N. Robinson & A. Ragozin (1984). "Maternal Stress and Social Support: Effects on the Mother-Infant Relationship from Birth to Eighteen Months." *American Journal of Orthopsychiatry* 54:224-235.

Cunningham, M. & A. Barbaree (1991). "Differential K-Selection versus Ecological Determinants of Race Differences in Sexual Behavior." *Journal of Research in Personality* 25:205-217.

Curry, D., R. Ball & R. Fox (1994). "Gang Crime and Law Enforcement Record Keeping." Washington, DC: U.S. Department of Justice, National Institute of Justice.

Dabbs, J. & R. Morris (1990). "Testosterone, Social Class, and Antisocial Behavior in a Sample of 4,462 Men." *Psychological Science* 1:209-211.

Daly, K. & M. Chesney-Lind (1988). "Feminism and Criminology." *Justice Quarterly* 5:497-538.

Daly, M. (1996). "Evolutionary Adaptationism: Another Biological Approach to Criminal and Antisocial Behavior." In G. Bock & J. Goode (eds.), *Genetics of Criminal and Antisocial Behaviour,* pp. 183-195. Chichester, England: John Wiley.

Daly, M. & M. Wilson (1985). "Child Abuse and Other Risks of Not Living with Both Parents." *Ethology & Sociobiology* 6:197-210.

Daly, M. & M. Wilson (1988a). *Homicide*. New York: Aldine de Gruyter.

Daly, M. & M. Wilson (1988b). "Evolutionary Social Psychology and Family Homicide." *Science* 242:519-524.

Daly, M. & M. Wilson (1994). "Some Differential Attributes of Lethal Assaults on Small Children by Stepfathers versus Genetic Fathers. *Ethology & Sociobiology* 15:207-217.

Daly, M. & M. Wilson (1996). "Violence Against Stepchildren." *Current Directions in Psychological Science* 5:77-81.

Daly, M., M. Wilson & S. Weghorst (1982). "Male Sexual Jealousy." *Ethology & Sociobiology* 3:11-27.

Dashkov, G. (1992). "Quantitative and Qualitative Changes in Crime in the USSR." *British Journal of Criminology* 32:160-165.

Davis, J. (1993). "Psychological versus Sociological Explanations for Delinquent Conduct and Gang Formation." *Journal of Contemporary Criminal Justice* 9:81-93.

Dawkins, R. (1982). *The Extended Phenotype*. Oxford: Oxford University Press.

de Waal (1996). *Good Natured: The Origins of Right and Wrong in Humans and Other Animals*. Cambridge, MA: Harvard University Press.

Degler, C. (1991). *In Search of Human Nature: The Decline and Revival of Darwinism in American Social Thought*. New York: Oxford University Press.

Dellarosa-Cummins, D. & R. Cummins (1999). "Biological Preparedness and Evolutionary Explanations." *Cognition* 73:37-53.

DeLozier, P. (1982). "Attachment Theory and Child Abuse." In C. Parks & J. Stevenson-Hinde (eds.), *The Place of Attachment in Human Behavior*, pp. 95-117. New York: Basic Books.

Dennett, D. (1995). *Darwin's Dangerous Idea: Evolution and the Meaning of Life*. New York: Simon & Schuster.

Denno, D. (1985). "Sociological and Human Developmental Explanations of Crime: Conflict or Consensus?" *Criminology* 23:711-740.

Depue, R. & P. Collins (1999). "Neurobiology of the Structure of Personality: Dopamine, Facilitation of Incentive Motivation, and Extraversion." *Behavioral and Brain Sciences* 22:491-569.

Diamond, J. (1992). *The Third Chimpanzee: The Evolution and Future of the Human Animal*. New York: Harper Collins.

DiLalla, L. & I. Gottesman (1989). "Heterogeneity of Causes for Delinquency and Criminality: Lifespan Perspectives." *Development and Psychopathology* 1:339-349.

Doudna, C. & F. McBride (1981). "Where are the Men for Women at the Top?" In P. Stein (ed.), *Single Life: Unmarried Adults in Social Context*, pp. 21-34. New York: St. Martin's.

Drake, R. (1995). "A Neuropsychology of Deception and Self-Deception." *Behavioral and Brain Sciences* 18:552-553.

Draper, P. & H. Harpending (1982). "Father Absence and Reproductive Strategies: An Evolutionary Perspective." *Journal of Anthropological Research* 38:255-273.

Draper, P. & H. Harpending (1988). "A Sociobiological Perspective on the Development of Human Reproductive Strategies." In K. MacDonald (ed.), *Sociobiological Perspectives on Human Development*, pp. 340-372. New York: Springer-Verlag.

Drigotas, S. & J. Udry (1993). "Biosocial Models of Adolescent Problem Behavior: Extensions to Panel Design." *Social Biology* 40:1-7.

Dugatkin, L. (1992). "The Evolution of the Con Artist." *Ethology and Sociobiology* 13:3-18.

Dupre, J. (1992). "Blinded by 'Science': How Not to Think About Social Problems." *Behavioral and Brain Sciences* 15:382-383.

Durkheim, E. (1951a). *The Division of Labor in Society*. Glencoe, IL: Free Press.

Durkheim, E. (1951b) *Suicide*. Glencoe, IL: Free Press.

Durkheim, E. (1982). *Rules of Sociological Method*. New York: Free Press.

Edelman, G. (1987). *Neural Darwinism. The Theory of Neuronal Group Selection*. New York: Basic Books.

Edelman, G. (1992). *Bright Air, Brilliant Fire*. New York: Basic Books.

Edgerton, R. (1992). *Sick Societies: Challenging the Myth of Primitive Harmony*. New York: Free Press.

Elliot, D., D. Huizinga & S. Ageton (1985). *Explaining Delinquency and Drug Use*. Beverly Hills: Sage.

Elliot, D., D. Huizinga & S. Menard (1989). *Multiple Problem Youth: Delinquency, Substance Abuse, and Mental Health Problems*. New York: Springer-Verlag.

Ellis, L. (1977). "The Decline and Fall of Sociology: 1975-2000." *American Sociologist* 12:56-66.

Ellis, L. (1987). "Criminal Behavior and r/K Selection: An Extension of Gene-Based Evolutionary Theory." *Deviant Behavior* 8:149-176.

Ellis, L. (1988). "The Victimful—Victimless Crime Distinction, and Seven Universal Demographic Correlates of Victimful Criminal Behavior." *Personality and Individual Differences* 9:525-548.

Ellis, L. (1989). *Theories of Rape: Inquiries into the Causes of Sexual Aggression*. New York: Hemisphere.

Ellis, L. (1991a). "A Synthesized (Biosocial) Theory of Rape." *Journal of Consulting and Clinical Psychology* 59:631-642.

Ellis, L. (1991b). "Monoamine Oxydase and Criminality: Identifying an Apparent Biological Marker for Antisocial Behavior." *Journal of Research in Crime and Delinquency* 28:227-251.

Ellis, L. (1995). "Dominance and Reproductive Success Among Non-Human Animals: A Cross-Species Comparison." *Ethology and Sociobiology* 16:257-333.

Ellis, L. (1996a). "A Discipline in Peril: Sociology's Future Hinges on Curing its Biophobia." *American Sociologist* 27:21-41.

Ellis, L. (1996b). "Arousal Theory and the Religiosity-Criminality Relationship." In P. Cordella & L. Siegel (eds.), *Readings in Contemporary Criminological Theory*, pp. 65-84. Boston: Northeastern University Press.

Ellis, L. (1998). "Neo-Darwinian Theories of Violent Criminality and Antisocial Behavior: Photographic Evidence from Nonhuman Animals and a Review of the Literature." *Aggression and Violent Behavior* 3:61-110.

Ellis, L. & M. Ames (1987). "Neurohormonal Functioning and Sexual Orientation: A Theory of Homosexuality-Heterosexuality." *Psychological Bulletin* 101:233-258.

Ellis, L. & P. Coontz (1990). "Androgens, Brain Functioning, and Criminality: The Neurohormonal Foundations of Antisociality." In L. Ellis & H. Hoffman (eds.), *Crime in Biological, Social, and Moral Contexts*, pp. 162-193. New York: Praeger.

Ellis, L. & H. Hoffman (1990). "Views of Contemporary Criminologists on Causes and Theories of Crime." In L. Ellis & H. Hoffman (eds.), *Crime in Biological, Social, and Moral Contexts*, pp. 50-58. New York: Praeger.

Ellis, L. & H. Nyborg (1992). "Racial/Ethnic Variations in Male Testosterone Levels: A Probable Contributor to Group Differences in Health." *Steroids* 57:72-75.

Ellis, L. & A. Walsh (1997). "Gene-Based Evolutionary Theories in Criminology." *Criminology* 35:229-276.

Ellis, L. & A. Walsh (2000). *Criminology: A Global Perspective*. Boston: Allyn & Bacon.

Elman, J., E. Bates, M. Johnson, A. Karmiloff-Smith, D. Parisi & K. Plunkett (1996). *Rethinking Innateness: A Connectionist Perspective on Development*. Cambridge, MA: MIT Press.

Ely, R., G. Melzi, L. Hadge & A. McCabe (1998). "Being Brave, Being Nice: Themes of Agency and Communion in Children's Narratives." *Journal of Personality* 66:257-284.

Ember, M. & C. Ember (1998). "Facts of Violence." *Anthropology Newsletter* (October):14-15.

Eysenck, H. (1982). "The Sociology of Psychological Knowledge, the Genetic Interpretation of the IQ and Marxist-Leninist Ideology." *Bulletin of the British Psychological Society* 35:449-451.

Eysenck, H. & G. Gudjonsson (1989). *The Causes and Cures of Criminality*. New York: Plenum.

Fagan, J. (1989). "The Social Organization of Drug Use and Drug Dealing among Urban Gangs." *Criminology* 27:633-669.

Farley, J. (1990). *Sociology*. Englewood Cliffs, NJ: Prentice Hall.

Farley, R. (1996). *The New American Reality*. New York: Russell Sage Foundation.

Farrington, D. (1987). "Implications of Biological Findings for Criminological Research." In S. Mednick, T. Moffitt & S. Stack (eds.), *The Causes of Crime: New Biological Approaches*, pp. 42-64. Cambridge: Cambridge University Press.

Farrington, D. (1996). "The Explanation and Prevention of Youthful Offending." In J. Hawkins (ed.), *Delinquency and Crime: Current Theories*, pp. 68-148. Cambridge: Cambridge University Press.

Feder, K. & M. Park (1989). *Human Antiquity*. Mountain View, CA: Mayfield.

Federal Bureau of Investigation (2000). "Crime in the United States: 1999." Washington, DC: U.S. Government Printing Office.

Fergusson, D. & L. Horwood (1995). "Early Disruptive Behavior, IQ, and Later School Achievement and Delinquent Behavior." *Journal of Abnormal Child Psychology* 23:183-199.

Figueredo, A. (1995). "The Epigenesis of Sociopathy." *Behavioral and Brain Sciences* 18:556-557.

Figueredo, A. & L. McCloskey (1993). "Sex, Money, and Paternity: The Evolutionary Psychology of Domestic Violence." *Ethology and Sociobiology* 14:353-379.

Fincher, J. (1982). *The Human Brain: Mystery of Matter and Mind*. Washington, DC: U.S. News Books.

Finkelhor, D. (1984). *Child Sexual Abuse: New Theory and Research*. New York: Free Press.

Fischbein, S. (1980). "IQ and Social Class." *Intelligence* 4:51-63.

Fishbein, D. (1992). "The Psychobiology of Female Aggression." *Criminal Justice and Behavior* 19:99-126.

Fishbein, D. (1998). "Building Bridges." *ACJS Today* 17:1-5.

Fisher, H. (1989). "Evolution of Human Serial Pairbonding." *American Journal of Physical Anthropology* 78:331-354.

Fisher, H. (1992). *Anatomy of Love. The Natural History of Monogamy, Adultery, and Divorce*. New York: W.W. Norton.

Fisher, H. (1998). "Lust, Attraction, and Attachment in Mammalian Reproduction." *Human Nature* 9:23-52.

Fletcher, R. (1991). "Mating, the Family, and Marriage: A Sociological View." In V. Reynolds & J. Kellett (eds.), *Mating and Marriage*, pp. 111-162. Oxford: Oxford University Press.

Flowers, R. (1988). *Minorities and Criminality*. New York: Greenwood.

Fox, R. (1991). *Encounter with Anthropology*. New Brunswick, NJ: Transaction.

Frank, D., P. Klass, F. Earls & L. Eisenberg (1996). "Infants and Young Children in Orphanages: One View from Pediatrics and Child Psychiatry." *Pediatrics* 97:569-578.

Freedman, D. (1997). "Is Nonduality Possible in the Social and Behavioral Sciences? Small Essay on Holism and Related Issues." In N. Segal, G. Weisfeld & C. Weisfeld (eds.), *Uniting Psychology and Biology*, pp. 47-80. Washington, DC: American Psychological Association.

Freud, S. (1961). *Civilization and its Discontents*. New York: W.W. Norton.

Garfinkle, I. & S. McLanahan (1986). *Single Mothers and Their Children: A New American Dilemma*. Washington, DC: The Urban Institute.

Gazzaniga, M. (1998). "The Split Brain Revisited." *Scientific American* (July):50-55.

Geary, D. (1998). "Functional Organization of the Human Mind: Implications for Behavioral Genetic Research." *Human Biology* 70:185-198.

Geary, D. (2000). "Evolution and Proximate Expression of Human Paternal Investment." *Psychological Bulletin* 126:55-77.

Gelles, R. (1991). "Physical Violence, Child Abuse, and Child Homicide: A Continuum of Violence or Distinct Behaviors?" *Human Nature* 2:59-72.

Giedd, J., J. Blumenthal, N. Jeffries, F. Castellanos, H. Liu, A. Zijenbos, T. Paus, A. Evans & J. Rapoport (1999). "Brain Development During Childhood and Adolescence: A Longitudinal MRI Study." *Nature Neuroscience* 2:861-863.

Gilder, G. (1976). *Sexual Suicide*. New York: Bantam.

Gilmartin, P. (1994). *Rape, Incest, and Child Sexual Abuse: Consequences and Recovery*. New York: Garland.

Gladwell, M. (1996). "The Tipping Point." *Subject to Debate* 10:1-11.

Glaser, D. (2000). "Child Abuse and Neglect and the Brain—A Review." *Journal of Child Psychology and Psychiatry* 41:97-116.

Glaser, D. & S. Frosh (1993). *Child Sex Abuse*. Toronto: University of Toronto Press.

Glueck, S. (1956). "Theory and Fact in Criminology: A Criticism of Differential Association Theory." *British Journal of Criminology* 7:92-109.

Glutton-Brock, T. & G. Parker (1995). "Punishment in Animal Societies." *Nature* 373:209-216.

Goldman, D., J. Lappalainen & N. Ozaki (1996). "Direct Analysis of Candidate Genes in Impulsive Behavior." In G. Bock & J. Goode (eds.), *Genetics of Criminal and Antisocial Behaviour,* pp. 183-195. Chichester, England: John Wiley.

Goldsmith, H. (1994). "Nature-Nurture Issues in the Behavioral Genetics Context: Overcoming Barriers to Communication." In R. Plomin & G. McClearn (eds.) *Nature, Nurture, and Psychology*, pp. 325-339. Washington, DC: American Psychological Association.

Goldstein, H. (1984). "Parental Composition, Supervision, and Conduct Problems in Youths 12 to17 Years Old." *Journal of the American Academy of Child Psychiatry* 23:679-684.

Gonczol, K. (1993). "Anxiety Over Crime." *Hungarian Quarterly* 129:87-99.

Gordon, R. (1997). "Everyday Life as an Intelligence Test: Effects of Intelligence and Intelligence Context." *Intelligence* 24:203-320.

Gottesman, I. & H. Goldsmith (1994). "Developmental Psychopathology of Antisocial Behavior: Inserting Genes into its Ontogenesis and Epigenesis." In C. Nelson (ed.), *Threats to Optimal Development: Integrating Biological, Psychological, and Social Risk Factors*, pp. 69-103. Hillsdale, NJ: Lawrence Erlbaum.

Gottfredson, L. (1986). "Social Consequences of the g Factor in Employment." *Journal of Vocational Behavior* 29:379-410.

Gottfredson, L. (1987). "The Practical Significance of Black-White Differences in Intelligence." *Behavioral and Brain Sciences* 10:510-512.

Gottfredson, L. (ed.) (1997a). "Intelligence and Social Policy." *Intelligence* 24:1-320.

Gottfredson, L. (1997b). "Why g Matters: The Complexity of Everyday Life." *Intelligence* 24:79-132.

Gottfredson, M. & T. Hirschi (1990). *A General Theory of Crime*. Stanford, CA: Stanford University Press.

Gottfredson, M. & Hirschi, T. (1997). "National Crime Control Policies." In M. Fisch (ed.), *Criminology 97/98*, pp. 27-33. Guilford, CT: Dushkin.

Gould, S. (1977). *Ontogeny and Phylogeny*. Cambridge: Harvard University Press.

Gould, S. (1991). "Exaptation: A Crucial Tool for an Evolutionary Psychology." *Journal of Social Issues* 47:43-65.

Gouldner, A. (1973). "Foreword." In I. Taylor, P. Walton & J. Young, *The New Criminology: For a Social Theory of Deviance*. London: Routledge & Kegan Paul.

Gove, W. (1985). "The Effect of Age and Gender on Deviant Behavior: A Biopsychosocial Perspective." In A. Rossi (ed.), *Gender and the Life Course*, pp. 115-144. Chicago: Aldine.

Gove, W. & C. Wilmoth (1990). "Risk, Crime, and Neurophysiological Highs: A Consideration of Brain Processes That May Reinforce Delinquent and Criminal Behavior." In L. Ellis & H. Hoffman (eds.), *Crime in Biological, Social, and Moral Contexts*, pp. 261-293. New York: Praeger .

Grafman, J. (1994). "Neuropsychology of the Prefrontal Cortex." In D. Zaidel (ed.), *Neuropsychology*, pp. 159-181. San Diego: Academic Press.

Grasmick, H., C. Tittle, R. Bursik & B. Arneklev (1994). "Testing the Core Empirical Implications of Gottfredson and Hirschi's General Theory of Crime." *Journal of Research in Crime and Delinquency* 30:5-29.

Grauerholz, E. & M. Koralewski (1991). "What is Known and Not Known about Sexual Coercion." In E. Grauerholz & M. Koralewski (eds.), *Sexual Coercion: A Sourcebook on Its Nature, Causes, and Prevention*, pp. 187-198. Lexington, MA: Lexington Books.

Gray, J. (1987). *The Psychology of Fear and Stress*. New York: McGraw-Hill.

Gray, J. (1994). "Three Fundamental Emotional Systems." In P. Ekman & R. Davidson (eds.), *The Nature of Emotion: Fundamental Questions*, pp. 243-247. New York: Oxford University Press.

Greenberg, D. (1980). *Crime and Capitalism*. Palo Alto, CA: Mayfield.

Greenough, W., J. Black & C. Wallace (1987). "Experience and Brain Development." *Child Development* 58:539-559.

Gress-Wright, J. (1993). "The Contraception Paradox." *The Public Interest* 113:15-25.

Griffiths, P. (1990). "Modularity and the Psychoevolutionary Theory of Emotion." *Biology and Philosophy* 5:175-196.

Groves, C. (1989). *A Theory of Human and Primate Evolution*. Oxford: Clarendon Press.

Groves, W. & R. Sampson (1987). "Traditional Contributions to Radical Criminology." *Journal of Research in Crime and Delinquency* 24:181-214.

Grusky, D. (1994). *Social Stratification: Class, Race, and Gender in Sociological Perspective*. Boulder, CO: Westview.

Gruter, M. (1991). *Law and the Mind: Biological Origins of Human Behavior*. Newbury Park, CA: Sage.

Gubernick, D., D. Sengelaub & E. Kurtz (1993). "A Neuroanatomical Correlate: Paternal and Maternal Behavior in the Biparental California Mouse (*Peromyscus Californicus*)." *Behavioral Neuroscience* 107:194-201.

Gunnar, M. (1996). *Quality of Care and the Buffering of Stress Physiology: Its Potential in Protecting the Developing Human Brain*. Minneapolis: University of Minnesota Institute of Child Development.

Guttentag, M. & P. Secord (1983). *Too Many Women: The Sex Ratio Question*. Beverly Hills: Sage.

Hall, E. (1987). "Adolescents' Perceptions of Sexual Assault." *Journal of Sex Education and Therapy* 13:37-42.

Hamburg, D. (1993). "The American Family Transformed." *Society* 30:60-69.

Hamilton, W. (1964). "The Evolution of Social Behavior." *Journal of Theoretical Biology* 7:1-52.

Hamparian, D., R. Schuster. S. Dinitz & J. Conrad (1978). *The Violent Few: A Study of Dangerous Juvenile Offenders*. Lexington, MA: D.C. Heath.

Hare, R. (1993). *Without Conscience: The Disturbing World of the Psychopaths Among Us*. New York: Pocket Books.

Hare, R. (1996). "Psychopathy: A Clinical Construct Whose Time Has Come." *Criminal Justice and Behavior* 23:25-54.

Harlow, H. & M. Harlow (1962). "Social Deprivation in Monkeys." *Scientific American* 206:137-144.

Harpending, H. & P. Draper (1988). "Antisocial Behavior and the Other Side of Cultural Evolution." In T. Moffitt & S. Mednick (eds.), *Biological Contributions to Crime Causation*, pp. 293-307. Dordrecht: Martinus Nyhoff.

Harris, G., M. Rice & V. Quinsey (1994). "Psychopathy as a Taxon: Evidence That Psychopaths are a Discrete Class." *Journal of Consulting and Clinical Psychology* 62:387-397.

Harris, J. (1998). *The Nurture Assumption: Why Children Turn Out the Way They Do*. New York: Free Press.

Harris, J., P. Vernon & D. Boomsma (1998). "The Heritability of Testosterone: A Study of Dutch Adolescent Twins and Their Parents." *Behavior Genetics* 28:165-171.

Harris, M. (1988). *Culture, People, Nature*. New York: Harper & Row.

Harrison, L. & C. Esqueda (1999). "Myths and Stereotypes of Actors Involved in Domestic Violence: Implications for Domestic Violence Culpability Attributions." *Aggression and Violent Behavior* 4:129-138.

Hawley, A. (1944). "Ecology and Human Ecology." *Social Forces* 22:398-405.

Hawley, A. (1950). *Human Ecology: A Theory of Community Structure*. New York: Ronald Press.

Hayner, N. (1933). "Delinquency Areas in the Puget Sound Region." *American Journal of Sociology* 39:314-328.

Hazard, J., W. Butler & P. Maggs (1977). *The Soviet Legal System*. Dobbs Ferry, NY: Oceana.

Heck, G. & A. Walsh (2000). "The Effects of Maltreatment and Family Structure on Minor and Serious Delinquency." *International Journal of Offender Therapy and Comparative Criminology* 44:178-193.

Heer, D. & A. Grossband-Shechtman (1981). "The Impact of the Female Marriage Squeeze and the Contraceptive Revolution on Sex Roles and the Women's Liberation Movement in the United States, 1960-1975." *Journal of Marriage and the Family* 43:49-65.

Henggeler, S., J. Edwards & C. Borduin (1987). "The Family Relations of Female Juvenile Delinquents." *Journal of Abnormal Child Psychology* 15:199-209.

Henry, B., A. Caspi, T. Moffitt & P. Silva (1996). "Temperament and Familial Predictors of Violent and Non-Violent Criminal Convictions: From Age 3 to Age 18." *Developmental Psychology* 32:614-623.

Henry, B., T. Moffitt, L. Robins, F. Earls & P. Silva (1993). "Early Family Predictors of Child and Adolescent Antisocial Behavior: Who are the Mothers of Delinquents?" *Criminal Behavior and Mental Health* 3:97-118.

Herbert, W. (1997). "The Politics of Biology." *U.S. News & World Report* (April 21):72-80.

Herman, J. (1990). "Sex Offenders: A Feminist Perspective." In W. Marshall, D. Laws & H. Barbaree (eds.), *Handbook of Sexual Assault: Issues, Theories, and Treatment of the Offender*, pp. 177-193. New York: Plenum.

Herrnstein, R. (1989). "Biology and Crime." [National Institute of Justice Crime File, NCJ 97216]. Washington, DC: U.S. Department of Justice.

Herrnstein, R. & C. Murray (1994). *The Bell Curve: Intelligence and Class Structure in American Life*. New York: Free Press.

Hill, K. & A. Hurtado (1996). *Aché Life History: The Ecology and Demography of a Foraging People*. New York: Aldine de Gruyter.

Hill, S., B. Bleichfeld, R. Brunstetter & J. Herbert (1989). "Cognitive and Physiological Responsiveness of Abused Children." *Journal of the Academy of Child and Adolescent Psychiatry* 28:219-224.

Himmelfarb, G. (1994). "A De-moralized Society: The British/American Experience." *The Public Interest* (Fall):57-80.

Hirschi, T. (1969). *The Causes of Delinquency*. Berkeley: University of California Press.

Hirschi, T. (1977). "Causes and Prevention of Juvenile Delinquency." *Sociological Inquiry* 47:322-341.

Hirschi, T. (1995). "The Family." In J. Wilson & J. Petersilia (eds.), *Crime*, pp. 121-140. San Francisco: ICS Press.

Hirschi, T. & M. Hindelang (1977). "Intelligence and Delinquency: A Revisionist Review." *American Sociology Review* 42:571-587.

Horgan, J, (1995). "The New Social Darwinists." *Scientific American*, October:174-182.

Horowitz, I. (1993). *The Decomposition of Sociology*. New York: Oxford University Press.

Hosking, G. (1985). *The First Socialist Society: A History of the Soviet Union from Within*. Cambridge: Harvard University Press.

Hrdy, S. (1980). *The Langurs of Abu: Female and Male Strategies of Reproduction*. Cambridge, MA: Harvard University Press.

Huff, R. (1989). "Youth Gangs and Public Policy." *Crime & Delinquency* 35:524-537.

Hur, Y. & T. Bouchard (1997). "The Genetic Correlation between Impulsivity and Sensation-Seeking Traits." *Behavior Genetics* 27:455-463.

Hurford, J., S. Joseph, S. Kirby & A. Reid (1997). "Evolution Might Select Constructivism." *Behavioral and Brain Sciences* 20:567-568.

Hurst, C. (1995). *Social Inequality: Forms, Causes, and Consequences*. Boston: Allyn & Bacon.

Huttenlocher, P. (1994). "Synaptogenesis, Synapse, Elimination, and Neural Plasticity in Human Cerebral Cortex." In C. Nelson (ed.), *Threats to Optimal Development: Integrating Biological, Psychological, and Social Risk Factors,* pp. 35-54. Hillsdale, NJ: Lawrence Erlbaum.

Inciardi, J. (1980). *Radical Criminology: The Coming Crisis*. Beverly Hills: Sage.

Insel, T. (1992). "Oxytocin and the Neurobiology of Attachment." *Behavioral and Brain Sciences* 15:515-516.

International Human Genome Sequencing Consortium (2001). "Initial Sequencing and Analysis of the Human Genome." *Nature* 409:860-921.

Jackson, P. (1991). "Crime, Youth Gangs, and Urban Transition: The Social Dislocation of Postindustrial Economic Development. *Justice Quarterly* 8:379-397.

James, W. (1986). "Hormonal Control of the Sex Ratio." *Journal of Theoretical Biology* 118:427-441.

James, W. (1987). "The Human Sex Ratio. Part 1: A Review of the Literature." *Human Biology* 59:721-752.

Jeffery, C.R. (1993). "Obstacles to the Development of Research in Crime and Delinquency." *Journal of Research in Crime and Delinquency* 30:491-497.

Jeglum-Bartusch, D., D. Lynam, T. Moffitt & P. Silva (1997). "Is Age Important? Testing General versus Developmental Theories of Antisocial Behavior." *Criminology* 35:13-48.

Jensen, A. (1998a). *The g Factor*. Westport, CT: Praeger.

Jensen, A. (1998b). "Adoption Data and Two g-related Hypotheses." *Intelligence* 25:1-6.

Jockin, V., V. McGue & D. Lykken (1996). "Personality and Divorce: A Genetic Analysis." *Journal of Personality and Social Psychology* 71: 288-299.

Johnson, R., A. Marcos & S. Bahr (1987). "The Role of Peers in the Complex Etiology of Adolescent Drug Use." *Criminology* 25:323-340.

Judge, T., C. Higgins, C. Thoresen & M. Barrick (1999). "The Big Five Personality Traits, General Mental Ability, and Career Success Across the Lifespan." *Personnel Psychology* 52:621-652.

Kagan, J., S. Reznick & N. Snidman (1987). "The Physiology and Psychology of Behavioral Inhibition in Children." *Child Development* 58:1459-1473.

Kalil, R. (1989). "Synapse Formation in the Developing Brain." *Scientific American* 261:76-85.

Kandel, E. & R. Hawkins (1992). "The Biological Basis of Learning and Individuality." *Scientific American* 267:79-86.

Katz, J. (1988). *Seductions of Crime: Moral and Sensual Attractions in Doing Evil.* New York: Basic Books.

Kemper, T. (1990). *Social Structure and Testosterone: Explanations of the Socio-Biosocial Chain.* New Brunswick, NJ: Rutgers University Press.

Kendler, K. (1983). "Overview: A Current Perspective on Twin Studies of Schizophrenia." *American Journal of Psychiatry* 140:1413-1425.

Kendler, K. (1995). "Genetic Epidemiology in Psychiatry: Taking Both Genes and Environment Seriously." *Archives of General Psychiatry* 52:895-899.

Kenrick, D. & J. Simpson (1997). "Why Social Psychology and Evolutionary Psychology Need One Another." In J. Simpson & D. Kenrick (eds.), *Evolutionary Social Psychology*, pp. 1-20. Mahwah, NJ: Lawrence Erlbaum.

Ketelar, T. & B. Ellis (2000). "Are Evolutionary Explanations Unfalsifiable? Evolutionary Psychology and the Lakatosian Philosophy of Science." *Psychological Inquiry* 11:1-21.

Kimura, D. (1992). "Sex Differences in the Brain." *Scientific American* 267:119-125.

Kirkpatrick, L. (1999). "Individual Differences in Attachment and Reproductive Strategies: Commentary on Buss & Greiling." *Journal of Personality* 67:245-258.

Kleck, C. & E. Patterson (1993). "The Impact of Gun Control and Gun Ownership Levels on Violence Rates." *Journal of Quantitative Criminology* 9:249-287.

Klein, D. (1995). "The Etiology of Female Crime: A Review of the Literature." In B. Price & N. Sokoloff (eds.), *The Criminal Justice System and Women: Offenders, Victims, and Workers,* pp. 31-52. New York: McGraw-Hill.

Klein, M. (1995). "Street Gang Cycles." In J. Wilson & J. Petersilia (eds.), *Crime,* pp. 215-236. San Franciso: ICS Press.

Knight, D. (1992). *Ideas in Chemistry: A History of the Science.* New Brunswick, NJ: Rutgers University Press.

Kochanska, M. (1991). "Socialization and Temperament in the Development of Guilt and Conscience." *Child Develoment* 62:1379-1392.

Kohn, T. (1970). *The Structure of Scientific Revolutions.* Chicago: University of Chicago Press.

Kornhauser, R. (1978). *Social Sources of Delinquency: An Appraisal of Analytical Methods.* Chicago: University of Chicago Press.

Kraemer, G. (1992). "A Psychobiological Theory of Attachment." *Behavioral and Brain Sciences* 15:493-541.

Kramer, P. (1993). *Listening to Prozac.* New York: Viking.

Krebs, D. (1987). "The Challenge of Altruism in Biology and Psychology." In C. Craw-ford, M. Smith & D. Krebs (eds.), *Sociobiology and Psychology: Ideas, Issues, and Applications,* pp. 81-118. Hillsdale, NJ: Lawrence Erlbaum.

Krebs, D. (1998). "The Evolution of Moral Behavior." In C. Crawford & D. Krebs (eds.), *Handbook of Evolutionary Psychology: Ideas, Issues, and Applications*, pp. 337-368. Mahwah, NJ: Lawrence Erlbaum.

Krebs, J. & N. Davies (1993). *An Introduction to Behavioral Ecology.* London: Blackwell.

Krueger, R., T. Moffitt, A. Caspi, A. Bleske & P. Silva (1998). "Assortative Mating for Antisocial Behavior: Developmental and Methodological Implications." *Behavior Genetics* 28:173-185.

Krueisi, M., H. Leonard, S. Swedo, S. Nadi, S. Hamburger, J. Lui & J. Rapoport (1994). "Endogenous Opioids, Childhood Psychopathology, and Quay's Interpretation of Jeffrey Gray." In D. Routh (ed.), *Disruptive Behavior Disorders in Childhood*, pp. 207-219. New York: Plenum.

Kuhn, T. (1970). *The Structure of Scientific Revolutions.* Chicago: University of Chicago Press.

Kyl-Heku, L. & D. Buss (1996). "Tactics as Units of Analysis in Personality Psychology: An Illustration Using Tactics of Hierarchy Negotiation." *Personality and Individual Differences* 21:497-517.

LaFree, G., K. Drass & P. O'Day (1992). "Race and Crime in Postwar America: Determinants of African-American and White Rates." *Criminology* 30:157-185.

LaFree, G. & K. Russell (1993). "The Argument for Studying Race and Crime." *Journal of Criminal Justice Education* 4:273-289.

Lahey, B. & R. Loeber (1994). "Framework for a Developmental Model of Opposi-tional Defiant Disorder and Conduct Disorder." In D. Routh (ed.), *Disruptive Behavior Disorders in Childhood*, pp. 139-180. New York: Plenum.

Lamanna, M. (1985). *Abortion: Understanding Differences.* New York: Plenum.

Lancaster, J. & C. Lancaster (1987). "The Watershed: Changes in Parental Investment and Family Formation Strategies in the Course of Human Evolution." In J. Lan-caster, J. Altman, A. Rossi & L. Sherrod (eds.), *Parenting Across the Lifespan: Biosocial Perspectives*, pp. 187-205. New York: Aldine de Gruyter.

Lanier, M. & S. Henry (1998). *Essential Criminology.* Boulder, CO: Westview.

Laub, J. (1983). "Urbanism, Race, and Crime." *Journal of Research in Crime and Delin-quency* 20:183-198.

Laub, J. & R. Sampson (1991). "The Sutherland-Glueck Debate: On the Sociology of Criminological Knowledge." *American Journal of Sociology* 96:1402-1440.

Laub, J. & R. Sampson (1993). "Turning Points in the Life Course: Why Change Mat-ters in the Study of Crime?" *Criminology* 31:301-325.

Lepowsky, M. (1994). "Women, Men, and Aggression in Egalitarian Societies." *Sex Roles* 30:199-211.

Leverson, R. (1994). "The Search for Autonomic Specificity." In P. Ekman & R. Davidson (eds.), *The Nature of Emotion: Fundamental Questions*, pp. 252-257. New York: Oxford University Press.

Levine, D. (1993). "Survival of the Synapses." *The Sciences* 33:46-52.

Levy, F., D. Hay, M. McStephen, C. Wood & I. Waldman (1997). "Attention-Deficit Hyperactivity Disorder: A Category or a Continuum? Genetic Analysis of a Large-Scale Twin Study." *Journal of the American Academy of Child and Adolescent Psychiatry* 36:737-744.

Lewis, D. (1991). "Conduct Disorder." In M. Lewis (ed.), *Child and Adolescent Psychiatry: A Comprehensive Textbook*, pp. 561-583. Baltimore: Williams & Wilkins.

Lewontin, R. (1982). *Human Diversity*. New York: Scientific American.

Leyton, E. (1986). "Hunting Humans: Inside the Minds of Mass Murderers." New York: Pocket Books.

Lilly, J. F. Cullen & R. Ball (1995). *Criminological Theory: Context and Consequences*. Thousand Oaks, CA: Sage.

Ling, W., D. Wesson, C. Charuvastra & J. Klett (1996). "A Controlled Trial Comparing Buprenorphine and Methodone Maintenance in Opioid Dependance." *Archives of General Psychiatry* 53:401-407.

Lipsitt, D., S. Buka & L. Lipsitt (1990). "Early Intelligence Scores and Subsequent Behavior." *American Journal of Family Therapy* 18:197-208.

Llinas, R. (1989). "The Intrinsic Electrophysiological Properties of Mammalian Neurons: A New Insight into CNS Functioning?" *Science* 242:1654-1664.

Loeber, R. & M. Stouthamer-Loeber (1986). "Family Factors as Correlates and Predictors of Juvenile Conduct Problems and Delinquency." In M. Tonry & N. Morris (eds.), *Crime and Justice: An Annual Review of Research* 7:29-149. Chicago: University of Chicago Press.

Loehlin, J., J. Horn & L. Willerman (1989). "Modeling IQ Change: Evidence from the Texas Adoption Project." *Child Development* 60:93-104.

Loehlin, T. & R. Nichols (1978). *Heredity, Environment, and Personality*. Austin: University of Texas Press.

Lopreato, J. & T. Crippen (1999). *Crisis in Sociology: The Need for Darwin*. New Brunswick, NJ: Transaction.

Lovejoy, C. (1981). "The Origin of Man." *Science* 211:341-350.

Low, B. (1998). "The Evolution of Life Histories." In C. Crawford & D. Krebs (eds.), *Handbook of Evolutionary Psychology: Ideas, Issues, and Applications*, pp. 131-161. Mahwah, NJ: Lawrence Erlbaum

Lubinski, D. & L. Humphreys (1997). "Incorporating Intelligence into Epidemiology and the Social Sciences. *Intelligence* 24:159-201.

Luks, F., F. Hansbrough, D. Klotz, P. Kottmeier & F. Tolete-Valcek (1988). "Early Gender Assignment in True Hermaphrodism." *Journal of Pediatric Surgery* 23:1122-1126.

Lykken, D. (1995). *The Antisocial Personalities*. Hillsdale, NJ: Lawrence Erlbaum.

Lynam, D. (1996). "Early Identification of Chronic Offenders: Who is the Fledgling Psychopath?" *Psychological Bulletin* 120:209-234.

Lynch, M. & W. Groves (1986). *A Primer in Radical Criminology*. Albany, NY: Harrow & Heston.

Lynn, R. (1990). "Testosterone and Gonadotropin Levels and r/K Reproductive Strategies." *Psychological Reports* 67:1203-1206.

Lynn, R. (1996). *Dysgenics: Genetic Deterioration in Modern Populations.* Westport, CT: Greenwood Press.

Lyons, M., W. True, S. Eusen, J. Goldberg, J. Meyer, S. Faraone, L. Eaves & M. Tsuang (1995). "Differential Heritability of Adult and Juvenile Antisocial Traits." *Archives of General Psychiatry* 53:906-915.

Lytton, H. & D. Romney (1991). "Parents' Differential Socialization of Boys and Girls: A Meta-Analysis." *Psychological Bulletin* 109:267-296.

Maccoby, E. (1992). "The Role of Parents in the Socialization of Children: A Historical Overview." *Developmental Psychology* 28:1006-1017.

MacDonald, K. (1988). "Socialization in the Context of the Family: A Sociobiological Perspective." In K. MacDonald (ed.), *Sociobiological Perspectives on Human Development*, pp. 320-339. New York: Springer-Verlag.

MacDonald, K. (1992). "Warmth as a Developmental Construct: An Evolutionary Analysis." *Child Development* 63:753-773.

MacDonald, K. (1997). "Life History Theory and Human Reproductive Behavior: Environmental/Contextual Influences and Heritable Variation." *Human Nature* 8:327-359.

Machalek, R. (1995). "Basic Dimensions and Forms of Social Exploitation: A Comparative Analysis." *Advances in Human Ecology* 4:35-68.

Machalek, R. (1996). "The Evolution of Social Exploitation." *Advances in Human Ecology* 5:1-32.

Machalek, R. & L. Cohen (1991). "The Nature of Crime: Is Cheating Necessary for Cooperation?" *Human Nature* 2:215-233.

Mackey, W. (1997). "Single-Parent Families Contribute to Violent Crime." In K. Swisher (ed.), *Single-Parent Families*, pp. 49-52. San Diego: Greenhaven Press.

MacLean, P. (1990). *The Triune Brain in Evolution: Role in Paleocerebral Functions.* New York: Plenum.

Magnusson, D. (1988). *Individual Development from an Interactional Perspective: A Longitudinal Study.* Hillsdale, NJ: Lawrence Erlbaum.

Mann, C. (1988). "Getting Even? Women Who Kill in Domestic Encounters." *Justice Quarterly* 5:33-51.

Mann, C. (1995). "Women of Color and the Criminal Justice System." In B. Price & N. Sokoloff (eds.), *The Criminal Justice System and Women: Offenders, Victims, and Workers,* pp. 118-119. New York: McGraw-Hill.

Marsh, R. & A. Walsh (1995). "Physiological and Psychosocial Assessment and Treatment of Sex Offenders: A Comprehensive, Victim-Oriented Program." *Journal of Offender Rehabilitation* 22:77-97.

Martindale, D. (2001). "Pink Slip in Your Genes." *Scientific American* 284:19-20.

Marx, K. (1977). *Karl Marx: Selected Writings.* (D. McLellan, ed.). Oxford: Oxford University Press.

Marx, K. & F. Engels (1948). *The Communist Manifesto*. New York: International.

Marx, K. & F. Engels (1965). The *German Ideology*. London: Lawrence and Wishart.

Masters, R. (1991). "Naturalistic Approaches to the Concept Of Justice." *American Behavioral Scientist* 34:289-313.

Matarazzo, J. (1992). "Psychological Testing and Assessment in the 21st Century." *American Psychologist* 47:1007-1018.

Matsueda, R. (1988). "The Current State of Differential Association Theory." *Crime & Delinquency* 34:277-306.

Matsueda, R. & K. Heimer (1987). "Race, Family Structure, and Delinquency: A Test of Differential Association and Social Control Theories." *American Sociological Review* 52:836-840.

Maughan, B. & A. Pickles (1990). "Adopted and Illegitimate Children Growing Up." In L. Robins & M. Rutter (eds.), *Straight and Devious Pathways from Childhood to Adulthood*, pp. 36-61. Cambridge: Cambridge University Press.

Mayes, L., M. Bornstein, K. Chawarska, O. Haynes & R. Granger (1995). "Informational Processing and Developmental Assessment in 3-Month-Old Infants Exposed Prenatally to Cocaine." *Pediatrics* 95:539-545.

Mazur, A. & A. Booth (1998). "Testosterone and Dominance in Men." *Behavioral and Brain Sciences* 21:353-397.

McBurnett, K., B. Lahey, P. Rathouz & R. Loeber (2000). "Low Salivary Cortisol and Persistent Aggression in Boys Referred for Disruptive Behavior." *Archives of General Psychiatry* 57:38-43.

McCartney, K., M. Harris & F. Bernieri (1990). "Growing Up and Growing Apart: A Developmental Meta-Analysis of Twin Studies." *Psychological Bulletin* 226-237.

McCrae, R., P. Costa, F. Ostendorf, A. Angleitner, M. Hrebickova, M. Avia, J. Sanz, M. Sanchez-Bernardos, M. Kusdil, R. Woodfield, P. Saunders & P. Smith (2000). "Nature Over Nurture: Temperament, Personality, and Life Span Development." *Journal of Personality and Social Psychology* 78:173-186.

McGue, M. (1994). "Why Developmental Psychology Should Find Room for Behavior Genetics." In C. Nelson (ed.), *Threats to Optimal Development: Integrating Biological, Psychological, and Social Risk Factors*, pp. 105-119. Hillsdale, NJ: Lawrence Erlbaum.

McGue, M., S. Bacon & D. Lykken (1993). "Personality Stability and Change in Early Adulthood: A Behavioral Genetic Analysis." *Developmental Psychology* 29:96-109.

McGue, M., T. Bouchard, W. Iacono & D. Lykken (1993). "Behavioral Genetics of Cognitive Ability: A Lifespan Perspective." In R. Plomin & G. McClearn (eds.), *Nature, Nurture & Psychology*. Washington, DC: American Psychological Association.

McGue, M. & D. Lykken (1992). "Genetic Influence on the Risk of Divorce." *Psychological Science* 3:368-373.

McLeod, J., C. Kruttschnitt & M. Dornfield (1994). "Does Parenting Explain the Effects of Structural Conditions on Children's Antisocial Behavior? A Comparison of Blacks and Whites." *Social Forces* 73:575-604.

McNaughton, N. (1989). *Biology and Emotion*. New York: Cambridge University Press.

Mealey, L. (1995). "The Sociobiology of Sociopathy: An Integrated Evolutionary Model." *Behavioral and Brain Sciences* 18:523-559.

Mears, D., M. Ploeger & M. Warr (1998). "Explaining the Gender Gap in Delinquency: Peer Influence and Moral Evaluations of Behavior." *Journal of Research in Crime and Delinquency* 35:251-266.

Mednick, S., W. Gabrielli & B. Hutchings (1984). "Genetic Influences in Criminal Convictions: Evidence from an Adoption Cohort." *Science* 224:891-894.

Merton, R. (1938) "Social Structure and Anomie." *American Sociological Review* 3:672-682.

Merton, R. (1968). *Social Theory and Social Structure*. Glencoe, IL: Free Press.

Messner, S. & R. Rosenfeld (1994). *Crime and the American Dream*. Belmont, CA: Wadsworth.

Messner, S. & R. Sampson (1991). "The Sex Ratio, Family Disruption, and Rates of Violent Crime: The Paradox of Demographic Structure." *Social Forces* 69:693-723.

Methwin, E. (1997). "Mugged by Reality." *Policy Review* (July/August):32-39.

Miller, L. (1987). "Neuropsychology of the Aggressive Psychopath: An Integrative Review." *Aggressive Behavior* 13:119-140.

Moffitt, T. (1993). "Adolescent-Limited and Life-Course-Persistent Antisocial Behavior: A Developmental Taxonomy." *Psychological Review* 100:674-701.

Moffitt, T. (1996). "The Neuropsychology of Conduct Disorder." In P. Cordella & L. Siegel (eds.), *Readings in Contemporary Criminological Theory*, pp. 85-106. Boston: Northeastern University Press.

Moffit, T., G. Brammer, A. Caspi, J. Fawcett, M. Raleigh, A.Yuwiler & P. Silva (1998). "Whole Blood Serotonin Relates to Violence in an Epidemiological Study." *Biological Psychiatry* 43:446-457.

Moffitt, T., A. Caspi, N. Dickson, P. Silva & W. Stanton (1996). "Childhood-Onset versus Adolescent-Onset Antisocial Conduct in Males: Natural History from Ages 3 to 18." *Development and Psychopathology* 8:399-424.

Moffitt, T., D. Lynam & P. Silva (1994). "Neuropsychological Tests Predicting Persistent Male Delinquency." *Criminology* 32:277-300.

Moffitt, T. & P. Silva (1988). "IQ and Delinquency: A Test of the Differential Detection Hypothesis." *Journal of Abnormal Psychology* 97:330-333.

Moir, A. & D. Jessel (1995). *A Mind to Crime*. London: Michael Joseph.

Molenaar, P., D. Boomsma & C. Dolan (1993). "A Third Source of Developmental Differences." *Behavior Genetics* 23:519-524.

Montagu, A. (1978). *Touching: The Human Significance of the Skin*. New York: Harper & Row.

Montagu, A. (1981). *Growing Young*. New York: McGraw-Hill.

Moore, C. & M. Rose (1995). "Adaptive and Nonadaptive Explanations of Sociopathy." *Behavior and Brain Sciences* 18:566-567.

Morash, M. & M. Chesney-Lind (1991). "A Reformulation and Partial Test of the Power Control Theory of Delinquency." *Justice Quarterly* 8:347-377.

Morris, A. (1987). *Women and Criminal Justice*. Oxford: Blackwell.

Moynihan, D. (1965). *The Negro Family: The Case for National Action*. Washington, DC: U.S. Department of Labor.

Nagin, D., D. Farrington & T. Moffitt (1995). "Life-Course Trajectories of Different Types of Offenders." *Criminology* 33:111-139.

Nagin, D. & R. Paternoster (1991). "The Preventative Effects of Perceived Risk of Arrest: Testing an Expanded Conception of Deterrence." *Criminology* 29:561-588.

Neisser, U., G. Boodoo, T. Bouchard, A. Boykin, N. Brody, S. Ceci, D. Halpern, J. Loehlin, R. Perloff, R. Sternberg & S. Urbina (1995). *Intelligence: Knowns and Unknowns. Report of a Task Force Established by the Board of Scientific Affairs of the American Psychological Association*. Washington, DC: American Psychological Association.

Nesse, R. (1990). "Evolutionary Explanations of Emotions." *Human Nature* 1:261-289.

Nesse, R. & A. Lloyd (1992). "The Evolution of Psychodynamic Mechanisms." In J. Barkow, L. Cosmides & J. Tooby (eds.), *The Adapted Mind: Evolutionary Psychology and the Generation of Culture*, pp. 601-620. New York: Oxford University Press.

Nettler, G. (1978). *Explaining Crime*. New York: McGraw-Hill.

Nielsen, F. (1994). "Sociobiology and Sociology." *Annual Review of Sociology* 20:267-303.

Nigg, J. & H. Goldsmith (1998). "Developmental Psychopathology, Personality, and Temperament: Reflections on Recent Behavioral Genetics Research." *Human Biology* 70:387-412.

Norton, E. (1987). "Restoring the Traditional Black Family." In L. Barnes (ed.), *Social Problems*. Guilford, CT: Dushkin.

O'Connor, T., K. Deater-Deckard, D. Fulker, M. Rutter & R. Plomin (1998). "Genotype-Environment Correlations in Late Childhood and Early Adolescence: Antisocial Behavioral Problems and Coercive Parenting." *Developmental Psychology* 34:970-981.

Oliveira, R. (1998). "Of Fish and Men: A Comparative Approach to Androgens and Social Dominance." *Behavioral and Brain Sciences* 21:383-384.

Padilla, F. (1992). *The Gang as an American Enterprise*. New Brunswick, NJ: Rutgers University Press.

Palmer, C. (1992). "The Use and Abuse of Darwinian Psychology: Its Impact on Attempts to Determine the Evolutionary Basis of Human Rape." *Ethology and Sociobiology* 13:289-299.

Palmer, C. & C. Tilley (1995). "Sexual Access to Females as a Motivation for Joining Gangs: An Evolutionary Approach." *The Journal of Sex Research* 32:213-217.

Panksepp, J. (1992). "A Critical Role for 'Affective Neuroscience' in Resolving What is Basic about Basic Emotions." *Psychological Review* 9:554-560.

Park, R., E. Burgess & R. McKenzie (1925). *The City*. Chicago: University of Chicago Press.

Passas, N. (1995). "Continuities in the Anomie Tradition." In F. Adler, & W. Laufer (eds.), *The Legacy of Anomie Theory*, pp. 91-112. New Brunswick, NJ: Transaction.

Pater, P. (1990) "The Study of Conflict." In J. Van der Dennen & V. Falger (eds.), *Sociobiology and Conflict: Evolutionary Perspectives on Competition, Cooperation, Violence and Warfare*, pp. 1-19. London: Chapman and Hall.

Paterson, G. & K. Yoerger (1993). "Developmental Models for Delinquent Behavior." In S. Hodgins (ed.), *Mental Disorders and Crime*. Newbury Park, CA: Sage.

Patrick, C. (1994). "Emotions and Psychopathy: Startling New Insights." *Psychophysiology* 31:319-330.

Paus, T., A. Zijdenbos, K. Worsley, D. Collins, J, Blumenthal, J. Giedd, J. Rapoport & A. Evans (1999). "Structural Maturation of Neural Pathways in Children and Adolescents: In Vivo Study." *Science* 283:1908-1911.

Pedersen, F. (1991). "Secular Trends in Human Sex Ratios: Their Influence on Individual and Family Behavior." *Human Nature* 2:271-291.

Perry, B. (1997). "Incubated in Terror: Neurodevelopmental Factors in the 'Cycle of Violence.'" In J. Osofsky (ed.), *Children in a Violent Society*, pp. 124-149. New York: Guilford Press.

Perry, B. & D. Polk (1997). "Personality Similarity in Twins Reared Apart and Together." *Journal of Personality and Social Psychology* 54:1031-1039.

Perry, B. & R. Pollard (1998). "Homeostasis, Stress, Trauma, and Adaptation: A Neurodevelopmental View of Childhood Trauma." *Child and Adolescent Psychiatric Clinics of America* 7:33-51.

Perusse, D. (1992). "Culture and Reproductive Success in Industrial Societies: Testing the Relationship at the Proximate and Ultimate Levels." *Behavioral and Brain Sciences* 16:267-283.

Pihl, R. & K. Bruce (1995). "Cognitive Impairment in Children of Alcoholics." *Alcohol, Health and Research World* 19:142-147.

Pine, D., J. Coplan, G. Wasserman, L. Miller, J. Fried, M. Davies, T. Cooper, L. Greenhill, D. Shaffer & B. Parsons (1997). "Neuroendocrine Response to Fenfluramine Challenge to Boys. Associations with Aggressive Behavior and Adverse Rearing." *Archives of General Psychiatry* 54:839-846.

Pinel, J. (2000). *Biopsychology*, 4th ed. Boston: Allyn & Bacon.

Pinker, S. (1997). *How the Mind Works*. New York: W.W. Norton.

Pinker, S. & P. Bloom (1992). "Natural Language and Natural Selection." In J.Barkow, L. Cosmides & J. Tooby (eds.), *The Adapted Mind: Evolutionary Psychology and the Generation of Culture*, pp. 452-493. New York: Oxford University Press.

Pitman, R. & S. Orr (1993). "Psychophysiological Testing for Post Traumatic Stress Disorder." *American Academy of Psychiatry and Law* 21:37-52.

Plato (1960). *The Republic and Other Works*. B. Jowett (trans.). Garden City, NY: Dolphin.

Platt, T. (1975). "Prospects for a Radical Criminology in the USA." In I. Taylor, P. Walton & J. Young (eds.), *Critical Criminology*, pp. 95-112. Boston: Routledge & Kegan Paul.

Plavcan, J. & C. van Schaik (1997). "Intrasexual Competition and Body Weight Dimorphism in Anthropoid Primates." *American Journal of Physical Anthropology* 103:37-68.

Plomin, R. (1994). "The Emanuel Miller Memorial Lecture 1993: Genetic Research and Identification of Environmental Influences." *Journal of Child Psychology and Psychiatry* 35:817-834.

Plomin, R. (1995). "Genetics and Children's Experiences in the Family." *Journal of Child Psychology and Psychiatry* 36:33-68.

Plomin, R. & C. Bergeman (1991). "The Nature of Nurture: Genetic Influences on 'Environmental' Measures." *Behavioral and Brain Sciences* 14:373-427.

Plomin, R., H. Chipuer & J. Loehlin (1990). "Behavioral Genetics and Personality." In L. Pervin (ed.), *Handbook of Personality Theory and Research*, pp. 225-233. New York: Guilford.

Plomin, R. & D. Daniels (1987). "Why are Children in the Same Family So Different from One Another?" *Behavioral and Brain Sciences* 10:1-60.

Plomin, R., J. DeFries & G. McClearn (1980). *Behavioral Genetic: A Primer*. San Francisco: W.H. Freeman.

Plomin, R., G. McClearn, D. Smith, S. Vignetti, M. Chorney, K. Chorney, C. Venditti, S. Kasarda, L. Thompson, D. Detterman, J. Daniels, M. Owen & P. McGuffin (1994). "DNA Markers Associated with High versus Low IQ: The IQ Quantitative Trait Loci (QTL) Project." *Behavior Genetics* 24:107-118.

Plomin, R. & S. Petrill (1997). "Genetics and Intelligence: What's New?" *Intelligence* 24:53-77.

Popenoe, D. (1993). "American Family Decline, 1960–1990: Evidence from the 1980s." *Journal of Marriage and the Family* 55:527-542.

Popenoe, D. (1994). "The Family Condition of America: Cultural Change and Public Policy." In H. Aaron, T. Mann & T. Taylor (eds.), *Values and Public Policy*, pp. 81-111. Washington, DC: The Brookings Institute.

Price, B. & N. Sokoloff (1995). "Theories and Facts About Women Offenders." In B. Price & N. Sokoloff (eds.), *The Criminal Justice System and Women: Offenders, Victims, and Workers*, pp. 1-10. New York: McGraw-Hill.

Quartz, S. & T. Sejnowski (1997). "The Neural Basis of Cognitive Development: A Constructivist Manifesto." *Behavioral and Brain Sciences* 20:537-596.

Quinney, R. (1975). "Crime Control in Capitalist Society: A Critical Philosophy of Legal Order." In I. Taylor, P. Walton & J. Young (eds.), *Critical Criminology*, pp. 181-202. Boston: Routledge & Kegan Paul.

Quinton, D., A. Pickles, B. Maughan & M. Rutter (1993). "Partners, Peers and Pathways: Assortative Pairing and Continuities in Conduct Disorder." *Development and Psychopathology* 5:763-783.

Raine, A. (1993). *The Psychopathology of Crime: Criminal Behavior as a Clinical Disorder*. San Diego: Academic Press.

Raine, A. (1997). "Antisocial Behavior and Psychophysiology: A Biosocial Perspective and a Prefrontal Dysfunction Hypothesis." In D. Stoff, J. Breiling & J. Maser (eds.), *Handbook of Antisocial Behavior*, pp. 289-304. New York: John Wiley.

Raine, A. & J. Dunkin (1990). "The Genetic and Psychophysiological Basis of Antisocial Behavior: Implications for Counseling and Therapy." *Journal of Counseling and Development* 68:637-644.

Raine, A., T. Lencz, S. Buhrle, L. LaCasse & P. Colletti (2000). "Reduced Prefrontal Gray Matter Volume and Reduced Autonomic Activity in Antisocial Personality Disorder." *Archives of General Psychiatry* 57:119-127.

Raine, A., J. Meloy, S. Bihrle, J. Stoddard, L. LaCasse & M. Buchsbaum (1998). "Reduced Prefrontal and Increased Subcortical Brain Functioning Assessed Using Positron Emission Tomography in Predatory and Affective Murderers." *Behavioral Sciences and the Law* 16:319-332.

Raine, A., P. Venables & M. Williams (1990). "Relationships between Central and Autonomic Measures of Arousal at Age 15 Years and Criminality at Age 24 Years." *Archives of General Psychiatry* 47:1003-1007.

Rakic, P. (1996). "Development of the Cerebral Cortex in Human and Non-Human Primates." In M. Lewis (ed.), *Child and Adolescent Psychiatry: A Comprehensive Textbook*, pp. 9-30. New York: Williams and Wilkins.

Raleigh, M., M. McGuire, G. Brammer, D. Pollock & A. Yuwiler (1991). "Serotonergic Mechanisms Promote Dominance Acquisition in Adult Vervet Monkeys." *Brain Research* 559:181-190.

Rasche, C. (1995). "Minority Women and Domestic Violence: The Unique Dilemmas of Battered Women of Color." In B. Price & N. Sokoloff (eds.), *The Criminal Justice System and Women: Offenders, Victims, and Workers,* pp. 246-261. New York: McGraw-Hill

Reige, M. (1972). "Parental Affection and Juvenile Delinquency in Girls." *British Journal of Criminology* 12:55-73.

Reiss, A., M. Abrams, H. Singer, J. Ross & M. Bencla (1996). "Brain Development, Gender and IQ in Children: A Volumetric Imaging Study." *Brain* 119:1763-1774.

Reiss, D. (1997). "Mechanisms Linking Genetic and Social Influences in Adolescent Development: Beginning a Collaborative Search." *Current Directions in Psychological Science* 6:100-105.

Reite, M. (1987). "Some Additional Influences Shaping the Development of Behavior." *Child Development* 55:596-600.

Ribchester, R. (1986). *Molecule, Nerve and Embryo.* Glasgow: Blackie.

Ridley, M. (1993). *Evolution.* Oxford: Blackwell.

Ritzer, G. (1988). *Contemporary Sociological Theory.* New York: Knopf.

Roberts, J. & T. Gabor (1990). "Lombrosian Wine in New Bottles: Research on Race and Crime." *Canadian Review of Criminology* 32:291-313.

Robinson, W. (1950). "Ecological Correlations and the Behavior of Individuals." *American Sociological Review* 15:351-357.

Rock, P. & S. Holdaway (1998). "Thinking About Criminology: 'Facts are Bits of Biography.'" In S. Holdaway & P. Rock (eds.), *Thinking about Criminology*. Toronto: University of Toronto Press.

Rodkin, P., T. Farmer, R. Pearl & R. Van Acker (2000). "Heterogeneity of Popular Boys: Antisocial and Prosocial Configurations." *Developmental Psychology* 36:14-24.

Rohner, R. (1975). *They Love Me, They Love Me Not: A Worldwide Study of the Effects of Parental Acceptance and Rejection*. New Haven: HRAF.

Rose, R., L. Bernstein, H. Judd, R, Hannish, M. Pike & B. Henderson (1986). "Serum Testosterone Levels in Healthy Young Black and White Men." *Journal of the National Cancer Institute* 76:45-48.

Rose, S. (1999). "Precis of *Lifelines*: Biology, Freedom, Determinism." *Behavioral and Brain Sciences* 22:871-921.

Rosenbaum, J. (1989). "Family Dysfunction and Female Delinquency." *Crime & Delinquency* 35:31-41.

Rosenfeld, R. (1986). "Urban Crime Rates: Effects of Inequality, Welfare Dependency, Region, and Race." In J. Byrne & R. Sampson (eds.), *The Social Ecology of Crime*, pp. 116-130. London: Springer-Verlag.

Rossi, A. (1977). "A Biosocial Perspective on Parenting." *Daedalus* 106:1-31.

Rossi, A. (1984). "Gender and Parenthood." *American Sociological Review* 49:1-19.

Rossi, A. (1997). "The Impact of Family Structure and Social Change on Adolescent Sexual Behavior." *Children and Youth Services Review* 19:369-400.

Rothbart, M. & S. Ahadi (1994). "Temperament and the Development of Personality." *Journal of Abnormal Psychology* 103:55-66.

Rothbart, M., S. Ahadi & D. Evans (2000). "Temperament and Personality: Origins and Outcomes." *Journal of Personality and Social Psychology* 78:122-135.

Rowe, D. (1992). "Three Shocks to Socialization Research." *Behavioral and Brain Sciences* 14:401-402.

Rowe, D. (1994). *The Limits of Family Influence: Genes, Experience, and Behavior*. New York: Guilford Press.

Rowe, D. (1996). "An Adaptive Strategy Theory of Crime and Delinquency." In J. Hawkins (ed.), *Delinquency and Crime: Current Theories*, pp. 268-314. Cambridge: Cambridge University Press.

Rowe, D. (1997). "A Place at the Policy Table? Behavior Genetics and Estimates of Family Environmental Effects on IQ." *Intelligence* 24:133-158.

Rowe, D. & B. Gully (1992). "Sibling Effects on Substance Use and Delinquency." *Criminology* 30:217-233.

Rowe, D. & D. Osgood (1984). "Heredity and Sociological Theories of Delinquency: A Reconsideration." *American Sociological Review* 49:526-540.

Rowe, D., W. Vesterdal & J. Rodgers (1999). "Herrnstein's Syllogism: Genetic and Shared Environmental Influences on IQ, Education, and Income." *Intelligence* 26:405-423.

Ruden, R. (1997). *The Craving Brain: The Biobalance Approach to Controlling Addictions*. New York: Harper Collins.

Ruffie, J. (1986). *The Population Alternative: A New Look at Competition and the Species*. New York: Random House.

Rushton, J. (1988). "The Reality of Racial Differences: A Rejoinder with Additional Evidence." *Personality and Individual Differences* 9:1035-1040.

Rushton, J. (1990). "Sir Francis Galton, Epigenetic Rules, Genetic Similarity Theory, and Human Life History." *Journal of Personality* 58:117-140.

Rushton, J. (1994). "The Equalitarian Dogma Revisited." *Intelligence* 19:263-280.

Rushton, J. (1995). "Race and Crime: International Data for 1989-1990." *Psychological Reports* 76:307-312.

Rushton, J. & A. Bogaert (1987). "Race Differences in Sexual Behavior: Testing an Evolutionary Hypothesis." *Journal of Research in Personality*, 21:529-551.

Rushton, J., D. Fulker, M. Neale, D. Nias & H. Eysenck (1986). "Altruism and Aggression: The Heritability of Individual Differences." *Journal of Personality and Social Psychology* 50:1192-1198.

Rushton, J., C. Littlefield & C. Lumsden (1986). "Gene-Culture Coeveolution of Complex Social Behavior: Human Altruism and Mate Choice." *Proceedings of the National Academy of Sciences* 83:7340-7343.

Rutter, M. (1996). "Introduction: Concepts of Antisocial Behaviour, of Cause, and of Genetic Influence." In G. Bock & J. Goode (eds.), *Genetics of Criminal and Antisocial Behavior*, pp. 1-20. Chichester, England: John Wiley.

Rutter, M. & H. Giller (1984) *Juvenile Delinquency: Trends and Perspectives*. New York: Guilford.

Ryan, W. (1971). *Blaming the Victim*. New York: Vintage.

Sagan, C. (1995). *The Demon-Haunted World: Science as a Candle in the Dark*. New York: Random House.

Sagarin, E. (1980). "Taboo Subjects and Taboo Viewpoints in Criminology." In E. Sagarin (ed.), *Taboos in Criminology*, pp. 7-21. Beverly Hills: Sage.

Sampson, R. (1985). "Race and Criminal Violence: A Demographically Disaggregated Analysis of Urban Homicide." *Crime & Delinquency* 31:47-82.

Sampson, R. (1995). "The Community." In J. Wilson & J. Petersilia (eds.), *Crime*, pp. 193-216, San Franciso: ICS Press.

Sampson, R. & J. Laub (1990). "Crime and Deviance over the Life-Course: The Salience of Adult Social Bonds." *American Sociological Review* 55:609-627.

Sampson, R. & J. Laub (1999). "Crime and Deviance over the Lifecourse: The Salience of Adult Social Bonds." In F. Scarpitti & A. Nielsen (eds.), *Crime and Criminals: Contemporary and Classical Readings in Criminology*, pp. 238-246. Los Angeles: Roxbury Press.

Sampson, R. & W. Wilson (2000). "Toward a Theory of Race, Crime, and Urban Inequality." In S. Cooper (ed.), *Criminology*, pp. 149-160. Madison, WI: Coursewise.

Saville, G. (1996). "Searching for a Neighborhood's Crime Threshold." *Suject to Debate* 10:1-11.

Scarr, S. (1981). *Race, Social Class, and Individual Differences in IQ*. Hillsdale, NJ: Lawrence Erlbaum.

Scarr, S. (1992). "Developmental Theories for the 1990s: Development and Individual Differences." *Child Development* 63:1-19.

Scarr, S. (1993). "Biological and Cultural Diversity: The Legacy of Darwin for Development." *Child Development* 64:1333-1353.

Scarr, S. (1995). "Psychology Will Be Truly Evolutionary When Behavior Genetics is Included." *Psychological Inquiry* 6:68-71.

Scarr, S. & K. McCartney (1983). "How People Make their own Environments: A Theory of Genotype→Environment Effects." *Child Development* 54:424-435.

Scarr-Salapatek, S. (1971). "Race, Social Class, and IQ." *Science* 174:1285-1295.

Schaff, A. (1970). *Marxism and the Human Individual*. New York: McGraw-Hill.

Schelling, T. (1971). "Dynamic Models of Segregation." *Journal of Mathematical Sociology* 1:143-186.

Schwendinger, H. & J. Schwendinger (1975). "Defenders of Order or Guardians of Human Rights." In I. Taylor, P. Walton & J. Young (eds.), *Critical Criminology*, pp. 113-146. Boston: Routledge & Kegan Paul.

Science for the People (1978). "Sociobiology—Another Biological Determinism." In A. Caplan (ed.), *The Sociobiology Debate*, pp. 280-290. New York: Harper & Row.

Segal, N. & K. MacDonald (1998). "Behavioral Genetics and Evolutionary Psychology: Unified Perspective on Personality Research." *Human Biology* 70:159-184.

Seligman, D. (1992). *A Question of Intelligence: The IQ Debate in America*. New York: Birch Lane Press.

Senger, H. (1993). "Human Rights and Crime." Paper presented at the 11th International Congress of Criminology, August 22-28, Budapest, Hungary.

Shallis, T. (1991). "Precis of *From Neuropsychology to Mental Structure*." *Behavioral and Brain Sciences* 14:429-469.

Shapiro, L. & T. Insel (1990). "Infant's Response to Social Separation Reflects Adult Differences in Affiliative Behavior: A Comparative Developmental Study in Prairie and Montane Voles." *Developmental Psychobiology* 23:375-394.

Shavit, Y. & A. Rattner (1988). "Age, Crime, and the Early Lifecourse." *American Journal of Sociology* 93:1457-1470.

Shaw, D. & R. Bell (1993). "Developmental Theories of Parental Contributions to Antisocial Behavior." *Journal of Abnormal Child Psychology* 21:493-518.

Shaw, C. & H. McKay (1972). *Juvenile Delinquency and Urban Areas*. Chicago: University of Chicago Press.

Shore, P. (1996). *Culture in Mind: Cognition, Culture, and the Problem of Meaning*. New York: Oxford University Press.

Shore, R. (1997). *Rethinking the Brain: New Insights into Early Development*. New York: Families and Work Institute.

Shover, N. (1985). *Aging Criminals*. Beverly Hills: Sage.

Sieff, D. (1990). "Explaining Biased Sex Ratios in Human Populations: A Critique of Recent Studies." *Current Anthropology* 31:25-48.

Simon, R. (1975). *Women and Crime*. Lexington, MA: Lexington Books.

Simons, R. & D. Blyth (1988). *Moving into Adolescence: The Impact of Pubertal Change and School Context*. Hawthorn, NY: Aldine de Gruyter.

Simons, R., J. Beaman, R. Conger & W. Chao (1993). "Stress, Support, and Antisocial Behavior Trait as Determinants of Emotional Well-Being and Parenting Practices among Single Mothers." *Journal of Marriage and the Family* 55:385-389.

Simons, R., C. Wu, R. Conger & F. Lorenz (1994). "Two Routes to Delinquency: Differences between Early and Late Starters in the Impact of Parenting and Deviant Peers." *Criminology* 32:247-274.

Singer, P. (2000). *A Darwinian Left: Politics, Evolution, and Cooperation*. New Haven, CT: Yale University Press.

Skinner, B. (1966). "The Phylogeny and Ontogeny of Behavior." *Science* 157:1205-1213.

Skinner, L., K. Carrol & K. Berry (1995). "A Typology for Sexually Aggressive Males in Dating Relationships. *Journal of Offender Rehabilitation* 22:29-45.

Skogan, W. (1991). *Disorder and Decline*. New York: Free Press.

Smith, D. (1993). "Brain, Environment, Heredity, and Personality." *Psychological Reports* 72:3-13.

Smith, M. (1987). "Evolution and Developmental Psychology: Toward a Sociobiology of Human Development." In C. Crawford, M. Smith & D. Krebs (eds.), *Sociobiology and Psychology: Ideas, Issues, and Applications*, pp. 225-252. Hillsdale, NJ: Lawrence Erlbaum.

Smuts, B. (1992). "Male Aggression Against Women: An Evolutionary Perspective." *Human Nature* 3:1-44.

Smuts, B. (1993). "Male Aggression and Sexual Coercion of Females in Non-Human Primates and Other Mammals: Evidence and Theoretical Implications." *Advances in the Study of Behavior* 22:1-63.

Snyderman, M. & S. Rothman (1988). *The IQ Controversy, the Media and Public Policy*. New Brunswick, NJ: Transaction.

Sokoloff, N. & B. Price (1995). "The Criminal Law and Women." In B. Price & N. Sokoloff (eds.), *The Criminal Justice System and Women: Offenders, Victims, and Workers*, pp. 11-29. New York: McGraw-Hill.

Solomon, R. (1980). "The Opponent-Process Theory of Acquired Motivation." *American Psychologist* 35:691-712.

South, S. & K. Trent (1988). "Sex Ratios and Women's Roles: A Crossnational Analysis." *American Journal of Sociology* 93:1096-1115.

Sowell, E., P. Thompson, C. Holmes, T. Jernigan & A. Toga (1999). "In Vivo Evidence for Post-Adolescent Brain Maturation in Frontal and Striatal Regions." *Nature Neuroscience* 2:859-861.

Spelke, E. (1999). "Object Perception: The Faculty of Segmenting Words into Objects." *http://humanitas.ucsb.edu/users/steen/CogSci/Spelke.html*

Spiro, M. (1980). *Gender and Culture: Kibbutz Women Revisited*. New York: Schocken Books.

Spoont, M. (1992). "Modulatory Role of Serotonin in Neural Information Processing: Implications for Human Psychopathology." *Psychological Bulletin* 112:330-350.

Stacey, J. (1993). "Good Riddance to 'The Family': A Response to David Popenoe." *Journal of Marriage and the Family* 55:545-547.

Stark, R. (1996). "Deviant Places: A Theory of the Ecology of Crime." In P. Cordella & L. Siegel (eds.), *Readings in Contemporary Criminological Theory*, pp. 128-142. Boston: Northeastern University Press.

Stattin, H. & Klackenberg-Larsson (1993). "Early Language and Intelligence Development and their Relationship to Future Criminal Behavior." *Journal of Abnormal Psychology* 102:369-378.

Steffensmeier, D. & E. Allan (1996). "Gender and Crime: Toward a Gendered Theory of Female Offending." *Annual Review of Sociology* 22:459-488.

Steffensmeier, D., E. Allan, M. Harer & C. Streifel (1989). "Age and the Distribution of Crime." *American Journal of Sociology* 94:803-831.

Suchy, Y., A. Blint & D. Osman (1997). "Behavioral Dyscontrol Scale: Criterion and Predictive Validity in an Inpatient Rehabilitation Unit Population." *Clinical Neuropsychologist* 11:258-265.

Suomi, S. (1980). *A Touch of Sensitivity*. WBGH Educational Foundation.

Sutherland, E. (1939). *Principles of Criminology*. Philadelphia: J.B. Lippincott.

Sutherland, E. & D. Cressey (1974). *Criminology*, 9th ed. Philadelphia: J.B. Lippincott.

Sutton, S. & R. Davidson (1997). "Prefrontal Brain Asymmetry: A Biological Substrate of the Behavioral Approach and Inhibition Systems." *Psychological Science* 8:204-210.

Svensson, T. (1992). "A Psychopharmacologist's View of Attachment." *Behavioral and Brain Sciences* 15:524.

Symons, D. (1987). "If We're all Darwinians, What's the Fuss About?" In C. Crawford, M. Smith & D. Krebs (eds.), *Sociobiology and Psychology: Ideas, Issues, and Applications*, pp. 121-146. Hillsdale, NJ: Lawrence Erlbaum.

Symons, D. (1992). "The Use and Misuse of Darwinism in the Study of Human Behavior." In J. Barkow, L. Cosmides & J. Tooby (eds.), *The Adapted Mind: Evolutionary Psychology and the Generation of Culture*, pp. 137-159. New York: Oxford University Press.

Sztompka, P. (1994). *The Sociology of Social Change*. Oxford: Blackwell.

Tambs, K., J. Sundet, P. Magnus & K. Berg (1989). "Genetic and Environmental Contributions to the Covariance Between Occupational Status, Educational Attainment, and IQ." *Behavior Genetics* 19:209-222.

Taylor, I., P. Walton & J. Young (1973). *The New Criminology: For a Social Theory of Deviance*. London: Routledge & Kegan Paul.

Taylor, J. (1992). *Paved with Good Intentions: The Failure of Race Relations in Contemporary America*. New York: Carroll and Graf.

Teicher, M., Y. Ito, C. Glod, F. Schiffer & H. Gelbard (1997). "Early Abuse, Limbic System Dysfunction, and Borderline Personality Disorder." In J. Osofsky (ed.), *Children in a Violent Society*, pp. 177-207. New York: Guilford Press.

Tellegen, A., D. Lykken, T. Bouchard, K. Wilcox, N. Segal & S. Rich (1988). "Personality Similarity in Twins Reared Apart and Together." *Journal of Personality and Social Psychology* 36:1031-1039.

Thornberry, T. (1987). "Toward an Interactional Theory of Delinquency." *Criminology* 25:863-891.

Thornhill, N. & R. Thornhill (1987). "Evolutionary Theory and Rules of Mating and Marriage Pertaining to Relatives." In C. Crawford, M. Smith & D. Krebs (eds.), *Sociobiology and Psychology: Ideas, Issues, and Applications*, pp. 373-400. Hillsdale, NJ: Lawrence Erlbaum.

Thornhill, R. & N. Thornhill (1992). "The Evolutionary Psychology of Men's Coercive Sexuality." *Behavioral and Brain Sciences* 15:363-421.

Thornhill, R. & C. Palmer (2000). *A Natural History of Rape: Biological Bases of Sexual Coercion*. Cambridge, MA: The MIT Press.

Tiger, L. (1990). "The Cerebral Bridge from Family to Foe." In J. van der Dennen & V. Falger (eds.), *Sociobiology and Conflict*, pp. 99-106. London: Chapman and Hall.

Toby, J. (1980). "The New Criminology is the Old Baloney." In J. Inciardi (ed.), *Radical Criminology: The Coming Crises*, pp. 124-138. Beverly Hills: Sage.

Tooby, J. (1999). "The View from the President's Table: The Most Testable Concept in Biology." *Human Behavior and Evolution Society Newsletter* 8:1-6.

Tooby, J. & L. Cosmides (1990) "On the Universality of Human Nature and the Uniqueness of the Individual: The Role of Genetics and Adaptation." *Journal of Personality* 58:17-67.

Tooby, J. & L. Cosmides (1992). "The Psychological Foundation of Culture." In J. Barkow, L. Cosmides & J. Tooby (eds.), *The Adapted Mind: Evolutionary Psychology and the Generation of Culture*, pp. 19-136. New York: Oxford University Press.

Tracy, P., M. Wolfgang & R. Figlio (1990). *Delinquency Careers in Two Birth Cohorts*. New York: Plenum.

Trasler, G. (1987). "Some Cautions for the Biological Approach to Crime Causation." In S. Mednick, T. Moffitt & S. Sack (eds.), *The Causes of Crime: New Biological Approaches*, pp. 7-24. Cambridge: Cambridge University Press.

Trevarthen, C. (1992). "Emotions of Human Infants and Mothers and Development of the Brain." *Behavioral and Brain Sciences* 15:524-525.

Trivers, R. (1972). "Parental Investment and Sexual Selection." In B. Campbell (ed.), *Sexual Selection and the Descent of Man, 1871-1971*, pp. 363-197. Chicago: Aldine.

Trivers, R. (1991). "Deceit and Self-Deception: The Relationship between Communication and Consciousness." In M. Robinson & L. Tiger (eds.), *Man and Beast Revisited*, pp. 175-191. Washington, DC: Smithsonian Institution Press.

Trudge, C. (1999). "Who's Afraid of Genetic Determinism?" *Biologist* 46:96.

Trunnel, E., C. Turner & W. Kaye (1988). "A Comparison of the Psychological and Hormonal Factors in Women with and without Premenstrual Syndrome." *Journal of Abnormal Psychology* 97:429-436.

Tsai, L. & R. Sapolsky (1996). "Rapid Stimulatory Effects of Testosterone upon Myotubule Metabolism and Sugar Transport, as Assessed by Silicon Microphysiometry." *Aggressive Behavior* 22:357-364.

Turkheimer, E. (2000). "Three Laws of Behavior Genetics and What They Mean." *Current Directions in Psychological Science* 9:160-164.

Turkheimer, E. & M. Waldron (2000). "Nonshared Environment: A Theoretical, Methodological, and Quantitative Review." *Psychological Bulletin* 126:78-108.

Udry, J.R. (1988). "Biological Predispositions and Social Control in Adolescent Sexual Behavior." *American Sociological Review* 53:709-722.

Udry, J.R. (1990). "Biosocial Models of Adolescent Problem Behaviors. *Social Biology* 37:1-10.

Udry, J.R. (1994). "The Nature of Gender." *Demography* 31:561-573.

Udry, J.R. (1995). "Sociology and Biology: What Biology Do Sociologists Need to Know?" *Social Forces* 73:1267-1278.

U.S. Bureau of the Census (2000). *The Black Population in the United States*. Washington, DC: U.S. Census Bureau.

U.S. Department of Justice (1993). *Survey of State Prison Inmates, 1991*. Washington, DC: Bureau of Justice Statistics.

van der Kolk, B. & M. Greenberg (1987). "The Physiology of the Trauma Response: Hyperarousal, Constriction, and Addiction to Traumatic Reexposure." In B. van der Kolk (ed.), *Psychological Trauma*, pp. 63-87. Washington, DC: American Psychiatric Press.

van den Berghe, P. (1987). "Incest Taboos and Avoidance: Some African Applications." In C. Crawford, M. Smith & D. Krebs (eds.), *Sociobiology and Psychology: Ideas, Issues, and Applications*, pp. 353-371. Hillsdale, NJ: Lawrence Erlbaum.

van den Berghe, P. (1990). "Why Most Sociologists Don't (and Won't) Think Evolutionarily." *Sociological Forum* 5:173-185.

Van Hooff, J. (1990). "Intergroup Competition in Animals and Man." In J. Van der Dennen & V. Falger (eds.), *Sociobiology and Conflict: Evolutionary Perspectives on Competition, Cooperation, Violence and Warfare*, pp. 23-54. London: Chapman and Hall.

Vandenberg, S. & G. Volger (1985). "Genetic Determinants of Intelligence." In B. Wolman (ed.), *Handbook of Intelligence: Theories, Measurements, and Applications*, pp. 3-57. New York: John Wiley.

Venables, P. (1987). "Autonomic Nervous System Factors in Criminal Behavior." In S. Mednick, T. Moffitt & S. Stack (eds.), *The Causes of Crime: New Biological Approaches,* pp. 110-136. Cambridge: University of Cambridge Press.

Vedder, R. & L. Gallaway (1993). "Declining Black Unemployment." *Society* 30:57-63.

Vila, B. (1994). "A General Paradigm for Understanding Criminal Behavior: Extending Evolutionary Ecological Theory." *Criminology* 32:311-358.

Vila, B. (1997). "Human Nature and Crime Control: Improving the Feasibility of Nurturant Strategies." *Politics and the Life Sciences* 16:3-21.

Vila, B. & L. Cohen (1993). "Crime as Strategy: Testing an Evolutionary Ecological Theory of Expropriative Crime." *American Journal of Sociology* 98:873-912.

Virkkunen, M. & M. Linnoila (1990). "Serotonin in Early Onset, Male Alcoholics with Violent Behaviour." *Annals of Medicine* 22:327-331.

Virkkunen, M., D. Goldman & M. Linnoila (1996). "Serotonin in Alcoholic Violent Offenders." In G. Bock & J. Goode (eds.), *Genetics of Criminal and Antisocial Behavior*, pp. 168-177. Chichester, England: John Wiley.

Voigt, L., W. Thornton, L. Barrile & J. Seaman (1994). *Criminology and Justice.* New York: McGraw-Hill.

Vold, G. & T. Bernard (1986). *Theoretical Criminology.* New York: Oxford University Press.

Vold, G., T. Bernard & J. Snipes (1998). *Theoretical Criminology,* 4th ed. New York: Oxford University Press.

Voss, H. & D. Petersen (1976), *Ecology, Crime and Delinquency.* New York: Appleton-Century-Crofts.

Walinsky, A. (1997). "The Crisis of Public Order." In M. Fisch (ed.), *Criminology 97/98,* pp. 8-15. Guilford, CT: Dushkin.

Wallis, C. (1987). "Children Having Children." In L. Barnes (ed.), *Social Problems,* pp. 10-16. Guilford, CT: Dushkin.

Walsh, A. (1990). "Illegitimacy, Child Abuse and Neglect, and Cognitive Development." *Journal of Genetic Psychology* 151:279-285.

Walsh, A. (1991) *Intellectual Imbalance, Love Deprivation, and Violent Delinquency: A Biosocial Perspective.* Springfield, IL: Charles C Thomas.

Walsh, A. (1992). "Genetic and Environmental Explanations of Violent Juvenile Delinquency in Advantaged and Disadvantaged Environments." *Aggressive Behavior* 18:187-199.

Walsh, A. (1995a). *Biosociology: An Emerging Paradigm.* New York: Praeger.

Walsh, A. (1995b). "Parental Attachment, Drug Use, and Facultative Sexual Strategies." *Social Biology* 42:95-107.

Walsh, A. (1995c). "Genetic and Cytogenetic Intersex Anomalies: Can They Help Us to Understand Gender Differences in Deviant Behavior?" *International Journal of Offender Therapy and Comparative Criminology* 39:151-164.

Walsh, A. (1997). "Methodological Individualism and Vertical Integration in the Social Sciences." *Behavior and Philosophy* 25:121-136.

Walsh, A. (1999). "Life History Theory and Female Readers of Pornography." *Personality and Individual Differences* 27:779-787.

Walsh, A. (2000a). "Behavior Genetics and Anomie/Strain Theory." *Criminology* 38:1075-1107.

Walsh, A. (2000b). "Evolutionary Psychology and the Origins of Justice." *Justice Quarterly* 17:841-864.

Walsh, A., J. Beyer & T. Petee (1987). "Violent Delinquency: An Examination of Psychopathic Typologies." *Journal of Genetic Psychology* 148:385-392.

Walsh, A. & L. Ellis (1997). "The Neurobiology of Nurturance, Evolutionary Expectations, and Crime Control." *Politics and the Life Sciences* 16:42-44.

Walsh, A. & L. Ellis (1999). "Political Ideology and American Criminologists' Explanations for Criminal Behavior." *The Criminologist* 24(6):1-27.

Walsh, A. & C. Hemmens (2000). *From Law to Order: The Theory and Practice of Law and Justice.* Lanham, MD: American Correctional Association.

Ward, D. & C. Tittle (1994). "IQ and Delinquency: A Test of Two Competing Explanations." *Journal of Quantitative Criminology* 10:189-212.

Warr, M. & M. Stafford. (1991). "The Influence of Delinquent Peers: What They Think or What They Do." *Criminology* 29:851-866.

Weisenfeld, A., C. Malatesa, P. Whitman, C. Granrose & R. Uili (1985). "Psychophysiological Response to Breast- and Bottle-Feeding Mothers to Their Infants' Signals." *Psychophysiology* 22:79-86.

Weiss, G. (1991). "Attention-Deficit Hyperactivity Disorder." In M. Lewis (ed.), *Child and Adolescent Psychiatry: A Comprehensive Textbook*, pp. 544-551. Baltimore: Williams & Wilkins.

Wellford, C. (1997). "Controlling Crime and Achieving Justice: The American Society of Criminology 1996 Presidential Address." *Criminology* 35:1-11.

Werner, E. & R. Smith (1992). *Overcoming the Odds: High-Risk Children from Birth to Adulthood.* Ithaca, NY: Cornell University Press.

West, D. & D. Farrington (1977). *The Delinquent Way of Life.* New York: Crane Russak.

Widom, C. (1989). "Child Abuse, Neglect, and Violent Criminal Behavior." *Criminology* 27:251-271.

Widom, C. & A. Ames (1988). "Biology and Female Crime." In T. Moffitt & S. Mednick (eds.), *Biological Contributions to Crime Causation*, pp. 308-331. Boston: Martinu Nijhoff.

Wikstrom, P. & R. Loeber (2000). "Do Disadvantaged Neighborhoods Cause Well-Adjusted Children to Become Adolescent Delinquents? A Study of Male Juvenile Serious Offending, Individual Risk and Protective Factors and Neighborhood Context." *Criminology* 38:1109-1142.

Wilbanks, W. (1987). "The Myth of a Racist Criminal Justice System." *Criminal Justice Research Bulletin*, Vol. 3. Huntsville, TX: Sam Houston State University.

Wilson, D. (1994). "Adaptive Genetic Variation and Human Evolutionary Psychology." *Ethology and Sociobiology* 15:219-235.

Wilson, D. & E. Sober (1994). "Reintroducing Group Selection to the Human Behavioral Sciences." *Behavioral and Brain Sciences* 17:585-608.

Wilson, E.O. (1975). *Sociobiology: The New Synthesis*. Cambridge, MA: Harvard University Press.

Wilson, E.O. (1990). "Biology and the Social Sciences." *Zygon* 25:245-262.

Wilson, E.O. (1998). *Consilience: The Unity of Knowledge*. New York: Knopf.

Wilson, G. (1983). *Love and Instinct: An Evolutionary Account of Human Sexuality*. New York: Quill.

Wilson, G., I. Sakura-Lemessy & J. West (1999). "Reaching the Top: Racial Differences in Mobility Paths in Upper-Tier Occupations." *Work and Occupations* 26:165-186.

Wilson, J.Q. & R. Herrnstein (1985). *Crime and Human Nature*. New York: Simon & Schuster.

Wilson, J.Q. & G. Kelling (1982). "Broken Windows: The Police and Neighborhood Safety." *The Atlantic Monthly* (March):29-38.

Wilson, M. & M. Daly (1985). "Competitiveness, Risk Taking and Violence: The Young Male Syndrome." *Ethology and Sociobiology* 6:59-73.

Wilson, W.J. (1987). *The Truly Disadvantaged: The Inner City, The Underclass, and Public Policy*. Chicago: University of Chicago Press.

Wolfgang, M., R. Figlio & T. Sellin (1972). *Delinquency in a Birth Cohort*. Chicago: University of Chicago Press.

Wolfgang, M., T. Thornberry & R. Figlio (1987). *From Boy to Man, From Delinquency to Crime*. Chicago: University of Chicago Press.

Wood, P., B. Pfefferbaum & B. Arneklev (1993). "Risk-Taking and Self-Control: Socialpsychological Correlates of Delinquency." *Journal of Crime and Justice* 16:11-130.

Woodger, J. (1948). *Biological Principles*. London: Routlege & Kegan Paul.

Woodward, V. (1992). *Human Heredity and Society*. St. Paul, MN: West.

Wrangham, R. & D. Peterson (1996). *Demonic Males: Apes and the Origins of Human Violence*. Boston: Houghton Mifflin.

Wright, R. (1994). *The Moral Animal: Evolutionary Psychology and Everyday Life*. New York: Pantheon Books.

Wright, R. (1995). "The Biology of Violence." *New Yorker* 71 (March 13):68-78.

Wright, R.A. & J. Miller (1998). "Taboo Until Today? The Coverage of Biological Arguments in Criminology Textbooks, 1961 To 1970 and 1987 to 1996." *Journal of Criminal Justice* 26:1-19.

Wright, W. (1999). *Born That Way: Genes, Behavior, Personality*: New York: Knopf.

Zahn, M. (1999). "Thoughts on the Future of Criminology. The American Society of Criminology Presidential Address." *Criminology* 37:1-15.

Zeifman, D. & C. Hazan (1997). "Attachment: The Bond in Pair-Bonds." In J. Simpson & D. Kenrick (eds.), *Evolutionary Social Psychology*, pp. 237-263. Mahwah, NJ: Lawrence Erlbaum.

Zuckerman, M. (1990). "The Psychophysiology of Sensation-Seeking." *Journal of Personality* 58:314-345.

Zuckerman, M., M. Buchsbaum & D. Murphy (1980). "Sensation-Seeking and Its Biological Correlates." *Psychological Bulletin* 88:187-214.

Zuravin, S. (1988). "Child Maltreatment and Teenage First Births: A Relationship Mediated by Chronic Sociodemographic Stress." *Journal of Orthopsychiatry* 58:91-103.

Index

Biography

Anthony Walsh is currently a professor of criminal justice at Boise State University, Idaho, where he teaches criminology, statistics, and criminal justice assessment and counseling. He received his Ph.D. in criminology from Bowling Green State University (Ohio) in 1983. Dr. Walsh has field experience in both law enforcement and corrections, and is the author of 12 books and 80 articles. His main accomplishment is marrying the sweetest and prettiest woman in the world.